TIMBER!

EDITED BY **WILLIAM A. DUERR**

IOWA STATE
UNIVERSITY PRESS,
AMES
1973

TIMBER!
TIMBER!
TIMBER!
TIMBER!

PROBLEMS / PROSPECTS / POLICIES

WILLIAM A. DUERR was formerly Distinguished Professor in the State University of New York and Professor of Forestry Economics in its College of Forestry, Syracuse. He is now Adjunct Professor in the College of Forestry, Syracuse, and Thomas M. Brooks Professor of Forestry in the Virginia Polytechnic Institute and State University, Blacksburg.

Photographs by Will Côté

❀

Composed and printed by
The Iowa State University Press

Library of Congress Cataloging in Publication Data

Timber Supply Policy Conference, Harriman, N.Y., 1970.
    Timber!
    Sponsored by the College of Forestry of the State University of New York.
    Includes bibliographical references.
    1. United States—Forest policy—Congresses.
2. Timber—United States—Congresses.   I. Duerr,
William Allen, 1911–   ed.   II. New York (State).
College of Forestry, Syracuse.   III. Title.
SD565.T56   1970   333.7'5'0973   72–1160
ISBN 0–8138–1700–5

CONTENTS

PREFACE

THIS BOOK IS ADDRESSED to those who are concerned with problems of environmental conservation—both professionals and laymen. Most of the chapters were written for a nationwide policy conference and were brought together under the title, "The United States Timber Supply." The conference was convened in November 1970 at Harriman, New York, by the College of Forestry of the State University of New York. Following a review of the background papers, representatives of government, conservation groups, industry, and the academic community exchanged ideas about forest policies and programs. (A list of the conferees is given on page xi.)

The conference closed with a summary and interpretation prepared by its secretary. This review, somewhat enlarged and then sent to the conferees for their criticism, appears as the semifinal statement in the book, Chapter 18. Three other additions have been made to the set of background papers: Chapter 1, on the identity of the timber-supply problem; Chapter 12, concerning international trade in wood products; and Chapter 19, bringing the timber-supply story up through 1971 and 1972, to the time of this book's publication.

Both the conference and this book were made possible through the interest and financial support of two foundations: Resources for the Future, Inc., and the New York Science and Technology Foundation.

Conference planning was the responsibility of a committee within the College of Forestry at Syracuse: Eric A. Anderson, Professor of Wood Products Engineering; William A. Duerr, then Professor of Forestry Economics; Russell E. Getty and Paul F. Graves, Professors of Forest Management; and Chairman John M. Yavorsky, Professor of Public Service and Continuing Education. For the management of the conference, the committee regrouped under the leadership of Dr. Graves, who played the major role in enlisting conferees and who served as Conference Chairman. Dr. Edward E. Palmer, President of the College, guided the committee's work and opened the conference with an informal keynote address. Ideas and material assistance, both in the conference and in the book, were generously given by John Fedkiw, of the U.S. Department of Agriculture, Robert E. Wolf, of the Interior Department, and the staff of the Forestry College's Office of Public Service and Continuing Education.

Special thanks are due to persons other than committee members who officiated at the conference. James S. Bethel, of the University of Washington, Michael F. Brewer, then of Resources for the Future, Inc., and Richard A. Skok, of the University of Minnesota, gave the opening reviews of background papers. Leon A. Hargreaves, of the University of Georgia, Otis F. Hall, of the University of New Hampshire, and Kenneth P. Davis, of Yale University, served as session chairmen. George R. Armstrong, of the State University of New York, offered the closing summary and interpretation of the conference.

The staff of Iowa State University Press, particularly Rowena James and Rosalie Koskimaki, were instrumental in improving the readability of the book.

My wife, Jean, shared the editorial responsibilities with me from the time we began to recruit authors until after the last proofs were read.

W.A.D.

Syracuse, New York

CONFEREES

(Participants in the Timber Supply Policy Conference, Harriman, New York, November 1970, and their affiliations at that time.)

JOHN A. BEALE, Department of Conservation, State of Wisconsin

PHILLIP S. BERRY, Sierra Club

JAMES S. BETHEL, College of Forest Resources, University of Washington

MICHAEL F. BREWER, Resources for the Future, Inc.

RUSSELL CAHILL, Council on Environmental Quality, Executive Office of the President

EDWARD P. CLIFF, Forest Service, United States Department of Agriculture

BERT L. COLE, Department of Natural Resources, State of Washington

T. K. COWDEN, United States Department of Agriculture

KENNETH P. DAVIS, School of Forestry, Yale University

JOHN FEDKIW, Office of The Secretary, United States Department of Agriculture

WAYNE W. GASKINS, Western Forest Industries Association

VERN L. GURNSEY, Boise Cascade Corporation

OTIS F. HALL, Institute for Natural and Environmental Resources, University of New Hampshire

LEON HARGREAVES, School of Forestry, University of Georgia

H. R. JOSEPHSON, Forest Service, United States Department of Agriculture

FRANK H. KAUFERT, School of Forestry, University of Minnesota

JOHN H. KYL, United States House of Representatives

HARLEY LANGDALE, JR., The Langdale Company

HARRISON LOESCH, United States Department of the Interior

S. H. MALLICOAT, Office of United States Senator Mark Hatfield

JOHN R. McGUIRE, Forest Service, United States Department of Agriculture

ROBERT W. MILLER, Office of Domestic and Business Policy, United States Department of Commerce

HARRY E. MORGAN, Weyerhaeuser Company

ARTHUR F. MUSCHLER, Edward Hines Lumber Company

ARTHUR W. NELSON, JR., U.S. Plywood-Champion Papers, Inc.

THOMAS C. NELSON, Forest Service, United States Department of Agriculture

BOYD L. RASMUSSEN, Bureau of Land Management, United States Department of the Interior

JACQUELINE SCHAFER, Conservative Party

J. E. SCHROEDER, National Association of State Foresters

GARY L. SEEVERS, Council of Economic Advisers, Executive Office of the President

ROBERT J. SEIDL, Simpson Timber Company

E. WARNER SHEDD, JR., National Wildlife Federation

RICHARD A. SKOK, School of Forestry, University of Minnesota

WILLIAM J. STOTT, Morgan Guaranty Trust Company

JOHN A. WEED, Morgan Guaranty Trust Company

JAMES G. YOHO, International Paper Company

JOHN A. ZIVNUSKA, School of Forestry and Conservation, University of California

INTRODUCTION

In 1968, some unusually sharp changes took place in the supplies and prices of U.S. standing timber, logs, and finished wood products, notably softwood lumber and plywood. By early 1969, the developments had become alarming. In some western lumbering centers, federal standing timber which had been selling for $70 per thousand board feet was being bid up by the sawmills and the veneer manufacturers to $150 and more. Many wood-using plants were having difficulty getting logs at any price. End-product values, too, were soaring: Lumber and plywood prices had risen anywhere from 50 to 100 percent within 12 months. Markets were in crisis with speculation running high and dealers hesitant to accept advance orders. The construction industry, newly charged with a goal of 26 million housing units for the next decade, felt the pinch keenly as it tried to respond. Home buyers found their dollars badly shrunken as wood shortage was added to labor scarcity and the high cost of borrowing.

The nation reacted strongly. Congress investigated. Subcommittees of the Senate and House Banking and Currency Committees were active, holding hearings, releasing summaries and recommendations, and offering remedial legislation. The President set up a Cabinet Committee, whose findings led to a variety of actions such as a temporary 10-percent increase in the allowable harvest of timber from federal forest lands and restriction of lumber and plywood purchases by the Defense Department. Log exports to Japan were curtailed.

Meanwhile, a profusion of further remedies was being proposed on all sides.

- Amend the Jones Act, which raises the cost of water-borne lumber from Alaska by requiring that it be shipped in U.S. vessels.
- Look for ways to increase wood imports.
- Manage and protect both federal and private timber lands more intensively.
- Produce timber along with recreation and other nonwood products on forest land.

- Work for genetic improvements and other technologic improvements in timber growing.
- Reform the timber appraisal and sales procedures for federal lands.
- Develop substitutes for wood products. Improve the efficiency of wood processing and distribution.
- Develop a national ethic which relates timber to welfare as conservation is now related to welfare.

The foregoing events and arguments provided the immediate motivation for the 1970 nationwide policy conference on the United States timber supply. The conference was conceived as a means of bringing together some of the leaders concerned, for the purpose of

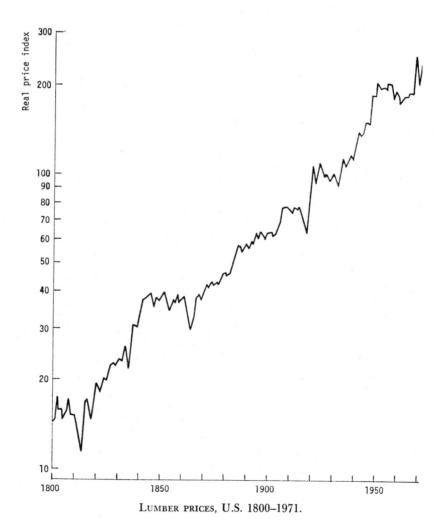

LUMBER PRICES, U.S. 1800–1971.

reviewing forest-land policies and programs and for exchanging ideas about their future directions.

The 1968–69 timber-supply crisis, viewed in perspective, is seen to be one of a series of such episodes which have punctuated the history of certain wood industries. The lumber story, which is the best documented and most notable, is told in Figure 1, where real price (in dollars of constant wholesale-market buying power) is plotted as an index number on a scale of years from 1800 to 1971. During these 17 decades, the real price of lumber multiplied approximately 20-fold. The trend line represents a persistent 1.8 percent annual increase. A substantial part of the secular upward push has been contributed by the periodic supply crises, most of which have come as the aftermath of war.

The timber-supply issue in the United States has two aspects. The short-term aspect usually becomes prominent when surging demands for construction materials and other wood products come up against the unresponsive supply of logs. The long-term aspect becomes evident when one looks ahead to the era, not many decades off, when only dramatic improvements in technology will permit the resource to satisfy the wants of a soaring population. The 1968–69 crisis was impressive because we were confronted simultaneously with both the short-term and the long-term aspects of the timber-supply issue.

The timber supply in question here is the supply of timber for all its uses: not merely lumber, veneer, and plywood, but also pulp and paper products, composition board, posts, poles, and many other commodities. Although each product has its own supply characteristics and its own trends in manufacturing technology and price, all products are drawn from the world's forest reservoir. Their raw-material requirements, along with the requirements for all forest values from water to scenery, are interrelated. Beyond the very short run, the timber supply—and, more broadly, the forest supply—may appropriately be viewed as a single subject.

The timber-supply conference was planned as an expression of concern for both the short term and the long, and for both timber resources and forest resources in general.

Papers for the timber-supply conference were addressed to three areas of concern:

1. Where we stand: What is the forest-resource position of the United States today? What is the timber-supply issue?
2. Where we are headed: What are the forest-resource prospects for the immediate future and the longer term? What are the opportunities for improving the timber supply?
3. Policies and programs: What have been the United States forest policies? What new policies and programs will be needed to meet the forest-resource issues of the future?

These issues hold great interest for nearly everyone: government, the conservation movement, wood industry, the forestry profession, research organizations, forestry schools, the general public. Land-resource management in the United States is of wider concern and lends itself to—indeed, demands—wider participation than ever before. Pressing needs are for study and discussion; for full comprehension of the issues and their implications; and for a progressive remedial program. The timber-supply conference was designed to encourage such study and discussion.

We hope the chapters in this book will provide a basis for such further study and discussion as may be undertaken in various regions of the country among persons who are concerned about United States timber supply—land managers and the users of the forest, public agencies and private interests, professionals and the general public. We hope, too, that the reading and discussion of this book will further these additional specific aims:

1. To bring out the available forecasts, in a world setting, of the type and extent of demands to be placed upon American forest resources.

2. To evaluate the capability of forest land owners and the manufacturers and purveyors of forest commodities to meet prospective demands.

3. To assess the sufficiency of the nation's forestry policies in light of prospective public dependency on forest resources, and to propose such additional goals and efforts as may be needed.

4. To elevate forestry to the rank of a prime national concern, emphasizing the close relation between our forests and our way of life and stressing our obligation to make plans for the one along with the other.

5. To put the subject of timber in the context of forest management as a whole, which includes the production and use of water, wildlife, recreational opportunities, and other services.

Timber-Supply Conference Committee:

ERIC A. ANDERSON
WILLIAM A. DUERR
RUSSELL E. GETTY
PAUL F. GRAVES
JOHN M. YAVORSKY

PART 1   TODAY'S PROBLEMS

1   A PERSPECTIVE

WILLIAM A. DUERR* AND BRUCE A. SCHICK**

WOOD AND ITS PRODUCTS—paper bags and paperboard cartons, tissue and newsprint paper, rayon, particleboard, lumber and wooden furniture, house framing and plywood sheathing, wooden beams, trusses, telephone poles, fenceposts, firewood—are the old-fashioned and new-fashioned materials of our civilization. Their role in our lives arises from the properties of wood: molecularly, a mine of interesting and useful chemical substances; microscopically, a loosely packed structure of fibers and cementing materials having valuable engineering qualities such as strength, resilience, and the capacity to insulate; macroscopically, a set of objects varied and pleasing to the eye; economically, a versatile, workable, traditionally abundant resource.

If wood were derived from mines in the middle of the desert, as are borax, salt, and oil in some cases, its impact upon other resources and upon people might well be minimal. The material would appear on the scene at the end of a freight journey, and man's primary concern would be to channel it into its various uses. However, the system which in fact exists for deriving wood is very nearly the opposite of this: At every turn, the process is thickly interwoven with human and natural events.

The trees from which wood is obtained are generally close neighbors of man and have long been so in many parts of the world. As a result, trees and forests are given deep cultural recognition: as shelter and hunting ground, as a fearsome place where enemies may lurk, as a source of material necessities, and as a religious and artistic symbol and a store of natural beauty and human tranquility. In poem, story, and song, forests and trees are endowed with a wide range of human and other animate qualities. Thus man lives with them, listens to them, talks with them, and calls on them for a wide variety of benefits.

---

* Thomas M. Brooks Professor of Forestry, Virginia Polytechnic Institute and State University, Blacksburg.

** Assistant Professor of Forest Economics, West Virginia University, Morgantown.

Benefits of the forest include timber, hunting ground, wildlife and watershed values; foraging areas for livestock; and opportunities for recreational, aesthetic, and sentimental enjoyment. All these resources are produced by man in concert. Every patch and parcel of his forest yields water and the services of watershed regulation; a place for hunting, nature study, and the contemplation of the scene; and a place for growing wood and edible plants. It even provides a pleasurable image for the dreamer who has never seen this forest and has no intention of visiting it.

THE FORESTRY SYSTEM

The system of creating forest benefits is extraordinarily complex. Its complexity results from the myriad interconnections from item to item within the system, and between the system and the rest of the world.

Within the system, for example, if the forest owner improves control over fires and other destructive agencies, he will work changes in the kinds of trees and their stocking and thus in the output of wildlife, water, and other benefits as well as wood. He will set similar changes in motion if he carries out silvical measures such as planting or seeding new trees or thinning out the timber growth. If he wants to increase wildlife or herbaceous vegetation or the yield of water, typically he must harvest some timber to create openings in the forest. Such openings may well change some of the characteristics of the soil and site and thus start new lines of succession of plants and animals and of soil flora and fauna. If he builds a new road, he will make the forest more accessible to recreationists and to loggers. If he wishes to preserve a woodland scene which people find attractive, he must arrest change, which is a nearly inexorable force, the stemming of which is itself a complex problem in resource management. If he attempts to let the forest be used for its full roster of benefits to people, he finds himself involved in the weighing of particularly complex trade-offs. Some of these are biologic: more trees, less forage. Some are engineering: more roads, less woods. Some arise from the community's culture, which may lead people to accept or dislike the juxtaposition of recreational development and logging activity—or to accept or dislike the appearance of this type of forest or that, or this or that silvical measure or system of wood harvest. Finally, in the ultimate cultural trade-off, if the owner opens his forest for widespread use by people—managers, loggers, home-site users, recreationists, or other human beings in sufficient number—he may be destroying people's image of the forest as wild land, including the image in the mind of the dreamer.

Whatever the origin of the trade-offs in forest-resource use, their weighing and resolution call for a set of criteria—that is to say, a scheme of values. It is in our culture that value schemes come into being and vie for acceptance. The thesis of this chapter is that the timber-supply problem is the manifestation of this vying where wood or its products are concerned.

The forest is a complex social-biologic-engineering system managed by people for myriad benefits. The quantity and quality of each benefit is influenced by the kind and amount of others produced. The resulting trade-offs are weighed by the people with whom the choices rest. Alternative criteria—value schemes—are at hand for this weighing. The timber-supply problem is the problem of deciding upon a scheme of values.

INTERCONNECTIONS WITH PEOPLE IN SPACE AND TIME

Between the forestry system and the rest of the world are interconnections which enlarge the scope of timber trade-offs and thus of the timber-supply problem. These interconnections occur across the range of people, places, and time.

Interconnections with people start with the ownership of the land: whoever has a voice in its management not only casts an influence on the forest but also feels the effects of whatever is done there and whatever outcomes ensue. For the private or the public landowner, the measures of management may consist simply of paying taxes or meeting other financial obligations, establishing a policy and reviewing it from time to time, and taking minimal required steps to protect the forest and its users and uphold the integrity of its boundaries. Such, for example, might be the program for a forest tract managed for wilderness hiking, camping, and related recreation. At the other extreme along the scale of management, and again for either private or public ownership, is the forest tract in which great amounts of resources are invested, not only in the form of land and trees which are the principal investments in the wilderness but also in a transportation network and in protection, watershed, timber, wildlife, and recreation developments. To such a forest, with its program of integrated management, people can come in large numbers from a wide band of surrounding communities to enjoy on-site activities or help oversee them, and forest products can flow out to consumers across the country.

In the last analysis, everyone is strongly forest-connected: Everyone consumes wood products, living in them or with them. Most people use water from the forest. Many people visit the forest as sightseers, recreationists, or hunters. And all persons of age are potential critics and partners in the management of forest lands, not only the public lands, but private holdings as well. Taking a proprietary interest in the forest, they may express and even enforce their views on what is right and wrong in resource management and what is beautiful and ugly and what affects their environment favorably and detrimentally.

Interconnections between the forest and people extend widely over space. Our highly urbanized society takes a large interest in distant forest lands as well as in the little patches and tracts close at hand. There is the dreamer's interest and that of the environmental activist and that of the forest-product consumer, and each one of us is a composite, in his own proportions, of these three. Wood commodities move great distances in interregional and international trade. In the United States, the principal foreign supplier is Canada, which provides much newsprint paper, lumber, and other wood products. Shipments also come from Scandinavian and European countries and from many of the tropical nations. And shipments—in smaller quantities—go out of the United States to numerous importers of roundwood and finished products.

Interconnections between the forest and people extend, too, over time. Such connections are strongly bonded by the fact that some forest enterprises may take a long while to bear fruit. A forest park featuring old-growth timber would take perhaps centuries to produce from bare ground. Veneer logs may take fifty years or more; pulpwood, no less than a decade or two. And almost any forest development requires some years to put into operation. The consequence is that we experience today the outcome of decisions long past, and current choices must anticipate long-delayed impacts upon society.

Every interconnection between forests and people is an interconnection between timber and people and a facet of the timber-supply issue.

THE FOREST-SUPPLY QUESTION

A large number of choices is open to American forestry. Many choices are associated with product mix: what relative proportions of scenery and wood and on-site recreation and water and so on to strive for. There are the choices with respect to the extent of national effort to be put into forest resources: how intensively to plan for their use, to protect them from physical damage, and to work for an enlarged output of services. There are the choices respecting how the forestry task is to be shared: notably, in what proportions among the millions of U.S. forest-land owners.

Each American forestry alternative represents not only a different set of benefits to consumers but also a different set of impacts upon all the persons whose concern is to create forest resources and make them available for human wants.

Whenever choices are to be weighed, a scheme of values is required for the weighing. Major policy decisions for forest supply require a set of values which will reflect the aims of the American people. It is at this point that the supply question grows into an issue, for the sets of values which come to hand are numerous and partly contradictory, and there is no consensus on their merits. As one searches through the testimony and the writings on forest-supply policy, including the subsequent chapters of this book, he finds the opportunity to classify the value schemes that he encounters. Although any such classification is arbitrary, it is helpful because it simplifies the issues and permits viewing them more objectively than might otherwise be possible.

Three schools of thought on forest-resource values can be distinguished: materialism, romanticism, and utilitarianism. These value schemes are not mutually exclusive. Not only do the three philosophies overlap but each person who has a position on the matter has, in his thinking, some elements of each. Forest-policy proposals are divisible, not into three sorts, but into a great many sorts, depending on the proportions of the basic ingredients present in each case.

MATERIALISM

The first of the three schools of thought emphasizes the material benefits that come from forest resources. It stresses resource production and is not pointedly concerned with consumption. Indeed, it takes the latter for granted because it assumes that forests are an absolute necessity. The theory is characterized by its special interest in two of the material outcomes of forest production: wood products and money profits.

That *wood holds primacy* among resource values is one tenet of materialism as applied to forestry. In resource conservation or in its exploitation, however the case may be, wood is first; all else is secondary:

> The first and foremost purpose of a forest growth is to supply us with wood material; it is the substance of the trees itself, not their fruit, their beauty, their shade, their shelter, that constitute the primary object. . . .[1]

Forests are an absolute necessity because wood is. Civilization cannot endure without wood—a circumstance which, the forestry materialists imply, fails to hold with respect to other goods or services of the forest:

> It may be stated without fear of contradiction that outside of food products no material is so universally used and so indispensable in human economy as wood. Indeed, civilization is inconceivable without

an abundance of timber. . . . So general and far reaching has its use become that a wood famine, however improbable its occurrence, would be almost as serious as a bread famine. We may become less wasteful, both as regards food and wood, but the necessity of wood, as far as we can foresee at present, will always be second only to the necessity of food, and far greater than that of any other material used in the arts.[2]

And again:

Every peacetime industry is dependent in some degree upon a supply of forest products. Food, clothing, and shelter of every kind require wood for their production. No wood, no agriculture, no manufacture, no commerce. Without the products of the forest, civilization as we know it would stop. In peace as in war the safety and prosperity of our country hangs upon a steady and generous supply of materials which the forest alone can produce.[3]

The materialistic belief in timber primacy is the belief, not only that wood is an essential commodity which stands foremost among all the forest's values, but also that if forest owners give attention to the timber supply, the supply of other forest benefits will automatically be assured:

It might be stated that forest regulation has for its chief object the provision for so managing rotation of cuttings on any given forest area that equivalent yields of harvestable timber can periodically, by periods of one year or longer, be obtained. Other objects of management, such as watershed protection and the stability of esthetic values, are usually secondary and follow naturally from attention given to the first.[4]

It follows from such reasoning that the nation need have no explicit concern for integrated forestry (which will supply all the forest goods and services in acceptable proportions). The conservation problem is simply to supply timber:

A remedy for . . . appalling waste must be found in a concerted effort to stop the devastation of our remaining forests and put our idle forest lands at work growing timber.[5]

Paralleling the forest materialists' faith in timber primacy is their faith in the *primacy of profit* in monetary terms.

We should consider [the acre of forest]: what it will cost to buy it, and to protect and carry it, what it will grow, how much and how fast, and everything that will have a commercial sales value, because we are interested first in the money which the acre will produce, and in its sawlogs only to the extent that they can be translated into money.[6]

And:

As the forests are transformed into useful materials and money, the vibration of the mills is the pulse of a great heart that forces a vitalizing stream of blood through innumerable business channels through whose tills and cash boxes the forest payrolls pass. To keep this pulse beating a continuing supply of forest resources is necessary.[7]

ROMANTICISM

In contrast to the materialistic approach and, to a degree, in rebellion against it, is romanticism. Its general expression is found in writings such as those of Emerson and Ruskin. These philosophers search for the spirit, the inner truth, of man and nature. They envisage a nature without man or with man as a nondespoiling participant. They seek a return to the *traditional values* of the simple, rural life, which they see cleansed of its dangers and squalor.

The contrast, and the superiority, of nature to man's works and material acquisitions is stressed by one writer in the following terms:

> Nothing could be more salutary at this stage than a little healthy contempt for a plethora of material blessings.
> Perhaps such a shift of values can be achieved by reappraising things unnatural, tame, and confined in terms of things natural, wild, and free. . . .
> Like winds and sunsets, wild things were taken for granted until progress began to do away with them. Now we face the question whether a still higher "standard of living" is worth its cost in things natural, wild, and free. For us of the minority, the opportunity to see geese is more important than television, and the chance to find a pasqueflower is a right as inalienable as free speech.[8]

Among spokesmen for the traditional values is Thoreau, who expresses the belief that one can find a richer existence by limiting his material possessions to his simplest needs. To observe and commune with nature provides values far beyond all but the most elementary of material wants. Indeed, a renewal of the traditional values is essential to civilization's survival.

An extension of the romantic school's traditional-value branch is that which extolls the *early ways of life* in rural America and implies that some turning-back of the clock is desirable. Here, for forestry, is a marriage of romanticism to timber-primacy materialism. Overlooked is the barrier presented by forests against farming and other developments which characterized the rural life. Extolled is the lavish use of wood and the heavy dependency upon wood which characterized the forefathers' culture: the split-rail fence meandering beside the field and wood, the log barn, the weathered siding of the house, the great pile of firewood for the long winter, the warmth of knotty pine paneling, the smell of the wood-burning cookstove, the comfort of the friendly hearth, and the good medicine of reflecting upon the days when the forest as a material was truly a mainstay of life.

Another extension of romanticism may be viewed as an outgrowth of its focus upon nature and natural values. Stressed here is the importance to man of *revival-recreation*—through communion with nature. There is again a marriage to materialism, this time to the profit-primacy form of it. The recreational values of the forest, which are accessible chiefly to persons who have profited in the material world sufficiently to afford them, are placed above other values and notably above timber:

> It is wholly natural that the people who are now living under the complex developments of modern civilization should turn to the outdoors for relief—a partial revertment to our more typical environment. What is more, with an increase of artificialities of modern human existence there will be an increasing demand for touch with our native habitat, the outdoors. The demand for outdoor recreation as the essential antidote for too much city is basic, is fundamental. The demand for recreation found in forested places is most permanent. It is part of the fiber of our being.
>
> A forest cannot be grown without producing recreation values for the man of today. Trees are an absolute essential for every recreation ground of modern humanity. Recreation is a basic, a genuine, an inseparable product wherever there is a forest.
>
> Recreation in general is a necessity, while recreation produced in the forest lands is the best style of that necessity we can find in the country.[9]

Here, as with the materialists, the forest is an absolute necessity—not, however, because of its timber, but because of its recreational resources.

UTILITARIANISM

The last of the three schools of thought, utilitarianism, follows such teachers as Bentham, J. S. Mill, Hobbes, and Locke. They held, in general, that the criterion for judging the goodness or rightness of an action is whether it contributes to the well-being of mankind. Utilitarianism has been described as the doctrine of the *greatest happiness* for the greatest number. One thinks immediately of the traditional forestry goal, the greatest good to the greatest number in the long run. In that respect, Gifford Pinchot, to whom the phrase is attributed, is purely utilitarian.

Utilitarianism rejects the criteria of both materialism and romanticism as a priori rules. On the other hand, it accepts either set of criteria or any other set which promises to meet the test of human beings' interest for the particular matter at issue.

In forestry, utilitarian thought makes at least three distinguishable points: first, an emphasis on human goals; second, an emphasis upon decision making and planning, especially the recognition of alternative courses of action and the weighing of them on the scale of human values; third, a stress upon a particular instance of recognizing and weighing alternatives—that is, integrated forestry. The first of these three points, the emphasis upon *human goals,* is illustrated by the following statement:

> The U.S. is a vast complex of more than 131 million individuals, each striving for a place in the sun. . . . Unrelated as people may appear as individuals, they are all consumers, and all have the rights to life, liberty, and the pursuit of happiness. Our great natural resources are nothing except as they are seen, used and enjoyed by people—or consumers. Thus, we plan, not for the glorification of a tree, not for the dedication of a bridge as a memorial to engineering genius, not for a sea of golden grain—but for the satisfaction of human needs.[10]

and by this:

> The goals in question are those of persons. I do not know whether other animals have goals or whether plants or inanimate objects have goals. It does not take much imagination . . . to read goals into the behavior of some of the entities external to man. But I do not care about such goals, except as man may be influenced by his concept of them. I am not interested in knowing what yonder stand of trees would ask for if it could speak. But I am concerned to know what the persons responsible for that stand are asking for, whether as a result of their own communion with nature or on some other basis. I am obliged to listen to a foolish man and turn a deaf ear even to a wise tree.[11]

And human goals are also stressed here:

> Foresters are specialists in forest science, and in the application of that science for the service of human needs. The farther forest science advances, the better will it be possible to fashion forest policies for the effective service of public needs.[12]

The second point of forestry utilitarianism, stressing *alternatives* and decision making-planning, follows easily from the first. Among the alternatives are trade-offs. Here is where the weighing process enters, in order to determine the best trade. Compromises are inevitable: One can seldom have anything cost-free. Furthermore, the compromise which represents people's interest today may not do so tomorrow; consequently, flexibility is a desirable quality to look for in programs when a decision is to be made:

> The . . . formula is exceedingly flexible, permitting changes in emphasis and type of use as conditions change and as public necessity requires. It regards all products and services of wildlands as having a potential place in the management picture.[13]

In this quotation, the third point of forestry utilitarianism is already evident: In recognizing alternatives and weighing plans for forest resource conservation, one is bound to look at the multiple products and services of the forest. Having done so, one is apt to plan for a combination of uses rather than to stress a single use, that is, he will in most cases find *integrated forestry* the best approach to the public interest. Integrated forestry may be thought of in social terms, something achieved in large areas, or in terms of individual patches of forest. Utilitarianism clearly diverges from both materialism, with its timber-primacy doctrine, and romanticism, with its recreation primacy:

> The task of forestry is to obtain from the natural resources in our charge all the values, utilities, and human benefits that are inherent in them.[14]

And again:

> Most forest lands possess inherently more than a single value. They produce wood and numerous byproducts. . . . The best forestry takes account of all of these values. . . . Forestry is a coordinated technique with many purposes and methods.[15]

And finally:

> You must carry the message of intelligent and constructive management of our forests to the man in the street. You must show him the vast difference in time required for growth and quality of wood fibre between a scientifically managed forest and one not so managed. But above all you must impress on him that our forests can—and must—be managed for *all* public values.[16]

THE ISSUE TODAY

The three philosophies represent three partly overlapping segments of a continuum: materialism at one end, romanticism at the other, and utilitarianism somewhere between. Materialistic thinking is still a part of the national frame of mind, and yet the fact that the materialist quotations bear the earliest publication dates, and bear none after the Second World War, is not altogether a coincidence. Few persons of this or the past generation who are concerned with forest resource policy follow a clearly materialistic line. The viable elements in materialism have, for the most part, been taken into the other two schools of thought. The elements that were not viable, such as the doctrine of timber primacy in resource management, are best left to rest undisturbed.

Two schools appear to suffice in interpreting today's forest-supply issue: romanticism and utilitarianism. It must be stressed again that these schools are not mutually exclusive. Although the basic philosophies are few, forest policies fall into a great many categories because of differences in the mix of philosophies they represent.

2   FEDERAL ASSESSMENT

SAUL NELSON*

In 1966 prices of Douglas-fir lumber, which had behaved quite circumspectly for some years, suddenly took off, rising 14 percent between December 1965 and May 1966, while softwood plywood jumped 20 percent. The Council of Economic Advisers was directed to chair an interagency group to examine the causes and consider what steps could be taken to reverse the trend. It became evident immediately that a number of specific problems could yield to vigorous government action, including heavy defense procurement, transportation bottlenecks, and restricted availability of public timber. The group recommended cut-back and close control of defense purchases, vigorous action by the Interstate Commerce Commission (ICC) to speed boxcar turnaround, and increased offerings of timber by the Forest Service and the Bureau of Land Management. These recommendations were quickly accepted, and in a short time the price trend reversed. It would be naive to claim too close a causal connection, since demand also began to slip at about the same time, but the actions adopted were certainly of some importance.

The extent of the rise and fall of softwood lumber and plywood prices in 1966 was not exceptionally great; the fluctuations had been about as great in 1959 and considerably sharper during the Korean War. In fact, it was only because of the Administration's general concern with the onset of inflation that the increases attracted the attention they did. Nevertheless, in retrospect it seems that this episode represented a premonitory signal of trouble.

One factor that should have been of concern was that the rise in prices occurred without any sharp jump in demand such as had occurred in 1959 and 1950: Housing starts of 720,000 units in the first half of 1966 were below the 780,000 reported during the same period of 1965, and total apparent domestic consumption of industrial roundwood in 1966 was less than 2 percent higher than in the previous year.

* Consulting Economist. Formerly Senior Staff Economist, President's Council of Economic Advisers, Washington, D.C.

In contrast, consumption in 1959, when the next preceding price increase had occurred, was 10 percent above 1958, and in 1950 consumption was 17 percent greater than in 1949. Moreover, there had been substantial increases in apparent consumption, ranging from 3 to 5 percent, in each of the years 1962–1965; yet softwood lumber prices had remained essentially stable, and the prices of softwood plywood had declined.

THE 1960S—A TIME OF LOOMING SCARCITY

Statistics suggest that a significant turning point may have been reached about 1961. Prior to that year, U.S. consumption of industrial timber products had shown no consistent trend for over a decade. Thereafter, consumption increased steadily. By 1966 it was 20 percent and by 1969, 25 percent higher than in 1961. In fact, except for the mini-recession of 1967, each year since 1961 has shown some further advance in timber consumption. This is especially noteworthy in view of the weak and erratic performance of the housing sector during the sixties. The 1963 peak of 1.64 million starts has never since been equalled.

The sensitivity of 1966 timber prices to a relatively small increase in demand suggested that the margin of unutilized resources had begun to narrow. A number of developments may have contributed to reducing the flexibility of supply response. The most critical of these was the sharp rise in prices of standing timber for sale and harvest ("stumpage") which began in 1963 and 1964; the average for Douglas-fir sold from national forests doubled between 1962 and 1966. This could only be interpreted as a progressive squeeze on the availability of timber to meet rising demand. In addition, the number of lumber mills was declining sharply for many reasons, including the failure of lumber prices to reflect the steep and steady increase in the cost of stumpage, as well as rising wages and limited supply of woods and mill labor.

While all these events were warnings of trouble ahead, it was not until 1968 that the seriousness of the problem became evident. The total apparent consumption of timber in that year—approximately 12.3 billion cubic feet, roundwood equivalent—was about 7 percent higher than during the dip in 1967, but only 2 percent greater than during 1966. Housing starts of 1.55 million, while substantially above the two preceding years, were only slightly higher than in 1965 and below the levels of 1963 and 1964. Yet prices took off with a vengeance. Softwood lumber rose 53 percent between December 1967 and the peak in March 1969, while softwood plywood jumped a staggering 110 percent.

Of course there were special factors involved. Dealers had gambled on lower prices and had been caught with depleted inventories. The winter of 1968–1969 was severe, and there were interruptions of production in the Northwest. The recurrent problem of freight car shortages arose again, aggravated by a dock strike in the Northeast. And of course the economy at large was subject to pervasive inflationary pressures.

It was clear that the problem was of truly major dimensions. In March 1969, the Cabinet Committee on Economic Policy appointed an interagency Task Force under the direction of Budget Director Mayo to study the situation and to recommend appropriate action. The Task Force in turn designated a staff-level working party.

The working party directed its attention first to the problem of skyrocketing prices. It found many superficial similarities to the pattern of 1966. Accordingly, it recommended similar steps, including action by the ICC to ease the transportation bottleneck, an increase in timber offerings from federal lands, and resumption of close supervision of defense procurement. In addition, the working party asked the State Department to talk informally to the Japanese, requesting them to cut back on their log imports. The Task Force had been appointed on March 7; these actions were approved by the President in a press release on March 19, setting some sort of record for speed. Again, as in 1966, these measures appear to have had a salutary effect, although the major credit for the subsequent sharp price reversal must obviously be attributed to the concurrent decline in the level of housing starts.

In 1966, the Task Force had been disbanded as soon as its recommendations had been submitted and appropriate action taken. In 1969, however, it was agreed that we could not be content with palliatives and that the time had come to look at the entire situation in longer perspective. Much more fundamental action was required if the nation's growing needs for softwood timber were to be met in the years ahead. Such action was especially urgent in view of the pressing need for a sharply expanded output of housing in accordance with the national goals endorsed by the Administration and Congress. At the same time, any program to increase timber supply had to accord equal weight to ensuring the preservation, and indeed enhancement, of the quality of the environment.

PROSPECTS FOR THE 1970S

The next task was projecting the demand for softwood timber at least through the 1970s and exploring ways by which that demand could be met. It was clear from the outset that price—more precisely, the price of softwood lumber and plywood relative to the general price level—had to be an important factor in any assessment. It entered both sides of the equation, since higher or lower relative prices would significantly influence the level of demand on the one hand and of supply on the other. A coordinated program was needed in order to avoid either a recurrence of the extreme price fluctuations of 1968–1969, with all their disruptive effects, or of so sharp an increase in relative prices as to impose a severe burden on the consumers of softwood products and especially on the housing industry.

Any estimate of the future course of prices was beset by an unusually high degree of uncertainty. In preparing the demand and supply forecasts, the Forest Service, which undertook the job, proceeded on the basis of five alternative price assumptions, expressed in terms of the relationship that prevailed during the years 1962–1967 between the prices of softwood lumber and plywood and the general wholesale price index and ranged from 100 to 130 percent of that level. In more current terms, the lowest price assumption was about 6 percent below, and the highest 22 percent above, the relationship during the first half of 1970.

Lumber and plywood prices during the early months of 1970 were depressed by the low rate of housing and construction generally, and thus some increase in relative softwood-product prices was to be anticipated as housing revived. A conservative expectation for the mid-1970s, assuming an early start on a program of accelerated management, would be an increase of at least 6 percent over the relative prices of the first half of 1970 (or 13 percent above the 1962–1967 average).

NATIONAL HOUSING GOALS

Turning first to the demand projections, one fairly firm peg to hang some numbers upon existed in the form of the national housing goals endorsed by the Administration and Congress. Even at its recent depressed level, housing constitutes over one-quarter of current softwood demand. If the housing objectives are to come anywhere near realization, they will represent by far the most rapidly growing increment into the mid-1970s. This fact provided those who put the estimates together with at least an objective starting point.

The housing-goal peg was far from being as solid as might have been desired. In the first place, while approved housing goals establish the total number of units to be built over the decade, the actual rate of construction depends on a host of factors including public and private financial resources, the availability of skilled manpower, and many others. Nevertheless, if the goals are to be approximated, total starts, excluding mobile homes and rehabilitations, must be of the order of 2.5 million per year by the mid-1970s. The path currently assumed anticipates that starts will be about 2.4 million in 1974, 2.5 million in 1975, and will then level off through 1978. This would involve about 70 percent more starts than in 1969 and far more than in any previous year.

Agreeing on the construction target still left a number of crucial questions. For example, lumber requirements per unit are significantly less for multi-family than for single-family dwellings, and it was assumed that the recent trend toward a larger proportion of the former would continue. Technology is constantly changing, as are design standards, and the efficiency of wood utilization is improving. Even such an apparently minor change as the introduction of the new lumber-dimension standards (analyzed in Chapter 10) should have a significant effect on total requirements. Shifts from lumber to plywood and particleboard and from wood products to substitute materials may be expected to continue. Utilization patterns will be strongly influenced by the relative prices of wood products prevailing at the time the units are being designed and constructed.

While the largest increment of demand is expected to come from housing, more than half of softwood timber will continue to go to nonhousing construction, packaging, pulpwood, and other uses. Consumption for these other uses may be expected to continue to grow as the economy expands, although the long-term trend toward somewhat slower growth than that of the economy as a whole should persist. Here, too, the size of the demand will be strongly influenced by relative prices.

RESULTS OF THE FORECASTS

In 1969, total softwood sawtimber consumption was 50 billion board feet (International $\frac{1}{4}$-inch scale), of which 14.6 billion was for housing and 35.3 billion for all other uses. On the conservative assumption that relative softwood-product prices in the mid-1970s would be about 6 percent above their level of January–June 1970 (13 percent higher than 1962–1967), consumption for housing could increase to nearly 25 billion board feet by 1975, while demand for other uses could rise to 37.6 billion board feet, for a total of 63 billion. (The rate of increase for these other uses, under this price assumption, averages about 2 percent per year for the period through 1978.) The total increment in softwood demand between 1969 and 1975 would thus be about 13 billion board feet, or over 25 percent.

The other price assumptions may be given briefly: It was estimated that with relative prices about 13 percent above the first-half-1970 level, total demand by 1975 would be of the order of 62 billion board feet, with about 24 billion for housing; and that with relative prices 22 percent higher, demand would be around 60 billion board feet, with about 23 billion for housing. (The two lower price assumptions were clearly unrealistic.)

In each case, it was estimated that the housing requirement

would remain somewhat stable for the balance of the decade, but that requirements for other uses would continue increasing at an annual rate of approximately 2 percent.

In other words, if the indicated demand was to be met, supplies would have to be increased by between 10 and 13 billion board feet between 1969 and 1975, or by 20 to 25 percent, and there would be some continuing growth thereafter. Recognizing all the uncertainties in such estimates, they do suffice to indicate the magnitude of the problem.

HOW CAN SUPPLIES BE INCREASED?

Increases in the supply of softwood timber can come from three sources: federal lands, mainly the national forests; state and private holdings; and net imports. The Task Force staff looked first at federal forests, since they represent the resource most readily responsive to actions by the federal government. The rate of utilization of this resource—that is, the amount of federal timber offered for sale in any year—has been the subject of increasingly intense controversy in recent years. Industry representatives have been highly critical of what they regard as much too conservative a policy, maintaining that offerings could be greatly increased without impairing sustained-yield and multiple-use objectives. These views have also gained the support of a number of academic forest economists.

On the other hand, conservation groups have become much more vocal and much more influential in the past few years. These groups have taken the opposite stand, arguing that the present rate of cutting on federal lands is excessive and damaging to the environment. Some have even resorted to the courts in efforts to block some of the timber sales offered by the Forest Service. The degree of their influence was clearly illustrated by the defeat of the proposed National Forest Timber Conservation and Management Act in the House in 1970. The Task Force had to take full account of this head-on clash of interests.

The second source of increased supplies, state and private holdings, presents a different set of problems. Commercial forest land in private hands exceeds the acreage of federal forests by about four to one. The ratio of usable growing timber is of course far narrower: In 1969, the cut from state and private holdings exceeded that from federal lands by less than two to one. Some of the major timber companies are developing and using their lands with high efficiency and due regard for the future, but this has not been true for the multitude of small holdings. There is vast room for improvement in the management of the latter. Unfortunately, this opportunity cannot be translated into major increments of supply over the short term. The challenge is to develop a comprehensive plan of encouraging and assisting private holders to undertake the programs and investments needed to permit them to realize their potential contribution to supply in the years ahead.

The third source is net imports which must come largely from British Columbia. The Task Force staff has had several visits from forest interests in that province, and Forest Service representatives have in turn gone to British Columbia to discuss the situation with the provincial authorities. There is every reason to believe that the cut in British Columbia can be increased substantially and that a large part of the increase would be exported to the United States, especially if prices were favorable.

THE LOG-EXPORT ISSUE

The question of exports has been blown up all out of proportion. It is true that the surge of log exports to Japan during the late 1960s had an adverse effect on some sawmills and plywood plants in the Northwest, especially to the extent that these exports raised stumpage costs in the national forests. It must be borne in mind, however, that some of these exports were of species not in high demand internally. More importantly, the focus of any analysis must be on net imports, rather than on gross imports and gross exports. As long as the U.S. is a net importer, the fact that some supplies are exported cannot be regarded as a vital consideration. Any curtailment of exports can only cause Japan to look to other sources for the supply it believes it needs. In this case, it would almost surely mean larger purchases from British Columbia which would, in turn, reduce the availability of Canadian lumber for export to the United States. The fact that the U.S. exports logs, whereas British Columbia insists on some degree of fabrication, is largely irrelevant in this connection. While there would not be a one-to-one correspondence between a curtailment of U.S. exports to Japan and a reduction of imports from Canada, they would no doubt substantially offset each other. Moreover, there are so many delicate factors involved in U.S. trade relations with Japan that any further moves to reduce log exports could entail quite serious penalties on other fronts.

The Task Force and its staff-level working party thus had to assess the timber-supply potential from all sources and to consider available means of mobilizing this potential, taking into account the constraints imposed by other essential objectives of national policy, especially sustained timber yield and environmental protection.

INCREASING FEDERAL, STATE, AND PRIVATE SUPPLIES

The Forest Service has consistently maintained that it cannot raise its offerings significantly unless it is authorized to proceed with a program of intensive management and unless the necessary funds are provided. If these steps are taken at an early date, the Service estimates that it might be able to offer 17 billion board feet for sale by 1975, or 2 billion more than were offered in 1969. By 1978, as the intensive management program yielded increasing benefits, a further increment of about 2½ billion board feet might become available. In 1969, the harvest from national forests fell about 1 billion board feet below the offering, reflecting low demand and low prices. With high demand and an improvement in relative prices, cutting may be expected to match the amount offered (or even run somewhat higher, to the extent that there had been a lag in cutting against previous sales). This would provide a supply increment of about 3 billion board feet for 1975, still some 10 billion short of the amount needed to meet the estimated demand on the basis of the conservative price assumption.

The size of the increment in supply that can be expected from private holdings and from higher net imports is clearly speculative. Both these supply sources are highly price-sensitive. The yield from private holdings will also be influenced by the nature, extent, and success of federal programs designed to assist the private sector. On the basis of the conservative relative-price assumption (6 percent over first half 1970), the Forest Service estimated that about 5 billion additional board feet would be available from private lands, plus about 1 billion more from net imports. However, it is at least equally probable that somewhat less would be available from private holdings and that exports would rise considerably more.

Such increments in timber supply would still leave an apparent gap of nearly 4 billion board feet, around 7 percent, between projected requirements and estimated supply on the conservative price assumption. This gap must be regarded as no more than a statistic. In practice, a balance between supply and consumption will be achieved one way or another. Normally, relative prices rise until balance is achieved. If all the underlying postulates used in the calculations prove correct, including a major acceleration of forestry programs— a very big "if"—balance could occur at a level of relative prices approximately 13 percent higher than in early 1970. Hopefully, achievement of a balance would not require any actual cutback in housing objectives, but rather, more economical utilization of wood and greater use of substitute materials.

The numbers presented here must be regarded as illustrative of the problem confronting us and as orders of magnitude rather than as precise forecasts. It is clear, however, that there is a problem: Realization of U.S. housing goals and satisfaction of the other needs of a growing economy will require a very considerable increase in the availability of softwood timber. The squeeze is likely to be most serious during the mid-1970s. It is equally clear that the needed increase in timber supply must be accomplished in ways compatible with the preservation and enhancement of environmental values. Public policy must address itself to this problem promptly.

The Task Force report released by the White House on June 19, 1970 set forth the basic dimensions of the problem and recommended a series of initial steps toward meeting it. These included action by the Forest Service to develop plans to increase the yield from national-forest lands in ways consistent with other objectives of forest management. The report suggested an increment of 7 billion board feet as a national-forest target for 1978. It recommended that the Service adopt a more flexible policy in establishing its offerings for each year, with a view to making supply more responsive to annual fluctuations in demand, but without jeopardizing intermediate or longer-term plans and objectives. It stressed the need for steps to augment the yield from private lands, and careful analysis of proposals designed to achieve this. It also urged that the Department of Housing and Urban Development, in cooperation with other agencies, push ahead rapidly with programs to encourage the development and facilitate the use of wood substitutes.

While the broad goals of policy seem clear, a host of questions still remain about the ways in which these goals could best be achieved, with due regard to all the basic objectives of public policy. The Task Force was aware that it did not have the solutions to such problems as how best to meet the physical needs of the economy while preserving environmental values, how best to develop the private potential at acceptable budgetary cost, how to answer the insistent criticisms from both industry and environmentalists regarding Forest Service management and disposal policies, and many others. The Task Force therefore recommended the designation of a panel of distinguished citizens to study these problems and to advise the Administration on solutions. The recommendation was carried out through appointment of the President's Advisory Panel on Timber and the Environment, chaired by Mr. Fred Seaton, former Secretary of the Interior.

3 TIMBER RESOURCES

H. R. JOSEPHSON* AND DWIGHT HAIR**

THE FOREST LAND RESOURCE of the United States includes some 760 million acres of forest land, about one-third of the 2.3 billion acres of total land area in the 50 states. Some two-thirds of this forest land, 510 million acres, is classed as commercial, that is, suitable and available for the growing of continuous crops of industrial wood products. The remaining forest land, 250 million acres, is classed as noncommercial. These lands are mostly of low productivity for timber growing. However, about 16 million acres of public noncommercial forests are productive lands but are reserved for recreation or other nontimber uses.

STATUS AND TRENDS

Although nominally available for timber production, commercial forest lands include some private holdings which have, in effect, been at least temporarily withdrawn from timber use: The owner's policy prohibits tree cutting. In general, the commercial forest lands are increasingly used for combinations of purposes, not only for timber but also for watersheds, recreation areas, wildlife habitat, and grazing. The noncommercial forests are primarily or exclusively valuable for such nontimber uses.

By far the major part of the nation's commercial forest land is in the eastern United States (North and South; see Table 3.1). The South accounts for 39 percent of the total and the North 34 percent. The West (Rocky Mountains and Pacific Coast) has the remaining 27 percent of the commercial forest area, plus most of the lands classed as noncommercial.

Since 1910, the area of commercial forest land in the United

---

* Director, Division of Forest Economics and Marketing Research, Forest Service, Washington, D.C.
**Assistant to the Director, Division of Forest Economics and Marketing Research, Forest Service, Washington, D.C.

States has increased by about 50 million acres. The gross gain in forest area in this period, resulting from the reversion of abandoned farmlands, amounted to some 85 million acres. However, there were withdrawals of about 35 million acres of forest lands for urban development, highways, airports, reservoirs, parks, wilderness and recreation areas, and for cropland development such as the recent surge of land clearing for soybean production in the Mississippi Delta.

Most areas converted from timber use to other purposes were stocked with trees. On the other hand, most abandoned farmlands reverting to commercial forest status were nonstocked lands which could contribute to timber yields only after a period of several decades. Immediate impacts of land-use changes on timber inventories, growth, and supplies available to industry thus have been, on the whole, much less favorable than the net changes in forest acreage would suggest.

Forest Survey data indicate that the rate of expansion of commercial forest area has been slowing down. In the fifteen years between 1953 and 1968, the net gain in area was about 8 million acres. Some further gains in forest area appear likely in the near future, in view of the projected decline in area needed for cropland and pasture. Within possibly a decade or so, however, losses of forest land to other uses appear likely to exceed gains, and consequently the area of commercial forest land can be expected to begin declining. The regions listed in Table 3.1 group the 50 states as follows:

TABLE 3.1 COMMERCIAL FOREST LAND IN THE UNITED STATES, BY REGION, 1953, 1963, AND 1968

(Thousand acres)

Region	1953	1963	1968
East:			
North	171,053	170,474	175,993
South	194,681	201,879	198,798
West:			
Rocky Mountains	66,383	66,100	66,112
Pacific Coast	70,185	69,847	69,310
Totals	502,302	508,300	510,213

1. North: Connecticut, Maine, Massachusetts, New Hampshire, Rhode Island, Vermont, Delaware, Maryland, New Jersey, New York, Pennsylvania, West Virginia, Michigan, Minnesota, eastern South Dakota, North Dakota, Wisconsin, Illinois, Indiana, Ohio, Iowa, Kansas, Kentucky, Missouri, and Nebraska.

2. South: Virginia, North Carolina, South Carolina, Georgia, Florida, Tennessee, Alabama, Mississippi, Arkansas, Louisiana, and Texas.

3. Rocky Mountains: Idaho, Montana, western South Dakota, Wyoming, Arizona, Colorado, and Nevada.

4. Pacific Coast: Alaska, Washington, Oregon, California, and Hawaii.

North and South together are referred to as East; Rocky Mountains and Pacific Coast, as West.

SOUTHERN FOREST LANDS

Southern forests include about 199 million acres of commercial forest land (Table 3.1), 39 percent of the U.S. total. About 42 percent of southern commercial forest lands support southern pine types, while hardwoods predominate on 58 percent of the total area:

Forest type group	Million acres
Loblolly-shortleaf pine	54.2
Longleaf-slash pine	26.0
Oak-hickory	56.4
Oak-gum-cypress	35.1
Oak-pine	25.0
Other	3.1
Total	198.8

The pine types provide the major part of the raw material for the southern lumber, plywood, and pulp industries.

Hardwoods are the climax species over much of the area occupied by pines, and trends in many areas indicate that hardwoods will replace pine unless management is greatly intensified or cutting practices drastically altered. Most of the oak-pine and oak-hickory types, for example, are on upland sites best suited to growing pines. Conversion of such areas to pine through hardwood tree removal and other cultural practices represents a highly promising management opportunity in many parts of the South.

Oak-gum-cypress types, which contain such valuable species as sweetgum, cherry-bark oak, and tupelo, occupy about 36 million acres in the South. These bottomland areas contain some of the most productive hardwood sites in the country. Nevertheless, in recent years, land clearing for field crops and pasture has caused a rapid reduction in the area of these forest types. A recent study in the Delta region of Mississippi, for example, showed that more than one-fifth of the bottomland forest had been cleared in a ten-year period. This rate of clearing was nearly four times that noted in earlier surveys.

NORTHERN FOREST LANDS

About 176 million acres of commercial forest land (34 percent of the national total) are found in the North (Table 3.1). Most of this area is in hardwood types:

Forest type group	Million acres
Spruce-fir	20.0
White-red-jack pine	10.9
Oak-hickory	61.0
Maple-beech-birch	33.7
Aspen-birch	24.0
Elm-ash-cottonwood	18.6
Other	7.8
Total	176.0

The oak-hickory forest is the most extensive type in the North, covering about 35 percent of the commercial forest area, and is a major source of hardwood sawlogs and veneer logs. In this type, as in the maple-beech-birch and the elm-ash-cottonwood types, the quality and value of the stands could be substantially increased by removing low-quality trees and in some cases by converting to more desirable species.

The aspen-birch type, which accounts for about 14 percent of the commercial forest, is concentrated in the Lake States region. This type is composed of relatively short-lived species that have taken over large areas of cutover lands and is a type primarily valuable for pulpwood. The swamp conifer forests of spruce, fir, and cedar occupy about 11 percent of the commercial forest land in the North; the pine type, 6 percent.

WESTERN FOREST LANDS

About 69 million acres of commercial forest land are located on the Pacific Coast and about 66 million acres in the Rocky Mountains (Table 3.1). Together these forest areas amount to 27 percent of the U.S. total. Most of the western forests are softwood forests:

Forest type group	Million acres
Douglas-fir	37.3
Ponderosa pine	35.9
Lodgepole pine	15.7
Fir-spruce	15.5
Hemlock-Sitka spruce	10.0
Other softwood types (including white pine, larch, and redwood)	9.9
Hardwood types	11.1
Total	135.4

The Douglas-fir type occupies about 28 percent of the commercial forest area in the West. Nearly half of the area in this type is on highly productive forest lands in western Washington, western Oregon, and northern California.

Ponderosa pine, occupying 27 percent of the commercial forest area in the West, occurs throughout eastern Oregon, eastern Washington, California, and the Rocky Mountains.

Douglas-fir and ponderosa pine stands are major sources of logs for high-quality lumber and plywood. Several other types of forest—particularly western pine, sugar pine, redwood, and larch—are also important sources of high-quality timber. In all these types, prompt regeneration of cut and burned areas is a major problem. And in the Douglas-fir region, large areas of high-site lands that have not regenerated promptly have been taken over by hardwoods.

The lodgepole pine and fir-spruce types each occupy about 11 percent of the western commercial forest area. These types are widely distributed at high elevations throughout the West. The hemlock-Sitka spruce type, 7 percent of the western commercial forest, occupies nearly all the commercial forest land in coastal Alaska and is also the characteristic type along the Washington and Oregon coasts. Most of the lodgepole pine, fir-spruce, and hemlock-Sitka spruce forests are overmature and susceptible to large losses from insects and diseases.

Timber mortality in the West, largely in overmature stands, amounted to 2.8 billion cubic feet in 1967. Reduction of this loss through conversion of old-growth to young-growth stands, increased salvage, and more effective protection programs could substantially increase timber supplies.

MAJOR IMPROVEMENTS

In recent decades, there have been major gains in timber-management intensity in all regions of the U.S. Expenditures for management programs by public and private groups have increased steadily to over $800 million a year.

Since the late 1920s, when the Clarke-McNary Act introduced effective fire control on private lands, the area of forest land burned over has dropped from around 40 million acres a year to a current level of around 4 million acres. At the same time, increasing proportions of the timber killed by fire have been salvaged. Timber losses from other causes, although still substantial, have been reduced by insect-control programs and other management efforts.

More attention has been given to harvesting practices to assure better regeneration, particularly on industrial and public forests. Annual tree planting has been increased from 139,000 acres in 1930 to about 1.4 million acres today. This rate is somewhat below the peak reached during the Soil Bank program of the late 1950s and early 1960s, as shown in Table 3.2.

Much of the planting, particularly on forest-industry holdings in the South, has been on former farm lands and on land where understocked hardwood stands could be converted to pine. Beyond this,

TABLE 3.2 ANNUAL PLANTING IN THE UNITED STATES
(Thousand acres)

Year	All land	Public land	Private land
1930	139	. . .	. . .
1940	519	265	254
1950	498	. . .	. . .
1960	2,102	265	1,837
1965	1,287	369	918
1969	1,374	389	985

both public and industrial planting after logging is becoming more widespread. Nevertheless, planting is still applied to only a small part of the cutover forest.

Removal of cull trees and other stand-improvement practices have been extended to include about a million acres annually. Commercial thinning of young stands, especially in the South and to some extent in the Douglas-fir region, is more common than heretofore. These cultural practices, while significant, are being applied to only a small portion of the forest lands which offer opportunities for better yields.

COMPETITION FOR LAND

Along with the intensified use and management of forest lands for timber production have come greater demands for nontimber uses of the forest. Increasing numbers of people want more withdrawals from commercial timber use, or modifications of forest land management, to provide nontimber goods and services such as wilderness and recreation areas and protection of the scenic and aesthetic values of the forested countryside.

With increasing population and income, recreational use of the forests has been expanding particularly fast. It is estimated that over a billion recreational visits are now made to forests and associated wildlands each year. Recent projections indicate that recreational use of forests by the year 2000 may be ten times the current level.

Demands for water for domestic and industrial use have been rising rapidly, and the upward trend is expected to continue. By the year 2000, for example, the nation's water requirements may be three times those of the early 1960s.

More than 250 million acres of forest land in the United States are grazed by domestic livestock. Demands for forage are expected to double and more by the end of the century, with a consequent intensification of grazing on all types of pasture and range. Forests also provide food and habitat for about 95 percent of the nation's big game animals, for roughly one-fourth of smaller game and furbearers, and for countless numbers of birds and other small animals.

Programs to establish multiple use of forest lands and improvement of the forest environment may impose important constraints on timber production in the years immediately ahead, the impact of multiple-use management on timber production may be largely confined to national forests and other public lands. Over a longer period, however, forest industries and many other private forest owners can be expected to encounter similar pressures for modification of timber management.

There is thus a growing need to develop and apply improved technology for multiple-use planning and multiple-use land management to achieve the optimum output of the many goods and services that can be derived from the nation's forest lands. Mutual understanding and support on the part of forest landowners and the public is essential if this goal is to be achieved.

TIMBER INVENTORIES IN THE EAST

In response to more effective programs of fire control and other management practices, timber inventories in the eastern United States have increased significantly in recent decades. Between 1953 and 1968, for example, inventories of softwood sawtimber (the board-foot measure of trees of a size and quality suitable for producing lumber and plywood) increased 42 percent in the South and 20 percent in the North (Table 3.3).

Total inventories of softwood growing stock (the cubic-foot meas-

TABLE 3.3 SAWTIMBER INVENTORY OF THE UNITED STATES ON COMMERCIAL FOREST LAND BY TREE TYPE AND REGION, 1953, 1963, AND 1968
(Billion board feet, international 1/4-inch rule)

Type and region	1953	1963	1968
Softwoods:			
North	60.7	67.7	72.6
South	188.1	234.3	266.7
Rocky Mountains	403.4	399.4	393.3
Pacific Coast	1,449.3	1,336.1	1,270.4
Totals	2,101.5	2,037.5	2,003.0
Hardwoods:			
North	191.0	221.5	239.4
South	193.6	193.2	194.8
Rocky Mountains	9.0	9.5	9.6
Pacific Coast	32.8	39.7	43.6
Totals	426.4	463.9	487.4
All Types:			
North	251.7	298.2	312.0
South	381.7	427.5	461.5
Rocky Mountains	412.4	408.9	402.9
Pacific Coast	1,482.1	1,375.8	1,314.0
Totals	2,527.9	2,510.4	2,490.4

TABLE 3.4 NET INVENTORY OF GROWING STOCK ON COMMERCIAL FOREST LAND IN THE UNITED STATES, BY TREE TYPE AND REGION, 1953, 1963, AND 1968
(Billion cubic feet)

Type and region	1953	1963	1968
Softwoods:			
North	26.9	32.4	35.5
South	54.3	65.9	74.0
Rocky Mountains	90.1	93.7	95.1
Pacific Coast	249.5	239.3	232.7
Totals	420.8	431.3	437.3
Hardwoods:			
North	82.1	101.0	111.9
South	70.3	73.1	74.9
Rocky Mountains	4.7	5.4	5.8
Pacific Coast	10.9	13.4	14.9
Totals	168.0	192.9	207.5
All Types:			
North	109.0	133.4	147.4
South	124.6	139.0	148.9
Rocky Mountains	94.8	99.1	100.9
Pacific Coast	260.4	252.7	247.6
Totals	588.8	624.2	644.8

ure of sound wood in trees 5 inches and larger in diameter at breast height, excluding rough and rotten trees) increased somewhat less than sawtimber in both the South and North (Table 3.4).

The increases in growing stock inventories since 1953 have been spread over all but the largest diameter classes (Table 3.5). The large

TABLE 3.5 NET INVENTORY OF SOFTWOOD GROWING STOCK ON COMMERCIAL FOREST LAND IN THE NORTH AND SOUTH, BY DIAMETER CLASS, 1953, 1963, AND 1968

Region and diameter class (Inches d.b.h.)	Inventory (Billion cubic feet)			Change (Percent)	
	1953	1963	1968	1953–68	1963–68
North:					
Poletimber:					
5.0–9.0	12.4	16.1	17.9	44.4	11.2
Sawtimber:					
9.0–13.0	7.5	9.3	10.3	37.3	10.6
13.0–19.0	4.9	5.4	5.7	16.3	5.6
19.0–29.0	2.0	1.5	1.5	−25.0	0.0
29.0 and over	0.1	0.1	0.1	0.0	0.0
Total sawtimber	14.5	16.3	17.6	21.4	8.0
South:					
Poletimber:					
5.0–9.0	15.0	17.8	19.6	30.7	10.1
Sawtimber:					
9.0–13.0	20.6	23.8	26.0	26.2	9.2
13.0–19.0	15.0	19.4	22.5	50.0	16.0
19.0–29.0	3.4	4.7	5.7	67.6	21.3
29.0 and over	0.3	0.2	0.2	−33.3	0.0
Total sawtimber	39.3	48.1	54.4	38.4	13.1

gain in quantity of softwood timber in the 13.0–19.0-inch diameter classes in the South is especially significant for the softwood lumber and plywood industries.

WESTERN INVENTORIES

In contrast to the upward trends in timber inventories in the East, softwood inventories in the West have been declining. Between 1953 and 1968, quantities of softwood sawtimber on the Pacific Coast dropped from 1,449 billion board feet to 1,270 billion, a decrease of 12 percent (Table 3.3). There was also a small drop, from 403 to 393 billion board feet, in the Rocky Mountains. These decreases in western timber inventories reflect the increase in harvesting of old-growth stands and the low level of growth in these western forests, resulting from heavy mortality in older stands and the recency of cutting on much of the young forest area.

HARDWOOD INVENTORIES, SOUTH VS. NORTH

Changes in hardwood timber inventories have differed substantially from the trends for softwoods. Hardwood inventories in the South have shown little change since 1953, mainly as a result of land clearing in the Delta region, heavy cutting, and stand conversion (Tables 3.3 and 3.4). Hardwood sawtimber inventories in the North, on the other hand, increased about 25 percent between 1953 and 1968.

Most of the recent increase in hardwood inventories in the North has been in the smaller diameter classes (Table 3.6). A major part of these increases in hardwood inventories was in the less desirable species such as the upland oaks, hickory, beech, cottonwood, and soft maple. There were also increases in the inventories of preferred species such as the select white and red oaks, hard maple, and yellow poplar. On the other hand, inventories of yellow birch and black walnut have declined.

TABLE 3.6 HARDWOOD INVENTORIES IN THE NORTH

Diameter class (Inches at breast height)	Inventory (Billion cubic feet)			Change (Percent)	
	1953	1963	1968	1953–68	1963–68
Poletimber:					
5.0–11.0	40.8	52.6	59.3	45.3	12.7
Sawtimber:					
11.0–15.0	19.5	24.5	27.3	40.0	11.4
15.0–19.0	11.8	13.6	14.8	25.4	8.8
19.0–29.0	9.5	9.7	9.9	4.2	2.1
29.0 and over	0.5	0.6	0.6	20.0	0.0
Total sawtimber	41.3	48.4	52.6	27.4	8.7

The relatively small quantity of hardwood sawtimber in the West has increased modestly in recent years (Tables 3.3 and 3.4). This increase was largely the result of the development of alder stands following clearcutting of softwoods, particularly on high-site lands in western Washington and western Oregon that were originally occupied by Douglas-fir.

TOTAL NET ANNUAL TIMBER GROWTH

Another important measure of the timber situation in the United States is the trend in net annual growth (that is, net after deduction of mortality losses from fire and other destructive agents). Since 1953, net annual growth has been increasing for both softwoods and hardwoods in all sections of the country (Tables 3.7 and 3.8). This has resulted both from reductions in mortality and from improvements in forest management practices.

Net annual timber growth in the United States totals about 10 billion cubic feet of softwoods and 7.4 billion cubic feet of hardwoods. Softwoods in the South have shown the largest increases in growth—for example, a 61-percent increase for growing stock and a 36-percent increase for sawtimber between 1952 and 1967. Growth of softwoods on the Pacific Coast and hardwoods in the North has also increased by lesser, yet still substantial, amounts.

TABLE 3.7 NET ANNUAL SAWTIMBER GROWTH AND REMOVALS ON COMMERCIAL FOR-
EST LANDS OF THE UNITED STATES BY TREE TYPE AND REGION, 1952, 1962, AND
1967

(Billion board feet, international ¼-inch rule)

Type and region	Growth			Removals		
	1952	1962	1967	1952	1962	1967
Softwoods:						
North	2.378	2.751	2.947	1.517	1.746	1.905
South	13.835	16.914	18.849	12.098	10.142	12.883
Rocky Mountains	3.232	3.419	3.470	3.173	4.302	5.039
Pacific Coast	8.600	10.132	10.908	21.465	21.623	24.243
Totals	28.045	33.216	36.174	38.253	37.813	44.070
Hardwoods:						
North	7.196	8.423	9.224	5.022	5.282	5.794
South	6.818	6.834	7.059	7.540	6.514	7.182
Rocky Mountains	0.102	0.114	0.120	0.015	0.021	0.024
Pacific Coast	0.724	1.004	1.133	0.062	0.282	0.397
Totals	14.840	16.375	17.536	12.639	12.099	13.397
All Types:						
North	9.574	11.174	12.171	6.539	7.028	7.699
South	20.653	23.748	25.908	19.638	16.656	20.065
Rocky Mountains	3.334	3.528	3.590	3.189	4.323	5.063
Pacific Coast	9.324	11.136	12.041	21.527	21.905	24.640
Totals	42.885	49.586	53.710	50.893	49.912	57.467

TABLE 3.8 NET ANNUAL GROWTH AND REMOVALS OF GROWING STOCK ON COMMERCIAL FOREST LAND IN THE UNITED STATES, BY TREE TYPE AND REGION, 1952, 1962, AND 1967

(Billion cubic feet)

Type and region	Growth			Removals		
	1952	1962	1967	1952	1962	1967
Softwoods:						
North	1.011	1.159	1.252	0.592	0.562	0.633
South	3.571	4.455	5.006	3.118	2.798	3.466
Rocky Mountains	0.933	1.069	1.148	0.538	0.736	0.868
Pacific Coast	1.927	2.379	2.560	3.325	3.395	3.884
Totals	7.442	9.062	9.966	7.573	7.491	8.851
Hardwoods:						
North	3.087	3.709	4.041	1.455	1.599	1.787
South	2.490	2.714	2.866	2.410	2.328	2.520
Rocky Mountains	0.051	0.076	0.091	0.002	0.004	0.004
Pacific Coast	0.253	0.344	0.383	0.029	0.078	0.097
Totals	5.881	6.843	7.381	3.896	4.009	4.408
All Types:						
North	4.098	4.868	5.293	2.047	2.161	2.420
South	6.061	7.169	7.872	5.528	5.126	5.986
Rocky Mountains	0.984	1.145	1.239	0.540	0.740	0.872
Pacific Coast	2.180	2.723	2.943	3.354	3.473	3.981
Totals	13.323	15.905	17.347	11.469	11.500	13.259

TIMBER GROWTH PER ACRE

Although total net annual growth has been increasing, average growth per acre is still far below that achieved in fully stocked, productive stands. The average net annual growth in 1967, in cubic feet per acre, is shown in Table 3.9.

For all commercial forest lands, net growth now averages about 34 cubic feet per acre, but this varies widely by region and class of forest ownership. In the South, for example, net growth on national forest and industrial lands averages around 50 cubic feet per acre, in contrast to about 37 cubic feet per acre on other public and private

TABLE 3.9 AVERAGE NET ANNUAL GROWTH IN THE UNITED STATES, 1967
(Cubic feet per acre)

Region	All owner- ships	National forest	Other public	Industry	Farm & miscel- laneous
North	30	29	29	39	29
South	40	50	38	53	36
Rocky Mountains	19	20	16	25	...
Pacific Coast	42	20	53	68	61
United States	34	25	33	52	33

holdings. In pine plantations, on the other hand, growth rates of 100 to 160 cubic feet per acre are being achieved in the South, and even higher rates have been attained on limited areas of cottonwood plantations.

On the Pacific Coast, net growth on forest industry and farm and miscellaneous holdings, where logging has been under way for many years, averages over 60 cubic feet per acre. On the national forests, which still contain a high proportion of old-growth timber, most growth is still lost to mortality, and net growth consequently averages only about 20 cubic feet per acre. Much higher growth rates could be achieved in this region, especially on high-site lands in western Washington, western Oregon, and northern California, with expanded investments for conversion of old-growth stands, thinning, salvage, protection, and other forestry measures.

In the North, net annual growth averages about 30 cubic feet per acre; in the Rocky Mountains, about 19 cubic feet per acre. These averages are also far below the levels that could be attained under intensive management.

COMPARISON OF GROWTH AND REMOVALS

In eastern United States, net annual growth of softwood timber in 1967, amounting to 6.3 billion cubic feet, was substantially above removals of 4.1 billion cubic feet (Table 3.8). In the West, net growth of 3.7 billion cubic feet was significantly less than removals of 4.7 billion cubic feet. In the East, these relationships reflect the resurgence of young-growth forests resulting from fire control and other forestry programs, plus relatively low levels of timber harvesting compared with previous levels. In the West, where most of the timber is still old-growth, cutting is relatively heavy, while growth in young stands has not yet had time to build up.

In the case of softwood sawtimber, net annual growth of 36.2 billion board feet in the United States was considerably less than total removals of 44.1 billion board feet (Table 3.7). Net growth of sawtimber in the South, 18.8 billion board feet, was 6 billion board feet above removals. Since 1967, however, much of this excess growth has been taken up by expansion of timber harvests for pulpwood, plywood, and lumber.

In the North, softwood sawtimber growth in 1967 was about 1 billion board feet more than removals.

On the other hand, on the Pacific Coast, where harvests consist in large part of the "allowable cut" in old-growth forests, removals of softwood sawtimber in 1967 were more than double the growth. In the Rocky Mountains, removals of softwood sawtimber were 1.5 times as great as net growth.

In the case of hardwoods, growth of growing stock amounted to 7.4 billion cubic feet in 1967—considerably more than removals of 4.4 billion cubic feet (Table 3.8). However, much of the growth occurs on small or low-quality trees, while most removals are of higher-quality trees.

Net growth of hardwood sawtimber in 1967, 17.5 billion board feet, also exceeded removals of 13.4 billion board feet. Net growth exceeded removals by a wide margin in the North; in the South, growth and removals of hardwood sawtimber were roughly equal.

Of the total removals of 13.3 billion cubic feet in 1967, roundwood products—including sawlogs, veneer logs, pulpwood, fuelwood, and miscellaneous products—accounted for 10.8 billion cubic feet, or 80 percent of the total. Additional logging residues, plus other losses from land clearing or other changes in land use, amounted to 2.4 billion cubic feet. Losses of forest land and timber to other uses were substantial in all regions, but were especially extensive in the river valleys of the South.

CHANGES IN GROWTH AND REMOVALS

In the 1962–1967 period, total softwood sawtimber removals in the United States increased 6.3 billion board feet, more than double the estimated 3 billion increase in net annual growth in this period (Table 3.7). The increase of 1.3 billion board feet of hardwood sawtimber removals approximated the rise in net annual growth in this period.

The rise in timber removals since 1962 largely reflects increases in harvests of sawlogs, veneer logs, and pulpwood. Between 1962 and 1967, output of these products rose 15 percent, to 9.9 billion cubic feet. By 1969, output had increased another 8 percent, to 10.6 billion cubic feet. Increases in output of these industrial wood products since 1962 have continued a trend extending back over several decades. During the past twenty years, for example, production of industrial roundwood from U.S. forests expanded 37 percent. As a result of improving utilization in this same period, shipments of processed items such as lumber, pulp, and particleboard rose more than 50 percent.

Until recent years, increases in production of industrial wood products were largely offset by decreases in production of fuelwood and miscellaneous roundwood products such as fence posts, mine timbers, piling, and similar items. However, the decline in the production of fuelwood has nearly run its course: Removals in future years are likely to move upward in line with the growing harvest of sawlogs, veneer logs, and pulpwood.

4   SUPPLY AND CONSUMERS

RALPH R. WIDNER*

PEOPLE CONSUME TREES. They also want the other benefits that flow from forests. The experience of the last several decades has shown that conflict between these two classes of demand cannot be resolved by the mere advocacy of multiple use, particularly when the issues involve the management of specific tracts of forest land.

While consumer demands, particularly for housing, and rising prices for wood are generating pressures for increased timber production on national-forest lands, a climate of opinion is spreading among the public favoring a de-emphasis of timber production in favor of ecologic, recreational, and watershed-protection benefits.

Such disparities in public attitudes—wanting to have the cake and eat it too—have been a consistent theme in American resource history. In the past, however, cries for more stringent logging controls have been accompanied by threats, real or imagined, of timber famine.

Today, the sufficiency or insufficiency of timber supplies is not necessarily the key issue for some segments of the consuming public. There appears to be some agreement that the basic forest resource exists—given more intensive application of genetics, fertilizers, and technology—to meet our present and foreseeable needs. The primary public disagreements center around the allocation of forest resources to competing demands and around the lands on which timber production shall be the dominant use.

Historically, we might expect the market place to be the final arbiter of the issue. To a certain extent, however, the question can no longer be completely resolved there. The arguments being put forth most strongly in opposition to increased timber production are in large part nonfinancial; a whole new set of social, political, and ecologic factors have been injected into what was once a rather simple short-run financial equation.

---

* Director, The Academy for Contemporary Problems, Columbus, Ohio.

CONSERVATIONIST–PRESERVATIONIST–ENVIRONMENTALIST

There has always been a fundamental schism in American conservation between the "preservationists" and the "resource developers," between the advocates of wilderness on the one hand and of multiple use on the other.

Today, widespread popular concern has grown beyond yesterday's simple differences of opinion on conservation policy. The preservationist movement has evolved into an "environmentalist" movement and it, in turn, has found common cause with the first well-organized, politically effective consumer movement in U.S. history. Its impact on future forest policy will be far-reaching.

One of the summary conclusions of the Fifth American Forest Congress in 1963 reads:

> There is no question but that on the bulk of American forest lands today, timber is carrying the economic load in supporting other forest uses. We should not thereby conclude, however, that this will continue to be true in the future. The pressures of urbanization are imposing new burdens on the forests and in some sections of the country, as population pressures grow, these other demands may supplant timber as the dominant forest resource demand.[1]

By 1970, this forecast had come true. The combined pressures of urbanization, rising consumption, intensive industrialization, and concomitant pollution of the environment led to a new public concern for the use of nonmaterial as well as material resources. A revolutionary alteration in public attitudes had begun.

An article in the February 1970 issue of *Fortune* reported:

> Noisy, militant, litigious, growing in strength and numbers, the conservationists are on the march. They believe their mission is desperately urgent—that unless Americans change some of their attitudes toward the environment, the country will literally destroy itself. . . . Clearly a growing number of Americans think the conservationists—or environmentalists, to give them a label that suits their newly expanded goals—may be right. The power of this burgeoning movement is being felt in the courts, in politics, and in the boardrooms of the nation's top corporations.

The article also pointed out that many now believe "that unless America abandons the notion that a growing population can prosper only through a growing output of goods drawn from an endless frontier of resources, and unless technological progress is restrained, then all the efforts to improve the environment will be in vain."[2]

The nonmaterialistic nature of many of the arguments being advanced by the environmentalists was emphasized by two professors of law quoted in the *Fortune* article. Joseph L. Saxe of the University of Michigan remarked: "We are beginning to see value in maintaining resources rather than merely exploiting them. The courts are going to have to respond to this new perspective."

In the same vein, James E. Krier, of UCLA, said: "The promised surge of environmental litigation calls for rethinking much of our substantive and procedural law. Much of that law was made during the prime of the old, proprietary lawsuit, which it suited well enough; it fits poorly, however, the frame of the new lawsuit brought to protect environmental values in the public interest. The common-law concepts of nuisance and waste, for example, are not responsive to the needs of environmental litigation. . . . they reflect a far too narrow and myopic view. . . ."

To many, it still seems conjectural whether the views of the environmentalists can withstand the heavy pressures which will be exerted by the mass of consumers for accelerated utilization of resources in the face of a growing population, demands by the economically deprived for a greater share in the material wealth of the country, and the rising aspirations of most Americans for better and better physical standards of living. The more skeptical economists are tempted to dismiss the environmentalist movement as a transient public fad that will soon pass in favor of some new popular infatuation. The rising prices which inevitably accompany more stringent resource utilization, they argue, would quickly disenchant the consuming public with rigorously restrictive policies of resource utilization.

ENVIRONMENTALIST-CONSUMER TIES

Environmentalists will undoubtedly have a profound impact on national policy during this decade. Their arguments are not new to American resource policy—indeed, they have been vociferously contended for over a century—but the situation is different today because environmentalists are achieving wide public acceptance simultaneously with the evolution of the first strong consumer movement in the country.

The congruence of interests between the environmentalists and the consumer movement is illustrated by a typical flyer issued to consumers at key locations in the Boston area by one organization, Boston Ecology Action:

> The packaging you take home today becomes trash tomorrow. This is costing you in terms of dollars and health. Packaging can be deceptive, disguising product contents. Packaging increases the cost of the products you buy. By converting trees to paper, it upsets the forest life cycle. You must pay high municipal taxes for trash disposal. When packaging is burned in building incinerators and city dumps, it contributes to air pollution. Burning paper gives off carbon monoxide and particulates. . . . Carry a bag or basket with you. Don't accept unneces-

sary paper bags. Remove excess packaging (like boxes around bottles and toothpaste tubes) at the store and ask the sales personnel to return it to the manufacturer.[3]

Environmentalists and consumer spokesmen have joined forces. They have not been reluctant to call attention to the costs or inconveniences which the public may have to bear if the nation de-emphasizes commercial in favor of noncommercial resource policies. The argument that these short-run costs should be borne in order to lighten the long-run costs imposed by deterioration of the national environment is readily accepted by many Americans in the face of the highly visible problems spawned by pollution and land abuse.

Inevitably, environmentalist attitudes have influenced the political climate. The President of the United States declared that environmental improvement would be the primary domestic concern of the 1970s. Congress confronts a welter of legislation dealing with the problem. State and local leaders have embarked upon new policies which would have been politically unthinkable five years ago.

The reception given the long-awaited report of the Public Land Law Review Commission is illustrative of the new attitudes. In an editorial on the report, the *Washington Daily News* applauded the Commission's recommendations for setting aside public lands for new towns, parks, wildlife areas, and wilderness, but took exception to the recommendations regarding timber: "The Commission proposes that 30 to 40 million acres of federal forest be designated for intensive tree-cutting under a 'dominant use' classification. This conflicts with the multiple-use approach in which recreation, wildlife, and water resources are given equal consideration."

Upon publication of the report, *Time* observed that "the main thrust of the report is a compromise between two conflicting policies. The Commission urges greater exploitation of federal lands for commercial use while simultaneously paying homage to environmental preservation." The article concluded that "an increasingly environment-conscious Congress may act only on those parts [of the recommendations] that reflect the current congressional mood."[4]

Science, the magazine of the American Association for the Advancement of Science, criticized the Commission's report as too favorable to commercial interests.[5]

While there is apparently little reluctance to earmark forest land for predominant use as recreation land, there is increasingly strong public resistance to the acceleration of timber production in many areas.

John D. Rockefeller IV, West Virginia's Secretary of State, wrote to the *Washington Post:*

Last fall my wife, Sharon, and I hiked along Otter Creek in Randolph and Tucker Counties, West Virginia. We agreed that it was one of the most beautiful areas in the eastern United States—with its large, majestic trees, its lush undergrowth, and the crystal-clear mountain stream rushing through sandstone boulders and over a series of waterfalls along the trail. We recommend this hike to anyone who loves the mountains. . . . We made a commitment then to work to preserve the Otter Creek we saw—largely untouched by the hand of man for nearly a century. . . . But there is already bad news. . . . The Forest Service has decided to permit logging in well over half of the Otter Creek area, over 10,000 acres in that part of the Monongahela National Forest. I think this was wrong. I applaud the efforts of the West Virginia Highlands Conservancy to spare from logging the entire 18,000 acres of the Otter Creek basin. . . . The federal government owns 808,000 acres of land in the Monongahela National Forest in eastern West Virginia. I believe that within this vast area we can afford to zone against logging and road building not only the 18,000 acres of the Otter Creek basin but also other areas such as Dolly Sods and the Cranberry back country. This can be done two ways. Congress can act, declaring national forests as wilderness areas, or the U.S. Forest Service can protect them by administrative decision. . . . In all of the United States east of the Mississippi River, Congress has declared only three wilderness areas. They are in North Carolina, New Jersey, and New Hampshire. Surely Congress should protect some wilderness areas in the mid-Atlantic region, and the Otter Creek basin in West Virginia is a most accessible and suitable candidate. At the very least the Forest Service should protect the area by administrative decision.

INTENSIVE TIMBER MANAGEMENT

The opposition which defeated the proposed National Forest Timber Conservation and Management Act of 1969 perhaps typifies the reasoning of opponents of increased timber production on the national forests. The Sierra Club submitted the following arguments to members of Congress:

1. Passage of the Act would foreclose possibility of additions to the National Wilderness Preservation System whenever the qualified area has even the potential for growing marketable wood.
2. Intensive forestry advocated by the Act will not bring good forestry to our public forests.
3. Remaining old-growth timber should be rationed out to produce future cutting cycles of 80 to 100 years, as the Forest Service has planned, rather than be sawed down as fast as modern machinery can do the job.
4. The current export of timber, over 4 billion board feet a year to Japan alone, belies the claim that the United States faces a massive timber shortage.
5. Housing needs of this country can be met through increased use of substitute products and modern construction concepts that will reduce the dependence on wood products and traditional building techniques.

In one letter addressed to members of Congress, the Sierra Club concluded: "Our national forests are too valuable to sacrifice them in the name of short-term economic benefits. To the extent that the nation may demand an increase in wood products, attention should be turned to our private timber-bearing lands, where 95 percent of the unstocked and understocked acreage lies. Skilled professional forestry on these lands would do far more to augment wood supplies than quick stripping of our public lands."

Terming the legislation the "Loggers Relief Act," the Sierra Club pointed out that "lumber consumption today in the U.S. is about the same as in 1910." It denied the existence of any timber shortage.[6]

The National Forest Products Association and the National Home Builders Association granted that lumber consumption in 1910 was 43.2 billion board feet compared to 43 billion board feet in 1968. But they pointed out the difference in "mix" of today's consumption of wood products compared to the century's first decade: In 1910, substantial portions of the timber cut in the U.S. were for fuel, railroad ties, and mine supports. Today, almost one-half of the cut is for building and industry, a little less than one-fourth for pulpwood, about 8 percent for plywood and veneer, and the rest for various industrial uses.

Answering the charge that exports of American timber belie the need for any concern over a timber shortage, the industrial organizations cited 1968 U.S. imports of over 6 billion board feet of finished lumber products, primarily from Canada. The industry then pointed to national commitments to build or rehabilitate 26 million units of housing, representing a doubling of demand for lumber.

Because of national economic conditions, the expected upsurge in housing starts in 1969 did not materialize and the expected further jump in the costs of plywood and softwood lumber did not occur in the last three quarters of 1969. In fact, after reaching a peak of 164.9 (1957–59 = 100) in April, the wholesale lumber price index declined, for a time almost continuously, approaching 120 at the end of 1970. During the same period, plywood prices dropped even more sharply. Nonetheless, there is a readily identifiable unsatisfied consumer demand for housing (and 80 percent of the frames for American homes are constructed of wood) that will have to be met during this decade.

RECONCILING CONFLICT

Can the conflicting aspirations of Americans as consumers and Americans as citizens wanting to withhold forest lands from intensive timber production be reconciled? Or are we likely to surrender, under the duress of rising prices, to short-run expedients which succeeding generations may painfully rue? Can multiple use be applied in land

and water management to help solve the conflict, or is it more likely to serve as a slogan for indecision about the most appropriate resource uses for specific forest areas?

An atmosphere of accommodation and farsightedness will have to be achieved before the present fractious debate over the proper use of the country's forest resources can be resolved.

The more candid environmentalists admit that the tactics of confrontation are not a very useful long-run policy. As Russell Train has observed: "We can't govern by protest, demonstration, and litigation. . . . You can't operate a going concern with protest as the main mechanism."

As the article in *Fortune* pointed out, "In private, some of the most intransigent among conservationists admit that the stress on obstruction is a temporary tactic. Eventually, they hope, the burden of defending the public interest in the environment will be taken up by public institutions. . . ."[7]

The environmentalists, for their part, will be forced to reconcile some of the internal contradictions inherent in their own position and, in particular, their opposition to increased utilization of a renewable resource such as timber in favor of other materials. Most of these other materials are derived from nonrenewable resources whose extraction or depletion most environmentalists either oppose or wish to discourage. It is not implausible to assume that the best long-run policy will be to rely more heavily on renewable rather than nonrenewable resources in meeting future consumption demands. Renewable resources can be more readily changed into materials whose residues cause less of a waste-disposal problem than many nonrenewable materials, which tend to persist in the environment. Many of those who espouse stricter resource controls also desire to provide the poor with safe and sanitary housing, good employment, and a more acceptable level of income. Meeting these objectives and simultaneously pursuing overly restrictive commercial resource policies will be difficult.

A substantial margin of conspicuous consumption could be controlled to help diminish some present demands on the timber resource, particularly in the case of pulpwood. Reuse could provide additional opportunities for reducing demands for raw resources. However, housing does account for the overwhelming share of timber demand and the enormous pent-up market for housing will have to be met. Suggesting other materials is no solution, for their use poses even more severe environmental problems than increased timber harvests.

Accommodation will require some very real changes in attitudes on the part of business, industry, and government. The commercial arguments which have played such an important role in formulating national resource policies during the past century will have to take their place in proper perspective with other resource considerations. Consumption for the sake of consumption will have to be curtailed.

The concerns of environmentalists are based on some profoundly pervasive problems affecting the future of the country and the race, and the climate of opinion that these concerns have engendered should be treasured and nurtured. The fundamentally commercial arguments previously used to secure passage of forestry legislation may be obsolete.

CONSERVATION BACKGROUND

Interestingly enough, even a century ago, the leaders of the forest conservation movement were not as concerned about the adequacies or inadequacies of timber supplies as they were about the effects of forest devastation upon the general environment. George Perkins Marsh lent a comprehensive vision to the early movement for forestry. Assurance of future commercial timber supplies played but a small role in his concern, and his perception was shared by many of the early forestry leaders.

The forest conservation movement in the state of New York was initially stimulated by the New York City Board of Trade and Transportation and the New York City Chamber of Commerce, more because of the effects which they thought forest devastation in the Adirondacks might have upon water supplies for the Erie Canal than upon the adequacy of future timber supplies. Their natural allies became those who were concerned about the impact which logging abuse had had upon forest recreation in the Adirondacks. Ultimately, these highly vocal groups had an enormous impact upon public opinion. Under the public pressures which developed in 1885 in New York, the timber resources of much of New York State were limited under the state constitution to two large forest preserves within which timber production was forever prohibited. Time after time, the people of New York State have refused to lift this iron-clad prohibition against timber production.[8]

Gifford Pinchot, who spent some of his early years as a forester working in the Adirondacks, bespoke his frustration on this point before an 1894 meeting of wealthy New York gentlemen farmers: "For ten years, we have been trying to provide suitable protection and management for the State Forest Preserves. At the end of that time, we find ourselves reduced to the conclusion that the very best thing we can do is to give up all hope of a sound and profitable management and simply content ourselves with putting it out of the power of the guardians of the forest to do it any harm."[9]

For very practical reasons, Pinchot found it necessary to place primary emphasis upon commercial arguments in favor of public forestry in order to secure passage of his legislation. His statement of the main objective of forestry, "to grow trees as a crop," substantially altered the earlier effect of such lay conservation leaders as Marsh. National resource policy was hammered out in an essentially commercial format.

For the last century, the commercial interests of the country dominated legislative decisions and public opinion. As a result, the disposition of resources was primarily governed by the needs and practices of those who utilized and processed these resources for public consumption.

Even in the 1880s, just before the Forest Preserve amendments were adopted in New York, it was inconceivable to many that resource policy could be discussed in any but a purely commercial sense. There was land to be homesteaded, timber to be harvested, minerals to be mined, rivers to be made navigable.

In the debate over a forest policy for New York State, Franklin Hough, a medical doctor who was later to play an important role in national forestry, found it unthinkable that anyone should suggest that vast tracts of forest be locked up in "preserves" or "parks": "With us no Government, State, or Nation will ever undertake reservations for this purpose. It may be done by individuals or groups for their own amusement but that is a matter that concerns nobody else. The sale of these privileges by government may be practicable and profitable in Europe but it is altogether out of place with us. Our taxpayers would never tolerate such an object of expense and it is to be regretted that the word 'park' has ever been used in this connection because it leads to the erroneous idea that expenses are to be increased for the enjoyment of those who have time or money to spend on sports or in woodland life."[10]

Public attitudes have changed considerably!

THE CONSERVATION ISSUE TODAY

The dominance of commercial viewpoints in American resource policy during the last century can be attributed primarily to the American belief in the need to develop the country and exploit the resources of a continent. Of prime importance was filling up and developing the interior. Today the country is filled up and the economy is the most highly developed in the history of mankind.

Inevitably, these changed circumstances are modifying widely held attitudes toward environmental questions. The commercial viewpoint no longer holds sole sway.

The existence of "public opinion" in the sense of a pervasive national consensus on key questions of policy is one of the myths of the democratic way of life. As Walter Lippmann pointed out in a study of public opinion made a half century ago, the great mass of the public is likely to remain apathetic or ignorant on most issues. It is aroused only when its own self-interest is involved, and usually this self-interest is clearly perceived only when the issue at hand intrudes upon the daily life of family and work.

In determining what public attitudes are likely to shape future resource policy, it is necessary to think of many "publics," not one. The political pulling and hauling of these self-interests, through organized groups, ultimately forms political decisions and shapes public awareness of an issue. It is this process which creates "a climate of opinion." The opinion may be held and understood, in fact, by only a small minority of the national electorate. As long as the general electorate remains apathetic or acquiesces through its silence, an opinion will prevail and ultimately affect political decisions.

Beginning in the early 1950s, ecologists from a number of disciplines awakened the leadership community to the existence of the highly intricate problems of environmental management. The work of these scientists eventually percolated into the political arena. A highly vocal Secretary of the Interior did much to popularize their findings.

The preservationists, given their own natural proclivities and interests, promptly seized upon the ecologists' ideas to reinforce their arguments on behalf of preservation.

Hough's argument that forest recreation was a luxury of the wealthy no longer applied in an affluent society in which the vast majority of citizens could afford to take advantage of the recreational amenities of the outdoors. With rapidly rising amounts of disposable income to spend on recreation, the public was no longer apathetic about such questions.

Public awareness has also been stimulated by the rapid metropolitanization of the United States, particularly since World War II. This sophistication has generated several environmental problems which the everyday citizen senses personally through stinging eyes, a rasping throat, slightly smelly drinking water, or constantly rising sewerage bills.

Because of the profound alterations in national life, the public became receptive to interests once thought to be the odd preoccupations of bird watchers and garden clubs. This receptivity was reinforced by the intricate network of communications media which reaches into every corner of American life. The process of creating a new "public opinion" accelerated.

Today, for the first time in U.S. history, consumer interests are close to attaining a balance of political power with commercial interests. Hereafter, political decisions about resource allocations will be the result of negotiation and not the result of unchallenged influence.

Is this possible?

In backing the proposed National Forest Timber Conservation and Management Act of 1969, industry interests were in favor of declaring timber production as the dominant use on approximately 97 million acres of national forests. In its report, the Public Land Law Review Commission recommended that 30 to 40 million acres of forest land be so classified. Conservation organizations were happy with neither recommendation, primarily because they feared that areas which they believed should be in the wilderness preservation system, or on which timber production should not be the dominant use, would be classified for such use before they could be set aside for other purposes. What environmentalists most fear is the piecemeal setting aside of areas of environmental, ecologic, or recreational interest while lands for intensive lumber production are designated en bloc. The consequent breakdown in trust leads to tactics of desperation.

PROSPECTIVE SOLUTIONS

The best solution appears to be simultaneous designation of two classes of forest so that both commercial and environmental interests can determine at the same time whether their needs are being satisfied. This can be accomplished only through a true multiple-use plan for national forests. As Orris Herfindahl has remarked:

> It should be recognized that there *are* benefits flowing from natural resources for which individuals cannot express their preferences in money terms simply because there is no feasible way for this to be done. In particular, it will not do to argue that society "needs" lumber or minerals but that scenery, etc., can always be dispensed with. This is an unreal choice, for the problem always involves a specific location. If consumers could express their preferences in economic terms, they might well indicate they want a particular slope to be forested rather than bare. . . . The "multiple use" solution, for example, is certainly applicable in many cases, but in some cases it turns out to be just a slogan serving to camouflage the complete sacrifice of one use to others.[11]

Accommodation might be achieved rapidly if Congress were to concentrate upon those aspects of the recommendations of the Public Land Law Review Commission which set up mechanisms for implementing a broad forest-use policy on all national forests.

Wilderness advocates point out that the areas of interest to them would contribute only a marginal amount of timber to meet national demands, perhaps as little as 1.2 percent. If this indeed turns out to be true, the basis for agreement can be reached quickly, and the nation can still meet its timber requirements without jeopardizing other forest values.

Each side must recognize the legitimacy of the other's interests. Herfindahl rightfully comments:

> While it may seem tactically wise—and may even be pleasant—to oppose all dam construction or to damn the wilderness enthusiasts as a minute nonworking portion of the population with perverted tastes, any progress toward a more suitable resolution of conflicts as they arise is going to be made by those who are less inflexible. An abandonment of fixed positions would be helpful.[12]

From the point of view of the consuming public, multiple use has meaning only so far as it is applied to the total inventory of national resources. It can rarely be applied in any perfect sense to small tracts of forest land. Within the whole framework of national resources, however, we can make provision for competing demands through intelligent planning. In this way, we can preserve a pluralistic system and assure even the minority the opportunity to meet its own requirements.

5   SUPPLY AND THE INDUSTRY

A. W. NELSON, JR.*

A COMPLETE HISTORY of the forest industry and its timber-supply problems is not necessary here, yet a clear understanding of where we are can be developed only from a historical viewpoint. It has been said that he who knows nothing of the past can understand little of the present and none of the future. This is certainly true of the timber-supply situation in the United States.

Much of the objection to helping the wood-using industry solve its timber-supply problem apparently comes from a segment of the public which still sees the industry in its old image as a despoiler of the forest—a broad categorization as "the lumber industry"—a viewpoint that is badly out of date.

Differences in point of view on timber supply go deep. Since before the turn of the century, a basic split in American schools of thought on conservation has existed between the aesthetic and the utilitarian. John Muir, founder of the Sierra Club, is identified with the aesthetic school of conservation, while Gifford Pinchot is identified with the utilitarian school. The two men worked together for a time to protect the new forest reserves set aside by President Grover Cleveland. They parted company, however, sometime prior to 1900 on the subject of wilderness preservation versus multiple use. Thus the issue is not a new one; its roots extend deep into U.S. history. What we are confronted with today is the same issue dressed up in late twentieth-century clothes.

We may have learned something about land management in the seventy or more years that have elapsed since Muir and Pinchot. We may be better equipped to resolve the issue between aesthetic and utilitarian values.

Lemuel R. Boulware, former Vice-President of General Electric in charge of Personnel and Community Relations, spent much of his life in the area of reconciling opposing views. The impact of his career on our society may be judged by the fact that a new word,

* Vice-President, Champion International Corporation, Atlanta, Ga.

"Boulwarism," has been coined by his admirers and critics. His book, *The Truth About Boulwarism,* outlines his premise that *when people are properly informed and know the problem they are arguing about, they usually move toward a solution, not toward a fight.* Surely this theory is valid in the area of land management.

EARLY HISTORY

The timber industry is reported to be the oldest industry on the North American continent. Early colonists were quick to seize the opportunity of shipping timber products from timber-rich America to timber-starved Europe. The saga of Eric the Red tells how Leif Ericson brought a cargo of wood from "Vinland" to the Norse settlements in Greenland. The Virginia Company, granted its charter April 10, 1606, was apparently the first to engage in manufacturing. Eight Poles and Dutchmen, specifically engaged for their skill in erecting sawmills, came to Virginia in 1608 and probably built the first sawmill in Jamestown. From then on, a solid stream of staves, masts, spars, balks, scantlings, wainscoating, tar, and pitch traveled from the new world to the old. The production of timber products also made possible the homes, shops, barns, and boats of the rapidly developing colonies.

Since forest products are heavy in relation to their value, and since the consumer is generally some distance from the forest, the question of transportation has always been a crucial one. Crude early-day transportation limited the kinds of material that could be extracted from the forest as well as the distances they could be sent to the consumer.

Initially, water was the important means for economical mass transport. Large volumes of timber were floated down streams, manufactured in streamside plants, and sent to consuming centers by boat. Development of the railways provided vastly greater access to forests and increased the use of wood. When the railroads could deliver supplies anywhere along their lines, demand for forest products rose rapidly and steeply. Thus, for example, a homesteader on the Great Plains was able to replace his sod hut with a wooden farmhouse and barn built from lumber hauled from the Lake States pineries by the new railroad.

The dual-wheel motor truck made possible the forest industry as we know it today, allowing the harvest of timber in terrain so rugged that railway construction was prohibitively expensive. Low-cost truck transportation made feasible the practice of forestry—through thinnings, selective cuts, scattered harvest cuts, and other measures. We are verging on yet another major step in transportation, with balloon and helicopter logging, woods chipping, and chip pipelines. Environmental-maintenance policies may well accelerate these developments.

MODERN HISTORY

In its formative years, the wood industry was migratory. Small water-powered—and, later, steam-powered—sawmills turned out lumber and other wood products for the early settlements of the eastern seaboard. The woods of Maine and New England furnished a timber supply for a period of more than 200 years. As the population moved west, the industry followed. The Lake States pineries, opened up after the Civil War, substantially contributed to the growth of the nation in the last third of the nineteenth century. It was then that forest industry began to take on the form of modern industry. Increasing greatly in size and complexity, enterprises in the Lake States acquired large tracts of timber, constructed logging camps, and organized railroad, sled, and water transportation. Frequently, the size and location of the sawmill required the construction of a company town. Organizations appeared which arranged for the transportation and sale of forest products. Originally, large-scale enterprises secured enough timber to amortize their investments in mill and logging equipment in fifteen or twenty years.

Logging was a rough and tumble business, and only the hardy and resourceful engaged in it. All the merchantable timber was cut. Frequently, only the best, clear first log of the tree was taken, giving rise to what many have called the "butt-log philosophy." The knotty upper portions of the tree were left in the woods because the price of clear lumber was so low that as long as it was available in plentiful supply, the public had no interest in second-grade "knotty lumber."

There were mixed emotions about what to do with the cutover lands. In some areas of the East, settlers cleared lands that had been logged and created many thousands of acres of productive and profitable farms. This happened so frequently that many lumber companies set up cutover-land sales organizations to facilitate transfer of the lands to settlers and homesteaders.

Although one of the easiest ways to clean up logged-over land was to burn the slash, more often than not the fire became uncontrolled and burned much of the surrounding countryside. Very little of the Lake States forest escaped one or more forest fires following logging.

When a company had cut all its own and any other available timber, it closed down the mill. In some instances, the owners stayed on in the community, investing in other types of business. The growth of the pulp and paper industry led some entrepreneurs into this line of activity, since considerable quantities of pulpwood remained after the sawmills had exhausted their supply of logs. The logging railroads were often torn up or abandoned, but in a significant number of cases, they became linked together to form the nucleus of the common-carrier rail system. As owners desirous of continuing in the lumber business reached the end of their timber supply in the Lake States, they turned to the southern pineries and to the West Coast.

New tracts of timber were acquired, new sawmills and towns were built, and more miles of logging railroad were constructed. The pattern was still liquidation. The high point of lumber production in the U.S. was reached just before 1910, with the manufacture of some 46 billion board feet, all produced from liquidating operations. In the West, many concerns also followed the liquidation pattern, shutting down whenever they ran out of a supply of timber.

VILIFICATION AND JUSTIFICATION OF INDUSTRY CONDUCT

The historical pattern of clearcutting, abandonment of facilities, and movement to a new location where the process was repeated lies at the core of the forest industry's timber-supply problem today. A small, vocal segment of the American public will not let the industry forget its past, will not give it credit for the attempts which it has made to achieve permanence, and will not acknowledge the leadership it has shown in rebuilding and stabilizing the forest resource. Today, 70-odd years into the twentieth century, proposals for harvesting timber can be greeted with cries of "rape," even when the proposals are within the allowable limits of sustained yield.

Since the highly emotional reaction to even scientifically organized timber harvesting is so widespread and persistent today, it might be worthwhile to analyze a few of its component parts. The idea is firmly fixed that the "lumberman destroyed the forest." However, much forest was literally destroyed by settlers who cut trees down, rolled them into piles, and set fire to them in order to clear the ground for farming. Strangely enough, this is greeted with approval: "characteristic hardy pioneer spirit," "hewing a home out of the wilderness," "making a contribution to society and to the building of our great nation."

The lumberman applied a similar hardy pioneer spirit: He made a contribution to society and to the building of our great nation by converting the trees in the forest to the lumber and wood products which built the cities, towns, and farms of America. This is not to say that he was without fault. If it were possible to make an accurate determination, the forest-products industry and those who engaged in it would be found to be no better and no worse than the average of all businesses during the formative years of our country.

As a matter of fact, the forest wasn't destroyed: It was just crudely harvested. The state of the art of forestry was as crude as plowing with a horse, cutting with a scythe, or reading by kerosene lamp. The harvesting method was a direct response to the economic conditions of the times. People conserve things of value. As long as timber was plentiful—an abundant supply in the next county, in the next state, or even out on the West Coast—the price of timber stayed low. Although many were concerned with the possibility of a timber famine, no one could see how another crop of timber could be grown economically.

VISIONS OF INDUSTRY PERMANENCE

Yet the idea persisted that trees could be grown and that the forest industry could become permanent. It was as visionary as sending a man to the moon. Trees grew too slowly. Who would pay taxes for 100 years before a tree was ready to harvest? Young trees produced only knotty lumber, which the public didn't want. Forest fires would wipe out the investment.

Despite claims of its detractors that the forest-products industry was interested only in liquidation and fast profits, the record indicates otherwise. Because of their closeness to the land and the growing trees, members of the forest industries were among the earliest to sense that the country's needs for forest products could not forever be met by the liquidation of old-growth forests. Somewhere along the line, a start had to be made toward putting the industry on a permanent footing by growing the timber needed instead of merely cutting the old growth which was already present on the land.

The crude harvesting of old-growth timber had one beneficial result. It proved that the forest was not destroyed; it was only altered. It showed that tree growth was, in fact, much more rapid than observers of the old-growth forest had suspected. It led to an appreciation of plant succession, a science which today has achieved worldwide recognition as part of the discipline of ecology.

Railroads were among the first to become actively concerned about their future source of wood supply. Then, as now, the wooden crosstie formed the foundation of the railroad, and perpetuation of the supply was a matter of great interest. Before the widespread use of wood preservatives, many railroads embarked on the growing of tree plantations of durable species such as catalpa. In spite of the time and money spent on them, these programs are little more than historical curiosities today. Natural regrowth of hardwoods in the East provided the continuing supply that the railroads needed. Nevertheless, the story illustrates that wood users had the courage to embark on an unknown venture entirely at their own expense.

Those who were in the forest-products business probably had the greatest incentive to stretch their supplies of timber. Originally, this merely took the form of lengthening the life of their individual operations. Protection from forest fires which could ruin vast areas of timber ranked high on the list, and various forest-fire-control cooperatives resulted. Technologic improvements such as the motor truck, which allowed harvesting otherwise inaccessible scattered stands, stretched the supply still further. Then came the revelation, to many different people at many different times and in many different places, that young-growth timber, if properly cared for, could develop into merchantable size and that the business might be able to survive on the timber that it grew or that others grew for it.

Thus the idea of a permanent forest-products industry was born. No one person or group can take credit for it. The idea was well established in Europe and it had been talked about in this country for many years as a philosophy. However, it remained for forward-looking members of the forest-products industry to grasp the opportunities for converting individual segments of the industry from a liquidation to a sustained-yield basis. The establishment of forestry schools after 1900 in this country and the development of the Forest Service organization of land managers and experiment stations gave rise to a body of knowledge which was of great assistance in the transition period.

The New Deal years saw a number of events which were to have lasting effect on the development of permanent forestry. Foremost was the Civilian Conservation Corps (CCC) program, which did much to establish forest-fire control in hitherto unprotected areas. The CCC built fire towers, trails, firebreaks, and access roads. It made a start in timber-stand improvement and insect and disease control. It planted trees on many thousands of acres of open or cutover land.

During the 1930s, many forest-products companies saw light at the end of the tunnel. Sustained-yield operation might just be possible. Young-growth timber was becoming acceptable in the market, forest-fire control was proven to be feasible with government help, trees were growing faster than expected, and a new factor, the pulp and paper industry, was increasing its consumption of small wood which could come from thinnings in young stands and from the tops of saw-log trees. If the pulp and paper industry could return some income to the forest owner in a relatively short time, this might be the key to putting forestry on an economical basis. Of considerable importance to the forest industry was the National Recovery Act (NRA) whose lumber-industry code contained a section on timber conservation and management. Although the NRA was declared unconstitutional, the lumber industry voluntarily agreed to keep the conservation section as an industry goal.

The nation's dependence on forest products was demonstrated in World War II. Furthermore, the ability of the country to manufacture quickly a vast quantity of lumber and of the carpenters to fabricate it quickly into cantonments, airfields, and buildings demonstrates the national necessity of keeping a viable forest-products industry capable of turning out vast quantities of a universal building material on relatively short notice. It goes without saying that access to an adequate supply of standing timber is a prerequisite to this phase of national-security planning.

At the conclusion of the war, the forest-products industry was able to return to its major task of converting to continuous, sustained-yield operation. The methods involved varied with the section of the country. Experience in the two major timber-producing regions, the South and the West, is illustrative.

DEVELOPMENT OF SOUTHERN INDUSTRIAL FORESTRY

As the pulp and paper industry moved into the South in the 1930s, its early history in New England and eastern Canada with declining supplies and ever-increasing costs of wood was fresh in the minds of those directing the movement. They vowed not to make the same mistake again and, with rare foresight, bought up tracts of cutover timberlands and established forestry departments, in some instances even before the mills were completed. This commitment by the industry to assume the responsibility for growing a portion of its raw material was an important turning point. The decision underscored a faith in the future. It was made, moreover, at a time when money was scarce, markets were uncertain, forestry was in its infancy, and the forest-fire threat was enormous. Nevertheless, numerous companies tackled the problems one by one as they came South, each applying its own brand of ingenuity to its own special circumstances.

The pulp and paper industry provided new jobs and pumped economic life into a South beset by twin woes, the depression and the boll weevil. The young stands of pine which had sprung up in the wake of the first cutting for lumber provided the raw material. Thousands of persons went to work in the woods, supplementing their meager agricultural incomes.

A new cash market for small trees in the form of pulpwood saved many thousands of farms from mortgage foreclosure. This experience proved that trees grow and that, where industry provided the markets, they could be converted into cash, utilizing land which could not be used for any other purpose. The very success of this operation created another problem. Would landowners, with their need for cash, clearcut their pulpwood stands? Would the South go through another wave of clearcutting and mill abandonment? Would this new resource be destroyed even as the hope it offered was just beginning to be understood and appreciated?

The industry became aware of the problem very early, for even though it had purchased cutover lands for reforestation, these lands could not support its whole wood requirement. The industry depended on the small, private, nonindustrial landowner to grow the major portion of its raw material. Forty years later, this situation still prevails.

Civic and government leaders became concerned because of the threat to community economic stability and talked of federal regulation of timber cutting. Discussions by industry leaders, the Forest Service, and community leaders led to the formation of the Southern Pulpwood Conservation Association (SPCA) in 1939. SPCA foresters teamed with foresters from the member pulp and paper companies to carry the forestry message into every forested county in the South. Forest-fire prevention, tree planting, thinning rather than clearcutting, and disease and insect control were preached and demonstrated. Movies, pamphlets, posters, essay contests, and field demonstrations were all used with great success. State legislatures were urged to appropriate more money for fire control and tree nurseries. A spirit of cooperation flourished. Major lumber-industry associations organized forestry departments. Surviving lumber companies cooperated in the movement.

Cooperation was not limited to the wood industry. Railroads, which hauled vast tonnages of raw material to the mills and carried the finished goods to market, soon realized that they had a stake in improving the timber-supply situation. Many railroads appointed forestry agents. One railroad held an annual field demonstration for state legislators. Another designed and built a successful tree-planting machine in its locomotive shops and made the drawings available. Banks bought tree-planting machines and lent them free of charge. Millions of tree seedlings were given to landowners by both lumber and pulp companies. The 4-H Clubs and Future Farmers of America planted millions of trees as part of their forestry projects. SPCA sponsored Boys Conservation Schools in each state in cooperation with the state forestry association. The Extension Service of the Department of Agriculture through its county agents, the Soil Conservation Service through its individual farm plans, and the Forest Service through its cooperative farm foresters all contributed to this effort.

The result of all the southern forestry activity was a vastly improved timber-supply situation. A declining resource trend had been halted and reversed. The importance of a renewable-resource-based industry to the U.S. was demonstrated when the new southern pine plywood industry began operating in 1964. Today, this industry, based on trees that weren't there just a few years ago, operates 30-odd plants and provides about one-fourth of the nation's softwood plywood requirements.

SOUTHERN FOREST RESOURCE ANALYSIS COMMITTEE

Although timber growth was ahead of depletion during the 1960s, industry leaders realized that the needs of the rapidly expanding population would require still greater forestry effort. Why not take a detailed look at the factors that had created a favorable growth-use ratio over the past thirty years? This analysis could provide guides to the new effort required to furnish the South's share of the nation's wood requirements through the year 2000.

In 1967, three industry associations—the Southern Pine Association, the Southern Hardwood Lumber Association, and the American Plywood Association—joined with the Forest Farmers Association, representing forest owners, to sponsor the Southern Forest Resource Analysis Committee. Operating with a modest budget, but with massive contributions of talent, the Committee produced a report entitled "The South's Third Forest." The report sets a timber-growth objective of 13 billion cubic feet (70 percent more softwood and 40 percent more hardwood growth than in 1968) as the South's share of national requirements in the year 2000. Thus the South's share is seen to be more than half the national total. The report stresses the maintenance of environmental integrity. For reaching its goals, it proposes a 14-point forestry program covering silviculture, marketing, taxation, land use, public information, and public support.

The taxation and public-support issues deserve special emphasis. At both federal and state levels, taxation is a cost of growing concern to the forest industry. The three-way race among tree growth, the compound-interest table, and government's need for tax revenue is of uncertain outcome. Forest industry gets three-fourths of its raw material from private lands and is concerned that taxes not wipe out the incentives to grow trees.

Achievement of the public-support objective will require greatly increased public understanding—especially urban understanding—of forestry principles: the need for pine plantations on the uplands instead of the hardwood forests which do poorly there, the need for equitable systems of long-term land classification for tax purposes, and the need for sustained-yield resource management on an efficient scale.

The Third Forest report views the present southern surplus of total cubic-foot timber growth over depletion, not as an invitation to relax efforts, but as verification that past forestry programs have worked and that the report's recommendations will produce desired results if they are followed as diligently as were the programs of the 1940s and 1950s.

WESTERN INDUSTRY'S SUPPLY PROBLEMS: RAW-MATERIAL SECURITY

In contrast to the South, the West is still largely concerned with the liquidation of old-growth timber and its orderly replacement with young growth. A high percentage of timber is in public ownership. Much of the road net is still to be built. The forest-products industry is dependent on public timber for much of its raw material, and some companies are totally dependent. Herein lies one of the western industry's problems: the public forests are not managed in such a way as to give wood users sufficient security in their raw-material supply.

Industry's need for raw-material assurance over a period at least equal to that required to amortize a plant has been recognized by the federal government on numerous occasions. The Sustained Yield Act of 1944 involved joint management of public and private timber. To provide economic security for the enormous investments required to utilize the pulp material from Alaskan national forests, the government has entered into fifty-year contracts. For a national forest in Alabama which lacked markets, the government was able to stimulate the installation of a forest-products plant by entering into a fifteen-year timber-supply contract.

Despite the existence of public policy favoring raw-material security, much of the western industry which is either wholly dependent or heavily dependent on government timber lives hand-to-mouth, buying relatively small amounts of timber by competitive bidding and often bidding in desperation when failure to be high bidder would mean a plant closure. Such arrangements are hardly conducive to increased investment, job tenure, community stability, or a permanent supply of building materials and other essential forest commodities.

INTENSIFYING PUBLIC FOREST MANAGEMENT

Another of the timber-supply problems in the West, as viewed from the industry standpoint, is the failure of public forest managers—principally the Forest Service—to intensify their practices in order to increase their wood output. In keeping with the purpose of the national forests, that is, to insure a supply of timber for the American people, much of national-forest management has been custodial, pending the time when the people's needs would require more intensive resource utilization. At present levels of funding, however, the Forest Service lacks the means to convert the custodial system into an active production system.

The Forest Service is bound by the Multiple Use-Sustained Yield Act of 1960 to manage the forests so that there need be no planned reduction of the cut in any period. In the absence of investment funds to increase timber growth—such as by thinnings, plantings, and timber-stand improvement—the current cut must be held down accordingly. If current or prospective growth can be accelerated, harvests can likewise be increased.

A good summary of the situation was given by Edward C. Crafts on May 23, 1969, before the Subcommittee on Forests of the House Agriculture Committee:

> Accepting the facts about softwood lumber and plywood with respect to demand, supply, and prices, the problem is what to do about it in the next 10 years so far as the national forests are concerned. Actually, the solution is rather simple, but not easy to attain. It means funding the Forest Service not only timber-resource management, but other activities as well, in accord with recommendations outlined in the report submitted by President Kennedy in 1961 for a "Development Program for the National Forests" with adjustments for updating and inflation. It also means adequate personnel ceilings. Actually, little or no new legislation is needed.
>
> It is my feeling that the Forest Service has been, and is being, pushed dangerously close to the brink with respect to timber management on the national forests. I do not believe in brinkmanship when it comes to depleting the natural resources of the United States.
>
> For many years in connection with its periodic reassessments of the timber situation, the Service has predicted a prospective shortage of softwood sawtimber, and this is exactly what is facing the industry now and why it is turning to the national forests as its own lands have been depleted of mature timber.
>
> There is a time gap until second-growth matures, when the industry must depend more heavily than in the past on public timber. That time gap is now. There is also excess sawmill capacity in relation to growth productivity, and no one wants to go out of business.
>
> I compliment the larger forest-industry operators for their generally progressive forest practices and for the growth on industry lands, which is more than that on national forests, although on a smaller acreage. Nevertheless, the fact remains that industry lands are short of softwood sawtimber.
>
> Forest Service lands have not been fully developed, nor have age classes and species composition been regulated adequately in a technical forestry sense. Intensive forest management is greatly needed.

CONSERVATIONIST REACTIONS TO INTENSIVE PUBLIC FORESTRY

Conservation groups initially agreed that more intensive management of commercial timber areas in the national forests were in their best interests because it would help safeguard the wilderness areas they were trying to protect. For example, on March 21, 1969, before the Senate Banking and Currency Committee, Lloyd Tupling, Washington representative for the Sierra Club, testified: "We do believe that more intensive management of the . . . areas that are designated for commercial timber purposes would be of benefit not only in the production of sawtimber, but if this could be done it would relieve the pressures on the wilderness areas we are trying to protect. So essentially there is no conflict in our position."

Later, however, the national preservation and recreation groups did an about-face. In their testimony on the proposed National Forest

Timber Conservation and Management Act of 1969, these groups made a number of contentions in strong opposition to more intensive timber management on the national forests. These contentions have received such wide publicity that they deserve serious point-by-point analysis. The following are eight of the arguments and industry comments on each one:

1. *Contention:* The proposal for intensified timber management is a raid on the national forests.

Comment: The Act of 1897 which established the national forests states, as a primary purpose, furnishing "a continuous supply of timber for the use and necessities of the citizens of the United States." The future need for more timber has been established. The amount required exceeds present yields because of low management levels. Increased yield requires higher sustained funding of timber growing. With increasing wood needs, if timber growth can be increased, existing cutting rates warrant review. Final decisions remain with the Secretary of Agriculture.

The preservationists implied that assured funding for forest management on public forest lands was a new idea. In actuality, assured funding was already in practice on the lands of the Bureau of Land Management of the U.S. Department of the Interior, the Department of Defense, and the state of Washington.

2. *Contention:* The proposal for intensified management ignores multiple use of the national forests; it threatens to overfund timber management and slight the rest of the national-forest program.

Comment: There is no intention, desire, or need to supersede the Multiple Use-Sustained Yield Act of 1960 in order to increase timber yield. The proposed programs would be subject to the Multiple Use Act. Increased financing of timber growing and consequent revision of the cutting rates do not abrogate multiple-use policies for the national forests. The Forest Service and the Secretary of Agriculture retain responsibility and authority for balancing national-forest uses. Existing authority imposes restraints on timber management, and there is no intent to terminate or influence this authority.

Although timber sales produce 98 percent of national-forest recepits, timber growing has always been funded at extremely low levels. New funds would help produce growth rates commensurate with wood needs. However, funding would be controlled by the appropriations committees of Congress, which control funding of all other federal programs.

Tree-growing practices—thinning, pruning, and prompt regeneration—enhance recreation, wildlife, and water yields. Nontimber uses of the national forests are separately funded under various statutes. But beyond this, the intensive timber-management proposal takes due regard for nontimber forest values.

3. *Contention:* The intensive-management proposal would result in classifying some 97 million acres of national forest as commercial forest land.

Comment: Land classification is not proposed as a function of timber-supply legislation. The Forest Service determines which lands should grow timber crops and which lands should be withdrawn from timber harvest. It would be pointless to invest public funds to grow timber commercially on lands which will not be used for production of timber.

Timber-supply proposals do not influence commercial-land determinations. They do not influence existing classifications. They do not require that all commercial timberlands be managed for high timber yields. The Forest Service reviews timber-growing plans at ten-year intervals and adjusts plans where other uses impose restraints. National forests total 187 million acres. Surely 97 million acres, or about half, could be called commercial. However, nearly one-quarter of these 97 million acres is already subject to limitations on timber production for the benefit of nontimber uses.

4. *Contention:* The intensive-management proposal would prevent any further additions to the national wilderness preservation system on areas with wood-growing potential.

Comment: The proposal would not affect present statutory policy and procedures regarding wilderness areas. At present, the allowable cut of timber is based on the total inventory of timber on lands the Forest Service thinks suitable for timber production; the timber-supply proposal would not alter this procedure. Indeed, the proposal would not preclude orderly consideration of the merits of any area for wilderness status.

5. *Contention:* The intensive-management proposal would allow old-growth timber to be sawed down as fast as modern machinery could do the job.

Comment: The proposed National Forest Timber Conservation and Management Act of 1969, against which the foregoing argument was directed, charged the Secretary of Agriculture, subject to the provisions of the Multiple Use-Sustained Yield Act of 1960, to "Revise the allowable annual harvesting rates in national forests to take into account (a) rotation ages estimated to be appropriate for markets and technology at the expected time of harvest, (b) the need for and benefits from use of high-level harvest options available within sustained-yield limitations, and (c) increased timber yields which will result from application of the measures authorized by Section 6 of this Act, as rapidly as possible after such measures have been undertaken: *Provided that appropriate reduction in allowable harvesting rates will be made if planned measures are not satisfactorily accomplished.*"

Faster-growing trees reach harvest size at an earlier age than slower-growing trees. The Forest Service would continue to set harvesting cycles as timber-growth rates were determined. Any accelerated harvesting of old-growth timber justified by intensified management would be controlled to be compatible with environmental maintenance and multiple-use requirements.

Under present levels of management, cutting will be almost exclusively in old-growth timber for the next sixty to ninety years on most of the western national forests. Even if old-growth cutting were increased, old-growth inventory is sufficiently large so that unforeseen failure of young growth to attain projected levels could be compensated through rapid reduction of the allowable cut.

6. *Contention:* The current export of timber, over 4 billion board feet a year to Japan alone, makes absurd the claim that the United States faces a massive timber shortage.

Comment: The United States is a net importer of lumber. More than 6 billion board feet are imported, primarily from Canada. Two billion feet of logs are exported, mostly to Japan, and about 1 billion board feet of lumber.

The Jones Act encourages export of Alaskan resources. Log-export curtailment legislation was passed in 1968—the industry-supported Morse Amendment to the 1968 Foreign Assistance Act, which limits log exports from western federal lands to 350 million board feet annually through 1971. Further curtailment is extremely complicated, and its results are speculative, because exports affect the ability to import. Also, current domestic demand is low.

7. *Contention:* National housing needs can be supplied by using wood substitutes.

Comment: Substitute materials may take some traditional wood markets but, at the same time, wood will capture new markets. Wood substitutes—steel, aluminum, plastics, masonry—use depletable raw materials. Only wood is grown. The markets for wood pay the costs of producing many of the other forest benefits.

8. *Contention:* The intensive-management proposal intends to have roads constructed through now roadless national-forest areas.

Comment: At an early stage, the proposed legislation would have provided advance roads for timber-salvage and cultural work. This provision was deleted in the final version because of wilderness-group objections. Timber growing and protection require roads, but supporters of the legislation did not want timber-growing funds used for road construction. Road-construction funds are appropriated under a separate statutory authorization, and amounts are increasing.

PUBLIC LAND LAW REVIEW COMMISSION

The Public Land Law Review Commission, established in 1964, made a far-reaching study of the public lands and published a report in 1970 which serves to throw more light on timber-supply conditions in the West.

The Commission's characterization of the federal forest lands serves to underscore the key position of these lands in the U.S. timber supply and thus the key importance of the federal forest-management program.

The Commission observed that the federal government has a dominant position in the nation's timber economy. The government owns some 20 percent of all the country's commercial forest land, nearly 40 percent of its supply of merchantable timber, and over 60 percent of its softwood sawtimber. The degree of potential federal control over the supply of timber, the Commission found, is greater than over that of any other commodity presently produced from public lands.

The Commission further characterized federal timber resources in these terms: Federally owned timber is vital to the wood economy of the country. It is vital to the economies of many communities. Federal policies with respect to the sale of this timber can result in the life or death of firms that use it. The federal government's dominance as a supplier of timber will continue in the future.

The Public Land Law Review Commission recommended that public lands to be used for timber production (within a multiple-use framework) be clearly designated, and it pointed out the benefits of public assurances regarding the timber supply from public lands: the creation of incentives for private investments in plant and equipment, the encouragement of long-range planning by timber-dependent communities, greater assurance of Budget Bureau support of public timber-management investments, and greater assurance that timber prices will be held down. The Commission emphasized that lands having a unique potential for other uses should not be included in timber-production units.

Among other notable Commission recommendations bearing upon the timber supply from western public forests were these: That timber-management operations be financed from a revolving fund made up of receipts from timber sales. That timber-sales procedures be simplified. That the construction of roads giving access to federal timber-production areas be speeded up. That communities and firms dependent on the public timber be given consideration in the management and disposal of this timber.

EVEN-AGED SILVICULTURE UNDER ATTACK

The timber-supply debate goes on. The silvicultural practice of harvesting intolerant (sun-loving, as contrasted with shade-loving) tree species by clearcutting in block or patches has come under attack in Congress, in the press, and in state legislatures.

The use of the clearcutting technique is questioned by its critics from an environmental standpoint. To set the record straight, the Forest Industries Council prepared a paper for the Council on Environmental Quality, entitled "Clearcutting—A Timber Management Tool in Perspective." There is much hard scientific evidence to support this method of harvest. It is ecologically sound because it is a simulator of the natural events such as fires, windstorms, and insect attacks that have led to the establishment of present even-aged forests of both pine and hardwood.

Admittedly, the sight of a recently harvested patch of forest may be jarring and aesthetically offensive to a casual visitor to the forest who cannot connect this event with his own use of forest products in his home and business. A similar reaction would no doubt be experienced by the casual visitor to a slaughter house who cannot connect what he sees with his own enjoyment of meat. The events in question are not pretty, but in both cases they do have promise of good things to come. Urban renewal can be placed in the same category.

People don't seem to react violently to such clearcut harvests as corn or wheat, which they see every year. In fact, the completion of a harvest is cause for rejoicing; the national holiday of Thanksgiving is a result. Perhaps it is the length of time a tree stands during its growth cycle that causes people to experience such shock when the tree is finally harvested.

6 SUPPLY AND FOREST OWNERS

THOMAS C. NELSON* AND ROBERT N. STONE**

MILLIONS OF INDIVIDUALS, thousands of corporations, and hundreds of public agencies influence timber supply through their ownership objectives and management policies. Timberland owners represent all segments of our society. Grouping this vast assortment masks meaningful differences, but nevertheless is necessary to make the subject manageable. In this chapter, the conventional categories are used: farm and miscellaneous private tracts, forest-industry holdings, national forests, and other public forest lands.

The pattern of ownership of the 510 million acres of commercial forest land (defined in Chapter 3) varies from region to region (see Tables 6.1 and 6.2 at end of chapter). Nationwide, 72 percent is privately owned and 28 percent is public, although in the South 91 percent, and the North 82 percent, is privately owned. The situation is much different in the West, where two-thirds of the commercial forest area is publicly owned. The predominance of private forest land in the East and of public ownership in the West traces back to the early development of the country.

Most private forest land is in farm and miscellaneous ownership. Such holdings account for 59 percent of the nation's commercial forest area and are located mostly in the East. Forest industries, defined as companies and individuals that operate wood-using plants, own one-eighth of the nation's commercial forest land. Industries own more forest in the South than in the North and West combined. Some of the most productive forest lands in the nation belong to the forest industries.

National forests, made up largely of lands reserved from the public domain, include about one-fifth of all commercial forest land. Other public holdings—federal, state, and local—total about 9 percent. More than three-fourths of the commercial forest land in national forests is in the West; the remainder is about equally divided between

* Deputy Chief, Forest Service, Washington, D.C.
** Principal Economist, Forest Service, Washington, D.C.

North and South. Nine-tenths of the other public commercial forest land is in the North and the West. In the North, other public forests are largely state- or county-owned; in the West, most are held by the Bureau of Indian Affairs or the Bureau of Land Management.

TIMBER QUANTITIES

The quantity of standing timber and its growth and removal tend, of course, to be distributed among classes of owner in somewhat the same proportions as the commercial forest acreage. However, differences in policy and in forest characteristics from one owner class and region to another vary the pattern. Statistical details are given in Tables 6.1 and 6.3 through 6.12. Some of the highlights are these:

Farm and miscellaneous private owners hold more growing stock than any other class of owner. However, because their lands are the least heavily stocked, they do not predominate to the degree that their acreage would suggest: Their share of the nation's total growing stock is 39 percent. But growth rate is rapid in these predominantly eastern forests. Their growth is especially large in the South, where it accounts for two-thirds of the regional total. Removals, too, are at a high rate: The farm and miscellaneous holdings are the East's major source of timber.

Growing-stock holdings of the forest industry account for 15 percent of the total. Thus nationally their stock is about proportional to their acreage. Half of all industry-owned timber is in the West, for the quantity per acre there is far greater than in the other regions—and greater, also, than that on other classes of holdings in the West. In every region, both timber growth and removal per acre are higher on forest-industry lands than on lands of other owners.

The national forests are located chiefly in the West, where they consist of predominantly old-growth timber on sites of less than average productivity and accessibility. These forests contain 35 percent of the nation's growing stock and 44 percent of its sawtimber but account for only 14 percent of the growth and 18 percent of the removal of growing stock. Taking the West alone, the corresponding percentages for the national forests are 60, 61, 36, and 41.

Public commercial-forest lands other than national forests hold 11 percent of the timber. For the country as a whole, these lands are about average with respect to timber stocking, growth, and removals.

CHARACTERISTICS OF NONINDUSTRIAL PRIVATE OWNERS

Most information about owners of small woodland tracts describes or classifies the woodland owner, his landholdings, and his forest land. In addition, a great deal is known about factors which bear on owners' woodland operations. It is known, too, that the small-woodland owner population, characteristics, and attitudes are constantly changing. Changes involve type of owner, size of woodland, owner's financial status, ownership objectives, and other variables.

A general characterization of nonindustrial private forest owners in respect to the availability of timber supplies from their holdings is given in Table 6.13. The tendencies summarized there are by no means invariable. For example, although low-income landowners tend to draw heavily on their woods for cash and thus deplete their growing stocks and their potential supply, it does not follow that all high-income owners do the opposite: Their timber supply, too, may be relatively low because they can afford to pass up financial opportunities and preserve their woods for recreational and aesthetic purposes. Again, the factors of age and past tenure do not consistently show the effects indicated in the table. But by and large, the factors listed provide insight into the timber-supply potentialities of farmers and miscellaneous forest owners.

In general, the greatest probability of small-woodland owner motivation for timber production exists where market demands are many and competitive, site productivity is high, and tract accessibility good. The factors of stand condition and stocking level are also tied directly to a landowner's prospects for increased timber producticity and supply.*

CHARACTERISTICS OF INDUSTRIAL AND OF PUBLIC OWNERS

The forest-industry classification stretches from one- and two-man operations producing fence posts or mine props to complex international corporations with highly technical production facilities and worldwide marketing channels for a variety of wood products. Forest industry owns land primarily to produce timber raw material for its plants. Over the years, industry has accumulated some of the finest timberlands and timber inventories in the nation. Recently, several of the larger corporations have extended their land operations well beyond timber into both recreational and residential uses.

In the past, wood-using firms could readily be classified by product. This was helpful for describing differences in the composition of the industry from region to region. It has recently become less meaningful because of integration within firms.

Today, major forest-products firms have developed national markets for many products, allowing closer utilization of more tree

---

* The authors are indebted to T. A. McClay, Research Forester in the Forest Service, for the use of his unpublished literature review in preparing this section.

species, sizes, and qualities and thus adding marginal timber to the usable supply. Increasing competition for timber and heavy concentrations of capital in modern high-capacity facilities have spurred the industry to insure its future wood sources through additional land-purchasing and leasing arrangements. This development is most apparent in the South, where wood-using plant capacity has been increasing and competition for stumpage is becoming keen. Land-ownership by southern forest industry has increased 12 percent since 1953. This expansion in acreage has been accompanied by substantial investments in forestry practices to accelerate wood production.

"Other public owners" range from federal agencies such as the Bureau of Land Management and the Bureau of Indian Affairs, managers of millions of acres of forest land, to states, counties, and school districts. Some schools have forests no larger than a few acres. Numerous public agencies include forest lands in their holdings and use them primarily for nontimber purposes. Examples are the Defense Department, National Park Service, Fish and Wildlife Service, Army Corps of Engineers, and state highway departments. Most of the lesser public holdings receive adequate protection and are actively managed, although their site productivity for timber production is below average. They are increasingly important for water, wildlife habitat, and outdoor recreation.

TRENDS IN LAND OWNERSHIP

Commercial forest acreage in the United States has increased about 1.5 percent during the last fifteen years, to about 510 million acres. This small gain was confined to the East. Fifteen-year gains or losses of commercial forest land by the major ownership classes are shown in Table 6.14. The nearly 32 million acres of forest added to miscellaneous private holdings, mostly from previous farm woodlands, make this the largest owner class. Farm-forest acreage declined sharply in the South and slightly in the West, but increased in the North in the last five years.

Additions of 4.5 million acres have brought forest-industry holdings to 65 million acres. All the gain has been in the East and most of it in the South. The leasing of forest land for timber production by forest industries is becoming more common, particularly in the South, where 3.7 million acres are under lease.[1]

Commercial forest-land acreage in public ownership has changed little over the last fifteen years. A reduction of lands managed by the Bureau of Indian Affairs was offset by gains in state ownership.

Net shifts in commercial forest area among ownership classes understate the wholesale movement of forest land among owners and the shifting land-use patterns. Recent studies illustrate the magnitude of these developments. In South Carolina, for example, the acreage which shifted into or out of the commercial-forest category was three times the net change in the category.[2] Among private owners, tenure averages about twelve to fifteen years, which means that a high percentage of the properties have new owners in a decade, although the properties remain largely within the same ownership category.

The amount of commercial forest land is expected to begin declining before the end of the century. Recent increases in commercial forest acreage came from abandoned cropland or pastures. Losses of forest land to urban development, highways, reservoirs, and land clearing were more than offset by farm abandonment. But this source of new forest is drying up.

In the future, two other aspects of ownership change may become more important in influencing timber supply. These are the trends toward more absentee ownership and the fragmentation and consolidation of landholdings accompanying the decline in farm numbers.

More than 58 percent of the U.S. population now lives in urban areas totaling about 1 percent of the land.[3] Even though the population is increasing rapidly, one-half of the counties in the country lost population between the last two national censuses. The exodus of people from these counties and most other rural areas adds to absentee ownership to the extent that landownership is retained. Areas with declining populations include many of the more heavily forested parts of the country. Rising incomes among urban families mean that growing numbers have the money to buy woodlands, taking them out of former uses such as timber production and devoting them to vacation or retirement purposes.

As land unneeded for agriculture is transferred to other uses, sizes of units may change. An old farm may be too small for an efficient tree farm, but may be far too large for a single vacation home site. The resulting fragmentation and consolidation of holdings influence the circumstances of timber production and thus the timber supply.

TRENDS IN TIMBER OWNERSHIP

Between 1963 and 1968, the quantity of timber growing stock increased nationwide by 20.6 billion cubic feet, or 3.3 percent (Table 6.15). Thus the growing stock increased chiefly on farm and miscellaneous private lands. Gains were also achieved by forest industry and on public holdings other than the national forests. The small gain on industry lands despite the additions to industry's land base, and the reduction on national forests, reflect conversion of old-growth to young-growth timber in the West.

The reduction of old-growth softwood stockpiles is more apparent in the trends for sawtimber, shown in Table 6.16. Total sawtimber declined between 1963 and 1968, although by less than one-half of 1 percent. Again, the decline centered on the national forests. The major increase was achieved on farm and miscellaneous private holdings.

AVAILABILITY OF TIMBER

Two rather distinct facets of timber availability are recognized by most authorities: (1) operability and (2) owner objectives.

The operability of timber depends on the cost of harvesting and transporting timber to market on the one hand, and its market value on the other. Cost factors include location, accessibility, timber quantity per acre, tract size, topography, and terrain. Market values relate to such items as tree size, quality, species, and usable length. Situations where timber values exceed costs offer operating possibilities. In the long term, a viable timber-producing situation must promise to cover costs of growing timber as well as of getting it to market.

Owner objectives condition timber availability. Where owners of forest land place substantial values on the trees for sentimental, aesthetic, or other nonmarket satisfactions—values which exceed what the trees are worth as timber—the timber is unavailable to the market.

The three major owner groups (considering all public owners as one) differ markedly in the operability of their forests.

Physical accessibility is of less concern to the industrial forest landowner than to most public forest managers. He has either constructed his processing plant adjacent or close to his timberlands or purchased timber holdings in the vicinity of his plant. The data offer evidence that industrial holdings have sufficient harvestable timber per acre (Tables 6.3 through 6.6). Considering the progressive forest-management programs of industry, one can accept the argument that timber size and quality are adequate. Industry, of course, is not immune to market slumps: It can find itself, at times, owning timber of species and qualities that cannot be utilized at a profit.

Mature stands in public holdings are, by and large, operable in terms of timber quantity, size, and quality. However, there is considerable public timberland in some sections of the country, particularly in the intermountain West, which lies outside the wood-procurement zones of industry. Lack of transportation systems, especially on western national forests, is an important factor limiting timber supply. Growing public concern about the maintenance of water quality and other environmental factors will probably retard development of additional national-forest road systems for timber harvesting.

In contrast, the small-scale private owner finds that as wood-using industry expands, location is less a problem each year. Nor is physical accessibility a problem. Rather, it is the condition of the timber stand which may render the forest inoperable. With the advent of automated harvesting equipment which performs most effectively in heavy timber, much timber now counted in the inventory will be increasingly costly to log.

TIMBER VS. OTHER FOREST VALUES

The three major owner groups are not alike in their objectives and thus are unalike in their influence upon timber supply.

As expected, the forest industry's primary objective is timber production. Public agencies—except for those dedicated to a preservation policy, such as the National Park Service and its state and local counterparts—have generally had a strong timber-supply objective. Within the confines of its legal authority, the Forest Service has as recently as 1970 reaffirmed its policy to develop and promote national programs that meet the nation's need for timber.[4] Practices on the national forests offer testimony to the implementation of this policy.

The objectives of the small-woodland owners and their relation to timber supply are the subject of considerable debate. One contention is that these owners have a variety of objectives incompatible with timber production and that therefore it is questionable if they can be counted upon to sell timber. Our conclusion, on the other hand, is that timber on the small holdings is and will be largely available for use.[5]

1. Although most studies of small-woodland owners emphasize the high proportion of these owners who have nonfinancial objectives, our data for the owners show heavy timber cuts and reduced inventories that are consistent with the seeking of higher rates of financial return.

2. Our limited studies show no reluctance among owners to sell timber and, on the whole, nationally, no significant withdrawal of timber.

3. Because of the temporary reasons for most withdrawals, it seems unlikely that more than a small share of timber can be considered "off the market" for a period long enough for mature timber to deteriorate.

4. The higher proportion of nonresidents than of residents unwilling to sell timber may substantiate the concern that the "new breed of owners" may adversely affect timber supply, but the magnitude of the effect will probably not be as great as is widely supposed.

5. Owners may be indifferent to small annual increments in timber value, but when they become aware of the cumulative value of their saleable timber, most owners seek the available profit.

Users of nontimber goods and services of the forest—water, recreational opportunities, wildlife, and range—are placing demands upon acreages formerly devoted to timber production. Demands for such goods and services as scenery, protection of endangered species, and wilderness are also making an impact upon forestry. What is the extent of these impacts? What are the projected effects? Quantifying them is difficult. It is estimated that of the 80,000,000 acres of commercial forest land in the national forests regulated for timber harvest (that is, included in the planned allowable cut), about 4 percent is managed under some form of modified silviculture to protect or enhance other forest values. Some provisions are also made to produce special vegetation for aesthetic purposes or wildlife habitat intermingled with the wood-producing trees. All in all, such modifications can be expected to reduce timber cut from the national forests by 3 to 5 percent.

The remaining acres of productive forest land in the national-forest system total about 17,000,000 acres not presently regulated due to inaccessibility or lack of markets and about 6,000,000 withdrawn by legislation or administrative order (wilderness, natural areas, and recreation developments).

In the future, the loss of national-forest timber yield attributable to nontimber uses will be determined by the skill of the managers in integrating the uses, the amount of land withdrawn from timber culture by legislation or administrative order, and the amount of federal funding for the development of the forest.

Industrial holdings, like the national forests, face expanding demands, but the general populace has not yet devised effective means of making itself heard in the private-land sector as it has in the public sector. The small-scale private woodland owner is more closely allied to the industrial than to the public sector in his forest-land bill of rights and decision processes.

Because of growing popular constraints upon the public timber supply, steps must be taken to increase timber production by the small-woodland owner. Demands on the public forest holdings will probably continue to intensify; people will demand and achieve a greater involvement in public-forest policy and programs; and popular concern for the quality of the environment will continue to be a dominant force. These factors will have major impacts on timber supply from public lands.

DEMAND-SUPPLY PROSPECTS

It is not the purpose of this chapter to arrive at solutions, or even alternatives, for meeting the nation's timber needs. However, some estimated output figures for the major ownership classes may be of value.

Assuming that relative timber-price levels will be held to 115 percent of 1962–1967 levels by 1980 and to 130 percent by 1990 and 2000 and that intensive management will be applied to all national-forest, other public, and forest-industry land, the nonindustrial private contribution of softwood sawtimber must be nearly doubled over present growth if forecast national demands by year 2000 are to be met.

Projections show that the public lands must supply most of the increases in softwood demands in the next ten years or so, but that farm and miscellaneous private woodlands must play a larger part in meeting increases in demand in the period beyond [1985]. Thus the increased harvests possible in the near future from national forests can buy the time needed to prepare the private lands to pick up the burden later.

The production of industrial timber from domestic forests in 1969 was estimated at 11.2 billion cubic feet, 19 percent higher than in 1959. The most recent Forest Service long-run projections indicate that the demand for timber will continue to increase in the decades immediately ahead.[6] Assuming prices at the 1962–1967 level, for example, it is estimated that demand for sawlogs will roughly double, veneer logs triple, and pulpwood quadruple by the year 2000. The latest data on timber inventories, growth, and removals indicate that softwood timber resources in the South and the Rocky Mountains can support somewhat larger timber harvests. However, demands for softwood sawtimber are expected to rise above supply in the early 1970s and to continue climbing. Thus, unless management is rapidly intensified, only sizeable increases in price will bring supply and demand into balance.

Most of the additional demand for hardwood lumber, and some of the demand for veneer and plywood in the next few years, can be met by hardwood timber resources in the North, where private ownership predominates.

Prospective longer-run shortages of both softwoods and hardwoods may be accentuated by losses of timber-producing land through conversion to cropland; through withdrawals for cities, highways, reservoirs, parks, and other uses; and through the imposition of constraints on timber practices to protect other forest values.

Forest Service studies indicate that with accelerated forest management, the nation's demands for softwood sawtimber can be met with little increase in prices, in the next decade at least. Accelerated management would involve such measures as planting, thinning, stand improvement, and increased protection against destructive agents. In the national forests, it would also require a large access-road program. In addition, research would have to develop new technology and increase the efficiency of timber production and utilization on all forests.

Management can be intensified on both public and private lands, particularly on farm and miscellaneous private forest tracts. These holdings comprise some 59 percent of the total area of commercial forest land. They provide nearly half of the raw material used by the forest industries today. The investment in management on these lands is, on the average, much below that on industrial and public lands, and growth per acre is low. If significantly more wood is to be grown on these nonindustrial forest holdings, the owners will need much more technical and financial assistance.

TABLE 6.1 COMMERCIAL FOREST LAND AND TIMBER INVENTORY, GROWTH, AND REMOVAL BY REGION AND OWNER CLASS, 1968
(Percent)

Region and class of owner or manager	Commercial forest land	Growing stock			Sawtimber		
		Inventory	Growth	Removal	Inventory	Growth	Removal
United States:							
Farm and misc. priv. owners	59	39	58	50	29	54	40
Forest industry	13	15	19	25	16	22	28
Forest Service	19	35	14	18	44	15	24
Other public agencies	9	11	9	7	11	9	8
Totals	100	100	100	100	100	100	100
North:							
Farm and misc. priv. owners	73	68	70	78	71	72	79
Forest industry	9	14	11	11	14	10	11
Forest Service	6	6	7	4	5	7	4
Other public agencies	12	12	12	7	10	11	6
Totals	100	100	100	100	100	100	100
South:							
Farm and misc. priv. owners	73	67	66	69	62	62	65
Forest industry	18	22	24	23	26	27	26
Forest Service	5	7	7	5	8	8	6
Other public agencies	4	4	3	3	4	3	3
Totals	100	100	100	100	100	100	100
West:							
Farm and misc. priv. owners	21	14	27	13	12	27	12
Forest industry	11	13	22	34	14	24	34
Forest Service	56	60	36	41	61	33	41
Other public agencies	12	13	15	12	13	16	13
Totals	100	100	100	100	100	100	100

TABLE 6.2 COMMERCIAL FOREST LAND BY OWNER CLASS AND REGION, 1968
(Million acres)

Class of owner or manager	North	South	West	Total
Farm and miscellaneous private owners	128.7	145.8	28.4	302.9
Forest industry	15.3	35.5	14.5	65.3
Forest Service	10.4	10.6	75.9	96.9
Other public agencies	21.6	6.9	16.6	45.1
Total	176.0	198.8	135.4	510.2

TABLE 6.3 GROWING-STOCK INVENTORY PER ACRE BY OWNER CLASS AND REGION, 1968
(Cubic feet)

Class of owner or manager	North	South	West	Total
Farm and miscellaneous private owners	776	681	1,797	826
Forest industry	1,337	940	3,083	1,507
Forest Service	941	1,036	2,740	2,359
Other public agencies	807	756	2,702	1,497
Totals	837	749	2,574	1,264

TABLE 6.4 SAWTIMBER INVENTORY PER ACRE BY OWNER CLASS AND REGION, 1968
(Board feet)

Class of owner or manager	North	South	West	Total
Farm and miscellaneous private owners	1,711	1,969	7,594	2,387
Forest industry	2,771	3,339	16,171	6,046
Forest Service	1,668	3,701	13,767	11,368
Other public agencies	1,483	2,411	13,362	5,997
Totals	1,773	2,321	12,680	4,881

TABLE 6.5 ANNUAL REMOVAL OF GROWING STOCK PER ACRE BY OWNER CLASS AND REGION, 1968
(Cubic feet)

Class of owner or manager	North	South	West	Total
Farm and miscellaneous private owners	15	28	22	22
Forest industry	18	39	113	51
Forest Service	10	29	26	25
Other public agencies	7	22	36	20
Totals	14	30	36	26

TABLE 6.6 ANNUAL REMOVAL OF SAWTIMBER PER ACRE BY OWNER CLASS AND REGION, 1968
(Board feet)

Class of owner or manager	North	South	West	Total
Farm and miscellaneous private owners	48	90	123	75
Forest industry	55	149	692	247
Forest Service	29	114	163	143
Other public agencies	20	72	228	105
Totals	44	101	219	113

TABLE 6.7 ANNUAL REMOVAL OF GROWING STOCK AS A PERCENT OF INVENTORY, BY OWNER CLASS AND REGION, 1968
(Percent)

Class of owner or manager	North	South	West	Total
Farm and miscellaneous private owners	1.9	4.2	1.2	2.7
Forest industry	1.3	4.2	3.7	3.4
Forest Service	1.1	2.8	1.0	1.0
Other public agencies	.9	2.9	1.3	1.3
Totals	1.6	4.0	1.4	2.1

TABLE 6.8 ANNUAL REMOVAL OF SAWTIMBER AS A PERCENT OF INVENTORY, BY OWNER CLASS AND REGION, 1968
(Percent)

Class of owner or manager	North	South	West	Total
Farm and miscellaneous private owners	2.8	4.6	1.6	3.1
Forest industry	2.0	4.4	4.3	4.1
Forest Service	1.7	3.1	1.2	1.3
Other public agencies	1.4	3.0	1.7	1.7
Totals	2.5	4.3	1.7	2.3

TABLE 6.9 NET GROWTH OF GROWING STOCK PER ACRE BY OWNER CLASS AND REGION, 1968
(Cubic feet)

Class of owner or manager	North	South	West	Total
Farm and miscellaneous private owners	29	36	40	33
Forest industry	40	53	62	52
Forest Service	36	50	20	25
Other public agencies	29	37	37	33
Totals	30	40	31	34

TABLE 6.10 NET GROWTH OF SAWTIMBER PER ACRE BY OWNER CLASS AND REGION, 1968
(Board feet)

Class of owner or manager	North	South	West	Total
Farm and miscellaneous private owners	68	109	148	95
Forest industry	82	200	260	185
Forest Service	77	192	68	83
Other public agencies	63	120	149	104
Totals	69	130	115	105

TABLE 6.11 GROWING-STOCK GROWTH AS A PERCENT OF INVENTORY, BY OWNER CLASS AND REGION, 1968
(Percent)

Class of owner or manager	North	South	West	Total
Farm and miscellaneous private owners	3.7	5.2	2.2	4.0
Forest industry	3.0	5.6	2.0	3.4
Forest Service	3.8	4.8	.7	1.1
Other public agencies	3.6	5.0	1.4	2.2
Totals	3.6	5.3	1.2	2.7

TABLE 6.12 SAWTIMBER GROWTH AS A PERCENT OF INVENTORY, BY OWNER CLASS AND REGION, 1968

(Percent)

Class of owner or manager	North	South	West	Total
Farm and miscellaneous private owners	4.0	5.6	1.9	4.0
Forest industry	3.0	6.0	1.6	3.1
Forest Service	4.6	5.2	.5	.7
Other public agencies	4.3	5.0	1.1	1.7
Totals	3.9	5.6	.9	2.2

TABLE 6.13 FACTORS RELATED TO TIMBER SUPPLY FROM NONINDUSTRIAL PRIVATE LANDHOLDINGS

Factor	Supply tends to be relatively—	
	High	Low
	Where factor is relatively—	
Land ownership:		
Woodland acres owned	Many	Few
Proportion of land wooded	High	Low
Assessed value of all land	High	Low
Owner's financial situation:		
Total assets	High	Low
Annual income	High	Low
Proportion of income available for saving and investment	High	Low
Investment alternatives	Low-return	High-return
Other characteristics of owner:		
Purpose of woods ownership	Timber production	Other
Interest in forestry	High	Low
Knowledge of forestry techniques	Much	Little
Tendency to adopt latest agricultural practices	Strong	Weak
Recent timber-marketing experience	Yes	No
Education	Much	Little
Occupation	Business or professional	Other
Age	Young	Old
Planning horizon	Long	Short
Past tenure on this property	Long	Short

TABLE 6.14 FIFTEEN-YEAR GAINS OR LOSSES OF
COMMERCIAL FOREST LAND BY OWNER CLASS

Class of owner or manager	Million acres
Farmers	−28.1
Miscellaneous private owners	+32.0
Forest industry	+ 4.5
Forest Service	+ 0.6
Indian Service	− 1.2
Bureau of Land Management	− 0.7
Other federal agencies	− 0.2
States	+ 1.1
County and municipal agencies	− 0.2

TABLE 6.15 INCREASE IN TIMBER GROWING STOCK BY OWNER CLASS, 1963–1968
(Billion cubic feet)

	1963	1968	Change
National forests	232.9	228.6	− 4.3
Other public holdings	62.1	67.5	+ 5.4
Forest industry lands	93.1	98.5	+ 5.4
Farm and miscellaneous private tracts	236.1	250.2	+14.1
Totals	624.2	644.8	+20.6

TABLE 6.16 TRENDS IN SAWTIMBER STOCKPILES BY OWNER CLASS, 1963–1968
(Billion board feet)

	1963	1968	Change
National forests	1,139.0	1,101.5	−37.5
Other public holdings	262.5	270.5	+ 8.0
Forest industry lands	393.3	395.4	+ 2.1
Farm and miscellaneous private tracts	706.6	723.0	+16.4
Totals	2,501.4	2,490.4	−11.0

PART 2   TOMORROW'S ISSUES

7　FUTURE EXPECTATIONS

E. M. GOULD, JR.*

"TIME," SAID SAINT AUGUSTINE, "is a three-fold present: The present as we experience it, the past as a present memory, and the future as a present expectation. . . . The future is not an overarching leap into the distance; it begins in the present."[1]

Sellar and Yeatman wrote an entertaining book based on the theory that history is not what really happened, but rather what people remember. The hilarious stew that they served up in *1066 and All That* is a real tribute to the fallibility of the human mind. Just as it is thought that no two snowflakes are exactly alike, so probably no two of us have identical memories of the past. The art of accurate verbal history has fallen into sad disrepair, and modern runes and sagas appear in so many books that few of us can read more than a small fraction. The fact that we all carry around with us rather highly personalized versions of mankind's experience on this earth is significant because we use memory selectively to fashion expectations about the future.

The future contains no fixed amount of time, because it starts with the rest of today and runs on indefinitely. Future expectations vary greatly in length. Those unfortunate enough to live a hand-to-mouth existence may look no further ahead than the next meal, whereas those who are better off are likely to have operating expectations that run through their lifetime and sometimes even their children's. Public and private institutions are likely to have guiding concepts of the future that are even more expansive.

This discussion really centers around the kind of expectations that can, in some significant way, help guide present activities. We should look at any forecast quizzically, asking, "If I thought this would come true, would I change anything I am doing today?" If the answer is yes, then the expectation can help and should be treasured. But if the event appears so peripheral to our interests or is

* Forest Economist, Harvard University, Petersham, Mass.

likely to happen so far in the future that we choose to stand pat, then the answer will be no, and we can forget that particular forecast. Useful expectations are therefore those that change present action and, like memories, are personalized and judgmental, depending on interest and temperament.

PROBLEMS IN FORECASTING

Expectations are bounded at one end by the present and stretch forward to some definable point of irrelevance. If they are also wide enough to include everything we believe will significantly affect our actions, how can we go about filling in such an expanse of blank canvas?

One bit of folklore says that history repeats itself. If the present can be placed at the right point in a cycle, the rest can be anticipated with confidence. This belief is corroborated by much of our common experience: The sun rises and sets with satisfying regularity; the seasons continue to march in an orderly manner; and most of the natural systems function in their accustomed way—in the words of an old New England deed, "So long as wood shall grow, water flow, and the memory of man runneth not back to the contrary." There seems to be every reason to believe that most of what is now ongoing will continue into at least the near future. The immediate foreground of expectations can therefore be filled in with finicky detail simply by extrapolating the immediate past.

Projecting today into tomorrow, even allowing for changes now underway, is useful only to a point, because the reliability of extrapolated trends diminishes rapidly. As lines are extended farther and farther into the future, minor errors are exaggerated into big ones, there is a rising probability that unforeseen events will create radical shifts, and human choice has greater scope for decisive change. This uncertainty has led some people to think that the past is practically irrelevant in determining much of the future. They point out that no two situations are similar in all important respects, so that the outcomes are very unlikely to be identical. If nothing is foreordained, human ingenuity must be relied upon to cope as best it can with an uncertain future.

In his book, *The Age of Discontinuity,* Peter Drucker has come up with an idea that borrows something from both points of view. He maintains that in some periods change takes place along fairly well-defined and predictable gradients, largely because many dominant, well-established concepts and systems are followed and refined for a considerable time. However, key ideas and forces are occasionally let loose in the world, and these so alter the state of human affairs that a major discontinuity occurs and events take off on a new and unpredictable course.

Interestingly enough, the same sort of thing seems to happen in nature. Ecologists at the Harvard Forest reconstructed the history of a piece of woodland in New Hampshire. They found that a pine-hemlock stand became established following a hurricane and fire in the 1600s. This stand developed smoothly along a growth gradient until 1938, when everything went down in another hurricane. Thereafter, an entirely new stand, dominated by hardwoods, became established. Thus the slow working of growth processes shaped the trend of development over most of the stand's life, but its basic composition, and therefore the character of the forest, was set by violent natural events. It seems likely that this is not an isolated instance, because most of the woods in our landscape are products of natural or man-made disturbances. This model of forest change, which includes long periods of trend-dominated development interrupted by major discontinuities, may be a reasonable analogue for the history of human development.

Foresters themselves once helped create a major discontinuity in the management concepts governing land, especially timberland. Ever since the profession took root and forecasts of the future have been needed, foresters have looked at the trees around them and have projected some measure of forest capability. In the process they have not overlooked the network of activities that connect the stump with the consumer, but there has been a strong tendency to view the forest as a "system" to be controlled and to relegate the rest to an "environment" beyond control. Foresters have been primarily preoccupied with tree problems; until recreation became important they gave less attention to human problems. This biocentric view has been unfortunate because the technical possibilities for adjustment in the system often lie chiefly outside the forest. Expectations based on the view from the woods are frequently deficient in the eyes of modern urban society.

Any speculation about man's future must revolve about the number of people there will be, where they will live, what they will do for a living, and how they will contrive to get along with one another. Although number, residence, livelihood, and conflict are all intimately related, some insight into reasonable expectations may be gained by dealing with these aspects of the future one at a time.

POPULATION

The question of numbers has been much in the public eye lately. Economics has long been called the dismal science because of Malthus' doleful idea that human fertility would always outstrip food production. Lately, some ecologists have taken over as chief pessimists with a belief that man's capacity to pollute the world has outstripped nature's recuperative powers. Just as Malthus misjudged human motivation regarding children, it is likely that these "doom-sayers" have underestimated human ingenuity.

Looking forward ten years, we can see with some clarity the numbers who will share this earth. Most of the mouths to feed and the hands to work can be counted in the people now alive. Of course the young must be nurtured, educated, brought to maturity, and then provided with something satisfying to do. With vision and luck, our present institutions can be flexible enough to absorb the increase of 10 or 20 percent that is likely to appear in the next decade. In industrial nations, numbers alone need be no problem, provided that young persons, with their enthusiasm for improving the quality of life, prove to be creative innovators rather than modern Luddites. The next few years should give a good clue to which road we are on.

In the short run, the less developed nations stand to gain the most from population control, because they can thereby avoid eating themselves to death and so enjoy something better than a marginal existence. But in the long run, all nations—the present "haves" and "have nots"—are equally interested in this basic means of reducing differences in national well-being. It seems unlikely that a stable world order can be created with the disparity in life style that now exists between the industrial and the agrarian nations.

How the question of population is finally decided, and the speed with which a solution is implemented, are critical elements in forming expectations about the future need for forests. There is little doubt that the United States can look after its own timber needs quite comfortably, given a little help from its logical trading partner to the north. However, there is small comfort in this highly parochial view if the needs of all the people in the world are to be served. Amelioration of the international picture will require a high order of technical and social innovation to grow more fiber and raise the living standard.

GEOGRAPHY

Although sheer numbers may not strain the developed nations in the next decade, the uneven geographic distribution of their citizens is another story.

People have been flocking to the urban areas of the United States ever since the second half of the nineteenth century, when industrialization started in earnest. By 1970 over three-quarters of the U.S. population lived in urban areas. During the 1960s, a great migration of rural people took place when black southerners moved to the industrial north. This kind of migration will have less impact in the future because there are so few rural dwellers left.

Population growth rates are much more manageable in the developed countries than elsewhere. The outlook for even the next decade is not very encouraging in the largely agrarian countries, especially those such as India, China, and the nations of South America that have large base numbers. A 3 or 4 percent increase in such populations each year can easily eat up gains from increased production. In these "Malthusian countries," where hand labor is the rule, a large family is a valuable earning asset: the united labor of an expanded family is needed simply to keep income above the starvation level. In an industrial country, on the other hand, children are expensive to raise and educate, and most parents choose smaller families and a higher standard of living. In due course, this same incentive may appear in the less developed countries, but it will probably not appear fast enough and therefore most of these countries must undertake positive programs of population control in order to survive.

The subject of population and the capacity of the world to provide comfortable and healthy life styles is currently fashionable. Even in the United States, where growth is about 1.8 percent, numbers can double in less than 50 years. With population control an important issue and techniques receiving a great deal of attention, the long-range picture is more promising than it was a few years ago. The question of stabilizing or at least controlling the number of passengers on "space ship Earth" is now a legitimate public issue that can be discussed without cataclysmic effects.

Most of the phenomenal growth in our economy during the current century has been based on the migration of underemployed farm people to more productive industrial work in the cities. Although these able-bodied workers were basic fuel for the economy, their influx was possible only because agriculture itself became an exceedingly industrial and productive activity. Large knowledge inputs in the form of capital goods and animal and plant husbandry now enable about one-twentieth of the population to produce more food and fiber than did half the population in 1900. And there is still a good deal of unexploited knowledge available as a base for further expansion. Agribusiness seems to be well able to service foreseeable needs during the next decade: Shortage of food is not likely to trouble advanced nations for many years to come.

Earlier foreign and rural migrants to the city were almost automatically absorbed into productive employment, because workers needed no more skill and education than they could get on the job. Today the situation is entirely different. Urban industries are becoming knowledge- rather than labor-based, and the most recent immigrants to the core city are not qualified to work until they have had extensive training. We have so far been unable to mobilize the resources needed to prepare these unskilled minorities to enter productive and therefore well-paid jobs. This has been especially true of blacks in city slums, but many others are in an equally unenviable position.

Unless hope of escaping the clutches of poverty can be encouraged by substantial accomplishment very soon, the poor pose a real threat to the whole social fabric. The disadvantaged are no longer spread thinly throughout the countryside, where joint action is difficult: they are concentrated in large numbers in the urban centers controlling the complex web of activities which make an industrial society productive. Serious disruption of the web is easy, and the costs for everyone could be exceedingly high. Top national priority therefore attaches to making the poor into productive citizens with a stake in the continued success of society.

The countryside still has plenty of problems, but they seem to be manageable compared to the difficulties seen in metropolitan areas. If urbanization has created the most efficient production and consumption conglomerates the world has seen, concentration of people at levels frequently greater than 10,000 per square mile has also created environmental diseconomies. Core-city transportation systems have metamorphosed through several instars from horses to steam to electricity and finally to autos, but the original settlement patterns remain and make technical changes more and more difficult. Congestion in central cities and surrounding suburban areas is currently reaching the point where only radically new innovations are likely to restore reasonable efficiency.

URBAN ISSUES

The problems of water supply, waste disposal, and dangerously contaminated air have also reached incipient crisis proportions in most large urban areas. Although the technical knowledge needed to remedy these difficulties is either at hand or well advanced through research, institutional arrangements have not yet been made. A high level of social inventiveness is needed in order to turn knowledge into timely action on an adequate scale. Any durable solution will have to deal with the problem of equity—distributing costs to the beneficiaries in ways that make the burden acceptable. Where rules concerning the use of "free access resources" such as air and running water have to be changed, the costs should be equitably shared among users. Although various levels of government will no doubt use tax money to reduce the public cost of many environmental-misfit operations, many cases can be corrected by changing private production processes. The cost of change would then be "internalized" and assessed against beneficiaries more or less automatically by the economic system.

In both the short and the long run, there is little doubt that most people will continue to live in urban areas. The imperatives of efficient production and consumption will all work in that direction until the advent of some yet-unknown major innovation. However, in the short run, the quality of life that central cities will be able to provide their citizens is likely to be unsatisfactory. In addition, change in the next few years will seem glacially slow until the nation makes the massive effort needed to solve the human and environmental problems that plague city people today. Meanwhile, the diseconomies created by deleterious functioning of the natural systems, and the normal impatience of the disadvantaged, will continue to reduce the efficiency of urban ways of life. We have reached the point where alternatives are sought by those who have the private resources to achieve a better life style. However, moving out will not solve the basic problem of providing the urban efficiency needed by a consuming society.

In industrial countries which are blessed with a large wooded estate, forest-land use can help solve a number of urban problems. For instance, a great deal of U.S. housing is blatantly bad and all of it costs too much. Here is a fertile field for developing new wood-based products that contribute to innovative designs making reasonably priced housing available to all, especially in the cities. New thinking about the connections among architecture, the human community, and the individual is badly needed to get urban people back into functioning neighborhoods that provide a sense of security and participation. We need an approach to structures that will bring individuals and their man-made and natural environments into an easy and satisfying relationship.

Involving foresters and industrialists in the task of urban improvement will be further complicated by the fact that the proponents of other forest values are competing vigorously for scarce land resources. Although many people are effectively stressing the need to use forests to generate clean air and water, to improve the spatial amenities of urban life, and to maintain some bit of nature in modern society, it is not yet clear how to get conservationists, preservationists, ecologists, industrialists, foresters, and planners to take a coordinated view. It seems evident that increasing scarcity is making multiple use a logical necessity at the very time when past deficiencies in performance under this rubric are undermining the whole concept.

PROSPECTS FOR INNOVATION

In the years immediately ahead, the vast majority of people will continue to earn their livelihood by producing the goods and services needed by others; only in the underdeveloped countries will many people live a subsistence way of life. Regardless of their form of government, people in the industrial countries will have to perform the functions of assembling resources, processing them, and distributing the resulting goods and a multitude of additional services to the places where they are needed. Almost everyone will be involved in some manner with these processes, and nearly all will belong to some organization participating in the work. The current shift of workers away from manufacturing, as it becomes more efficient, and toward more and more demanding public and private services is likely to continue during the next decade, as will the need for general organizational chores.

A major element in any expectation of the future is the great durable infrastructure of production plants, farms, and transportation, power, and communication networks. Most of this infrastructure will be in use throughout the coming decade, and a great deal of it even fifty years hence. The traditional industries—steel, automobiles, agriculture, and chemicals—will still loom large several decades from now even though the big growth will probably come from some of the more modern industries: electronics, computers, and similar knowledge-based activities. But any look at the near future must figure on using most of our present production plant, and even in the long run much of it will stay with us.

Considering the time required for major investment programs to mature, most new plants and other facilities for the next decade are already on the drawing boards. Although the pace of the economy will affect the rate of change, it seems unlikely that the next five to ten years will see much that is now completely unknown as a product or production process. Unless they are stimulated by the powerful drive of necessity, truly innovative systems will be slow in coming and unlikely to dominate economic activity even five decades hence.

Forests are a relatively stable element in any resource equation because their growth is slow measured in human terms. However, their social values are subject to change by human decision. New processes that utilize wood in different ways can change supplies-in-being almost overnight. Social control over forest use—allocations for wilderness; constraints on burning, harvesting, or recreational use; or the demands of mechanization on forest operations—can redefine "productive forest land" very quickly. Thus while trees continue their slow growth, their potential for satisfying human needs is subject to continuous and rapid change, especially during periods of discontinuity.

One theory of innovation states that great changes are most likely to occur when the need is widely felt and when relevant technical skills are well developed. On this theory, we should expect to see some relief of urban congestion: mass transit systems that function door-to-door; decentralization to avoid the diurnal flood to and from the office and shop; the improvement of electronic communication to generate systems that move information to people where they live rather than moving the people.

Better and cheaper housing is probably more inhibited by inflexible human institutions than it is by technical infeasibility. The proliferation of local construction rules has gone beyond the needs of health and safety; labor regulations siphon off gains from new techniques; financial and business institutions are less than responsive to the changing situation. All these limitations cry out for a systems approach to relieve the constraints on where and how we live.

Demands for a healthy and comfortable environment are just beginning to be widely articulated. In the relatively near future, we can expect that considerable change will be made in production processes to reduce the more deleterious environmental effects of industry. In the long run, the greatest change will probably result from dropping the idea of "final consumption" and viewing production, consumption, disposal, and reuse as a single materials-cycling process. Such a view can lead to considerable revision of ideas about consumer demand and the goods and services needed to satisfy it. If people reject built-in obsolescence, excessive packaging, hard pesticides, and other things that create objectionable long-term side effects in the environment, our present systems of production will still work, but considerable change in procedures will be needed.

GETTING ALONG WITH ONE ANOTHER

Learning to live together with a tolerable level of conflict appears to be a full-time job over the foreseeable future. Seeking the elimination of conflict is not realistic: There are too many real differences in interest among the people of the world to think that strife can magically disappear. However, it is not beyond hope to devise systems of conflict resolution which are more effective and leave fewer lasting scars than present systems, and which escape such heavy penalties for failure as our present procedures entail. The job of controlling conflict between the sexes, within the family, between generations, between workers and managers, between managers and owners, and among nations is tremendous but central.

The most grievous outcome for the world would be a dispute ending in nuclear warfare, but responsible governments have learned a good deal about avoiding ultimate disaster during twenty-five years of living with the nuclear threat. The substitute, limited warfare, is becoming more unpopular with every passing day, at least when used by a big power such as the United States. Almost certainly we will see this style of settling conflicts given up in the United States. However, this policy may encourage adventures by some of the smaller powers who have much to gain and comparatively little to lose. It is not yet clear what can be substituted for the threat of force as a steadying influence in international relations. Innovations in this area deserve top priority. Only in the long run does a basic shift in international dealings toward more pacific methods seem possible. Meanwhile, agile footwork will still be needed to avoid catastrophe.

In the United States and a good deal of the rest of the world, much of the immediate future will be dominated by conflicts arising because the young dream dreams and the old fear change. The current revolt of youth against the establishment is real and will probably persist through much of the coming decade. The root of the matter is not so much the recognized government-business-university complex, but rather the fact that practically all the significant tasks in a modern society are performed by some kind of organization. The proliferation of organization itself, with areas of overlapping and dovetailed activity, makes older theories of social order obsolete. As Drucker (*The Age of Discontinuity*) has noted, the old idea of a social order where governments had neat layers such as federal, state, and local to perform assigned public tasks, while business firms did all the private tasks, simply doesn't fit a modern society. Today, private research houses make public policy recommendations for governments; public schools are sometimes run by private contract. Universities do both public and private research and planning, and all the lines that once seemed so clear are now blurred, indistinct, and outside accepted social theory.

Organization, which appears to be essential for getting things done in a complex society, makes it difficult for individuals to feel that they make a meaningful contribution or significantly control their private destinies. Developing social mores that will help individuals and organizations play their essential roles in a responsible and responsive way must take equal priority with efforts to rationalize international relations. At the moment, a host of new advocates is promoting wider participation in forest-land-use decisions. It is hoped that the next few years will produce positive and responsible roles for such special publics as the Sierra Club and Nader's Raiders. While applying the brakes may be useful in any decision-making process, the full value of such efforts will come only when they help articulate and develop viable alternatives so that the public can choose more intelligently.

REPRISE

Since we can't leap into the future, but must get there from here one step at a time, how does the journey promise to start? Although tomorrow will be a day much like today, at some point changes big and little will combine to set new goals and directions. Only if we are both wise and lucky will we carry forward the best in our culture and leave behind the worst. The prevalence of social ferment today suggests we are about to pitch over a divide that will mark the 1970s as a time of discontinuity.

We will need more of almost everything during the next decade just to maintain those features of our present lifestyle which have survival value. Raising the living standards of the undernourished and underprivileged in industrial countries is essential just as it is in the developing countries now that instant transmission of words and pictures creates global anticipations.

At times, the U.S. economy behaves badly, society is discomfited, and malaise spreads. Unfortunately, most of the remedies proposed at such times center on technical adjustments in economic or social machinery. Such a mechanical view of the problem has limited utility unless we decisively improve the bleak expectations which people hold and which produce poor social performance.

At the moment, the most pressing social problem is alienation caused by the people's loss of faith in the capacity of public and private institutions to adjust to a changing world. The past has demonstrated that social machinery can respond if given enough time. Widespread, massive, and almost instant information has injected a new element of urgency into the need for response. Daily and hourly exposure to system failures—war, poverty, discrimination, disorder, environmental deterioration—produces a gut feeling for change in all these things—right now! The time available to make needed adjustments in the complex social web has probably been permanently lessened. We must learn to deal with a foreshortened time dimension as well as with a shrinking world. This lesson is as valid for foresters as it is for statesmen.

By definition, a time of discontinuity is a period of rapidly changing and transient expectations due to great uncertainty about the future. Such a time may offer unparalleled opportunities to improve the lot of mankind, if we diligently exercise our human instinct to search, learn, and adapt.

8   TIMBER RESOURCE PROSPECTS

H. J. VAUX*

THIS ASSESSMENT of timber-supply prospects rests on the assumption that forestry will continue to move in today's directions under today's policies. Thus it attempts to provide some sort of benchmark against which the need for new policies and new directions may be judged.

The approach to timber-resource prospects requires analysis of the factors affecting supply and demand: available forest area, present growing stock, prospective timber-management practices, and timber growth on the supply side; and domestic economic development and the international balance of timber trade on the demand side.

The relatively distant time horizon within which the assessment is to be made creates special problems. Judgments about the magnitude and direction of numerous elements in the assessment are speculative. Indeed, as we try to look beyond 1975 into an increasingly distant future, uncertainty becomes the key economic characteristic with which we have to deal.

A second and more subtle difficulty arises from the fact that the nature and influence of many of the several factors affecting supply and demand shift substantially as we move toward more remote time horizons. For example, in the "near term" (about 1975), supply is dominated by existing stocks and producers' market expectations of the future. But in the "long term" (about 2020), supply is much more strongly influenced by available timber-management techniques and their cost, by present long-run expectations concerning demand, and by public resource policies. And in the "mid term" (about 2000), the relative importance of these several factors affecting supply will be still different.

AVAILABLE LAND

The prospective 1975 timber supply will differ from current supply (1) if there are significant changes in merchantable-timber inven-

---

* Professor of Forestry, University of California, Berkeley.

TABLE 8.1 AREA OF COMMERCIAL FOREST LAND IN THE UNITED STATES ON JANUARY 1, 1968, BY REGION AND CLASS OF OWNERSHIP
(Thousand acres)

Region	All ownership	National forests	Other public	Forest industry	Farm and miscellaneous
North	175,992.5	10,342.2	21,643.9	15,328.3	128,678.1
South	198,798.1	10,589.0	6,877.1	35,531.7	145,800.3
West	135,422.0	75,939.4	16,574.7	14,510.0	28,397.8
Totals	510,212.5	96,870.6	45,095.7	65,370.0	302,876.2
Proportion of total	100.0	19.0	(Percent) 8.8	12.8	59.4

SOURCE: Division of Forest Economics and Marketing Research, Forest Service, United States Department of Agriculture.

tories between now and then and (2) if timber-harvesting policies of owners change in response to changed price expectations or other factors. The timber inventory in the near term will depend primarily on the present level of stocks modified by such land withdrawals, timber growth, and timber harvest as may occur between now and 1975.

The area of commercial forest land reported by the Forest Service as of January 1, 1968, is shown in Table 8.1. What changes in this basic factor of production are likely to take place if forestry continues in today's directions under today's policies?

In the past, the principal changes in reported commercial forest land area have been due to (1) conversion of forest land to agricultural, urban, or other nonforest land uses, (2) reservation or purchase of forests for wilderness, park, or other forest uses from which commercial wood production is excluded by the owner's policy, and (3) reversions to the commercial forest category, primarily from abandonment of agricultural cultivation. The aggregate net impact of such changes has been relatively small during the past fifteen years. Outside the West, the net change in commercial forest area was less than 7.5 million acres, or 2 percent of the total commercial forest (regions are defined in Chapter 3).

But the recent relative stability may not persist. A look toward the future reveals three factors that seem likely to work in the direction of reducing land input for timber supply. One is additional reservations of publicly owned land for uses which preclude timber production. This factor may be expected to operate most forcibly on the 92.5 million acres now in public ownership in the West, where the principal remaining stands of old-growth timber are located. To the extent that publicly owned commercial forests in the North are favorably located, they, too, may come into demand for restricted recreational or open-space uses. The impacts of this factor are likely to be pretty well worked out in the West during the next ten or fifteen years. By that time it seems probable that either reservation or utilization will have taken place on most western forests. Elsewhere, this kind of reduction of the commercial forest-land base will probably persist as long as population and real income continue to rise.

A second factor which will tend to reduce the area available for commercial timber growing is further public acquisition of forest land now in private ownership for recreation and open-space uses. Acquisitions for such purposes under the Land and Water Conservation Fund Act amounted to 800,000 acres in the first four years of the Act's existence, and the funds available for such programs have recently been expanded. By no means all the land so acquired comes from the commercial forest category, but some of it does, and that class of land is often the most attractive resource for recreation and open-space purposes. Significant reductions in private commercial forest area from this cause seem likely to continue until well beyond the near-term horizon of 1975.

COMMERCIAL FOREST LAND

A third factor that tends to reduce land input for timber supply is the growing discrepancy between "commercial forest area" as now defined in the nationwide Forest Survey and the area of land which will actually contribute to the timber supply. Commercial forest land is land "which is producing or is capable of producing crops of industrial wood and not withdrawn from timber utilization by statute or administrative regulation . . . generally capable of producing in excess of 25 cubic feet per acre of annual growth."[1] There appear to be three separate deficiencies in this definition.

The first deficiency is that the definition includes land of such low timber-growth potential. What are the costs and returns of growing timber on land whose productivity is as low as 25 cubic feet per acre per year? Although detailed and comprehensive estimates of the costs and returns do not appear to have been made, the available data suggest that lands of such low productivity may be uneconomic for timber growing.

Marty and Newman calculated rates of return on intensified timber-growing programs for the various type-site conditions found on national forests. Their results indicate that 25 percent of the commercial forest area on national forests would yield a rate of return to management intensification of less than 3 percent.[2] Such a low rate of return strongly suggests that these lands are submarginal for economical timber growing at the levels of stumpage price projected by Marty and Newman.

The Forest Service's "Douglas-Fir Supply Study" reports entire working circles which yielded negative rates of return to specified management-intensification programs.[3] The conclusion seems almost inescapable that considerable land included in such working circles is below the economic margin for timber growing.

Although the land in question in each of these examples is by definition "commercial forest land," there appears to be no economic justification for considering the land as a factor of production contributing to long-term future timber supply. If the long-term economic justification for devoting these lands to timber production appears questionable, it seems equally questionable that ordinary commercial timber-harvest operations should be conducted on such land merely because it now supports merchantable old growth. The rising value of old-growth forests for recreational and amenity purposes makes it proper to challenge the validity of including in estimates of near-term timber supply the quantity of timber on lands of such low productivity that they cannot sustain an economic timber-growing enterprise in the long term. Such land (site productivity class IV) is estimated to include more than 25 percent of the commercial forest land on western national forests. Additional low-productivity "commercial" forest is undoubtedly included in current inventories for the North and South.

The second deficiency in the definition of commercial forest land arises because of the wide diversity of ownership intent among non-farm miscellaneous private owners. It has been estimated, for example, that not more than 10 percent of such owners in densely populated northeastern states are interested in growing commercial timber on their land. A significant (but unknown) proportion appear to be adverse to timber growing. Yet almost 60 percent of the land defined as commercial forest in the New England and mid-Atlantic states is held by these miscellaneous owners. Economic incentives may be of little avail in bringing land in such ownership into the effective timber-supply picture.

Finally, as a third deficiency in the definition of commercial forest land, there is the likelihood that continuing locally significant withdrawals will be made for freeways, airports, reservoirs, urban sites, and other nonforest uses.

The weight of the three deficiencies is sufficient warning that the time has come to replace the simple "open frontier" assumption inherent in the definition of commercial forest land with a more realistic one based on increasing competition for land of all kinds. This may require some scaling down of timber-supply forecasts.

Few, if any, factors are in sight which can offset to any significant degree the potential reductions in the supply of timber-growing land. The process of agricultural-land abandonment, which added substantially to the commercial forest-land resource following World War I, no longer operates significantly in this direction. Improvements in access and in information which resulted in a 10 percent increase in estimates of commercial forest in the West as recently as 1960 are also an unlikely source of future increases.

Political developments will largely determine the extent of near-term withdrawals. Should national priorities be reordered by 1975, reductions of available inventories from this source on the order of 2 to 3 percent might eventuate.

TIMBER INVENTORY IN 1975

As reported by Josephson and Hair in Chapter 3, timber growth increased significantly between 1952 and 1967. Its trend in the near term is likely to be influenced primarily by the level of timber harvesting. Between 1962 and 1967, annual timber removals rose faster than did annual growth in both softwoods and hardwoods, in each of the regions. The result is particularly evident in the Pacific Coast and Rocky Mountain regions. On the Pacific Coast, annual sawtimber growth rose only 905 million board feet between 1962 and 1967. During the same period, annual removals increased 2.73 billion board feet.

The near-term outlook is for continuing expansion of timber removals. Further increases in plywood and pulpwood consumption at recent rates, along with lumber use at about the 1968 level, would result in 1975 removals 13 percent above the 57.5 billion-board-foot level reported for 1967. These trends assure an accelerated decrease in inventories in the West, where 1975 sawtimber stocks are likely to be 6 to 7 percent below 1967 levels. These decreases should be offset in part by increases of the order of 10 percent in the North and South, with only a 1- to 1½-percent decrease in sawtimber nationwide due to the net excess of removal over growth.

The outlook for timber inventories in 1975 based on projections of growth and cut trends is shown in Table 8.2.

TABLE 8.2 SAWTIMBER INVENTORY AND ITS NEAR-TERM CHANGE, BY REGION

Region	Inventory (Billion board feet)		Change (Percent)	
	1968 actual*	1975 projected	1963–68 actual	1968–75 projected
North	312	345	+4.6	+10.6
South	461	502	+8.0	+ 8.9
West	1,717	1,610	−4.0	− 6.2
Totals or averages	2,490	2,457	−0.4	− 1.3

* Data from Division of Forest Economics and Marketing Research, Forest Service, United States Department of Agriculture.

NEAR-TERM SUPPLY OUTLOOK

In addition to inventory changes, such as those estimated in Table 8.2, near-term supplies of stumpage will be influenced by timber owners' management policies. In the North, where more than 73 percent of the forest is in farm and miscellaneous ownership, timber inventories on such holdings declined 7.3 percent between 1963 and 1968 despite a 2.6 percent increase in forest area. Thus, the inventory increases in the North projected in Table 8.2 are likely to be confined largely to public and industrial holdings. This might permit nominal increases in timber output from such forests. The extensive farm and miscellaneous private woodlands may well contribute somewhat less to supply than they currently do, both because of further expected declines in inventory and because of the probable increase in the proportion of the inventory held for noncommodity forest uses. The 1975 stumpage supply in the North will probably be little changed from 1968 levels. If this region follows the general trend of growing demand for wood and increases its consumption, a moderate rise in stumpage values may be in store.

In the South, sawtimber inventories on the predominant farm and miscellaneous forest holdings expanded between 1963 and 1968, but at a somewhat lesser rate than the 8-percent increase for all forests. Thus, some expansion in near-term timber supply is likely. This should be sufficient to accommodate increases in regional consumption without significant upward movements in stumpage prices.

In the West, public ownership accounted for over 73 percent of the timber inventory in 1968. An additional 14 percent was in industrial ownership. Little significant change in these proportions is to be expected in the near term. The dominant factor now affecting western supply is the allowable-cut policy on public and industrial timber lands, since other owners control less than 13 percent of the inventory. Although allowable cuts from public lands moved upward prior to 1968, continued region-wide expansion of this element in supply may be increasingly difficult to achieve in the years immediately ahead. Improved inventory and site data, which have been a significant source of increased allowable cuts in the past, are unlikely to yield further increases. Contractions in allowable cuts because of reservations for noncommodity purposes will probably more than offset any possible increases from public lands.

On industrial holdings in the West, increases in allowable cut may be justified by new programs of intensified timber management. A few industrial properties have already expanded output on this basis by as much as 20 percent. But the net effect of such increases in the near term may be sufficient only to offset the declining trend of output from all industrial forests, which has characterized the period since 1955.

Timber removals in the West increased $1\frac{1}{4}$ percent per year between 1953 and 1968 and by twice that rate in the last five years of the period. Continued near-term increases in timber removals of at least 1 percent per annum appear likely in view of the outlook for expanding wood-products demand, the current dominance of the West as a timber supplier (two-thirds of the 1967 national cut), and the presence of substantial installed but unutilized sawmill capacity. This pressure for expanding the cut in the face of quite inelastic standing-timber supply strongly suggests further significant increases in market prices of western stumpage.

In sum, the trends described would lead, by 1975, to an expansion of timber removals for the entire United States by up to 10 percent of 1967 levels. Part of this increase would be met by a 7- to 8-percent increase in net growth, and the remainder would be absorbed by a $1\frac{1}{4}$- to $1\frac{1}{2}$-percent decline in sawtimber inventories. Continuing pressure on stumpage prices would produce significant near-term increases in the West and possibly in the North as well.

As perspective on this sketch of the near-term timber-supply outlook, testimony by Chief Forester Cliff in October 1969 on the general timber supply outlook noted that "the projected increases (in timber supply) are not large enough to meet demands for very long. Projected softwood sawtimber supplies, for example, fall below projected demands in the early 1970s."[4] Allowing for some differences in the usage of terminology, the Chief's description of the near-term outlook appears to be essentially the same as the one given here. To the extent that comparison between different projection approaches is possible, the near-term supply outlook I have suggested also seems consistent with that presented for the South by the Southern Forest Resource Analysis Committee in 1969.[5]

These near-term projections suggest 1975 removals of softwoods about $7\frac{1}{2}$ billion board feet above 1967. The Cabinet Task Force on Softwood Lumber and Plywood estimated that requirements of softwoods to meet national housing goals in 1974 would be more than 11 billion board feet above 1967.[6] Thus, the present projection confirms the Task Force conclusion that unless an early start toward expansion of timber supply is made, achievement of housing goals will exert strong upward pressure on softwood prices.

FACTORS AFFECTING TIMBER CONSUMPTION IN THE LONG TERM

The preceding analysis of the near-term timber-supply outlook assumed that the upward trend of wood-products demand and of timber removals characteristic of the last fifteen years would continue to 1975. Near-term inventories and supply have thus been evaluated against the assumption of a demand for wood largely independent of supply and reflecting currently established economic forces. But when we turn to the long term and try to gauge what might happen by year 2020, a different approach is required, an approach that must take account of the interdependencies between supply and demand which may be distinctly important over a period of decades.[7]

Within the span of the next fifty years, interrelated shifts in timber demand, supply, and consumption are virtually certain to occur. In order to try to identify which ones may be important, the following approach is taken: Demand and supply are appraised independently, each on the assumption that presently identifiable trends are sustained into the future. Such projections of supply and demand are then modified in the light of the probable effects of each on the other during the long term. Finally, estimates of potential consumption are derived from the modified projections.

FACTORS AFFECTING DEMAND IN THE LONG TERM

The population of the United States doubled in the first fifty years of the present century and has fallen just short of sustaining that rate of increase in the last two decades. If the latter, more conservative, rate of growth is projected to 2020, the population in that year would be 380 to 385 million, or about 86 percent above the present level.

Long-term projections of gross national product are more speculative than those for population growth and, as Dr. Gould has implied in Chapter 7, they may be largely irrelevant as a guide to wood demands in the long term. For whatever they may be worth, most projections would associate a GNP of $3,500 to $4,000 billion current dollars with the suggested 2020 population of 380 million; in other words, about a four-fold increase over the 1969 annual rate. Such a result would slightly more than double the present GNP per capita.

Although a four-fold expansion in wood demand is also conceivable, other factors seem likely to moderate the prospective expansion. In recent years, the proportion of GNP devoted to services has been increasing somewhat. Further rises in per-capita income might accelerate this increase, with a consequent relative decrease in the demand for physical structure raw materials, including wood.

Concern over environmental pollution will probably stimulate replacement of the present open-ended systems for controlling production with closed systems of economic and social control. Emergence of closed-system controls over production will tend to hold in check the prospective increase in both output and new raw-material input per unit of total economic activity. In the forest-products field, such a development would bear most significantly on pulp products, the segment of wood demand which has shown the largest growth over the past forty years.

Such a basic realignment of our production/consumption systems would undoubtedly check the forces which have thus far sustained the growth in demand for many forest products. On the other hand, it would open up the possibility of revolution in the competitive relationships among commodities, bringing to wood vast new technological obligations. Society might at long last capitalize on the basic properties of cellulose, designing production-consumption systems that are highly efficient from the standpoint of closed-system economies. Efficiency criteria for such systems are vastly different from the ones presently in use.[8] The biodegradable character of cellulose may prove to be a major advantage of wood in such a context. The renewability of timber supplies will also be an asset compared to metals. In addition, trees are a relatively efficient source of plant fiber. In the very long run, renewable resources such as wood may be favored by society over nonrenewable ones, but it may take longer for this force to become dominant than the fifty-year horizon with which we are dealing.

RESEARCH, DEVELOPMENT, CONSUMER RELATIONS

The real possibility that a major technologic and institutional restructuring of our society, comparable in scope to the industrial revolution, may mark the period between now and 2020 emphasizes uncertainty as a key characteristic of the long-term outlook. The demand for timber will probably be most affected by, first, the research and development aimed at exploiting wood's adaptability to closed-system economies and, second, the industries' work to establish and maintain consumer preference for products made of wood.

On both the preceding counts, wood starts from a relatively disadvantaged position. Historically, the effort, both public and private, expended on research and development in wood production and marketing has been very modest compared to the effort in nonwood sectors. Outlays in 1965 were about $100 million, less than 1 percent of the value of wood products sold in that year.[9] Moreover, the major objective of wood research and development has been to solve near-term and mid-term problems. Some research fundamental to the long-term problems of demand has been accomplished, but its magnitude appears puny compared to the dimensions of the job. In the past the structure of the industries has not been conducive to research effort.[10] The federal and state forest products laboratories have shown interest, but their contributions appear relatively minor in the face of tasks whose complexity and magnitude are at least equal to those of a moon shot and whose significance for the long term on earth is probably far greater.

CONCENTRATION THROUGH MERGERS

Recent mergers of forest-products firms into large corporate units, particularly where they are based on extensive timber holdings, may be removing some of the obstacles to research and development. But a number of the large units now seem to be heavily preoccupied with near-term questions. Clearly, the mere emergence of large corporate entities is not enough to ensure that long-term research and development problems will be perceived, formulated, and dealt with.

Comparable observations could be made about efforts to influence consumer preferences for wood. The same industrial characteristics which have held research and development low and focused on near-term problems have given wood an image of unconcern toward consumers.

Although the potential demand for wood in the long term seems great, the extent to which this potential may actually be realized probably depends more than ever before on the kinds of research, development, and consumer-education programs that are mounted during the next couple of decades. Both the public and wood-using industries should understand that significant expansion of the economy's wood sector can be an essential, constructive step in adapting to the constraints of Spaceship Earth. There should also be a general understanding that the underdeveloped forest resource holds great long-term potentialities for growing more timber. Unless these points are recognized and acted upon, the expansive view of future wood demand conjured up by prospective population and GNP is likely to prove illusory.

The outlook for demand can be clarified by an examination of the long-term timber supply, provisionally assuming a 100-percent increase in demand by the year 2020, a relatively modest assumption in view of apparent potentials.

LONG-TERM SUPPLY OUTLOOK: LAND USE

The factors affecting the land base for commercial timber growing in the long term include the same ones enumerated earlier in connection with the near-term outlook. In addition, there is the growing possibility of extended use of forested areas for primary residential purposes. Dr. Gould, in Chapter 7, has alluded to the critical problem of urbanization and the probability of some kind of "discontinuous" development in response to it. One possibility is extensive nonfarm residence in rural areas. Such a ruralizing of the population might have a substantial impact on the availability of commercial forest land.

The Southern Forest Resource Analysis Committee estimated

that within the next thirty years the following net reductions in timber-growing land might occur in the South:

Conversion to agriculture	3 million acres
Urban and industrial expansion	2 million acres
Rights of way, etc.	1 million acres
Parks and recreation areas	3 million acres
Reservoirs, etc.	1 million acres
Total net reduction	10 million acres

The Committee also noted that the loss of land inputs could be much higher if multiple-use management is not widely practiced on the remaining commercial-forest acreage.[11]

Losses of land inputs from similar causes will be experienced in the North and West. A net nationwide reduction on the order of 30 million acres, almost 6 percent of the 1968 total, would not be surprising. Growing-stock losses from attrition of the land base will be relatively larger than area losses, since land converted to nonforest uses is usually better stocked at the time of conversion than is the time of conversion than is land reverting to forest use.

TIMBER INVENTORIES

The annual growth of timber in 1967, estimated by the Forest Service at 17⅓ billion cubic feet, represented a 2.7 percent return on growing stock. Compared to the situation fifteen years earlier, annual growth had risen 4 billion cubic feet, or 30 percent. Forty-five percent of the growth was in the South, 31 percent in the North, and 24 percent in the West.

During the same fifteen-year period, timber removals rose from 11½ billion cubic feet per year to 13¼ billion. Thus, the growing-stock input to the timber-supply system has been increasing about 3½ billion cubic feet per year. This additional input will contribute to further increases in growth in the future. In the West, conversion of slow-growing old-growth forests to managed stands will also increase future growth.

Under the assumption that present trends will continue, the end of the era of increasing nationwide timber growth seems to be in sight. Projection of past trends in growth against timber removals incident to a doubling of the demand for wood indicates that removals would exceed growth by 2005. Thereafter, inputs of stocks into timber growing would begin to decline. The forest capital plant would begin to shrink, and reduction in growth would shortly ensue. Coupled with the still-rising trend of withdrawals resulting from demand expansion, an accelerating reduction in total annual growth would develop shortly after the year 2020.

The outlook appears considerably more ominous if it is examined in relation to tree species. Timber withdrawals bear more heavily on softwoods than they do on hardwoods. Between 1952 and 1967, about 66 percent of the growing-stock removals were softwood. During the same period, only about 57½ percent of the growth was softwood. Projecting these relationships, one concludes that softwood removals would begin to exceed softwood growth in 1990. Other things being equal, the period of accelerating decrease in softwood growth might thus begin no later than 2000.

A SUPPLY MODEL

The meaning of these trends, with their several complex interactions, can perhaps be best explained by presenting a single model of long-term timber supply. Although the theoretical basis for projecting timber supplies in the long term has been generally understood for a number of years, the amount of actual data which lend themselves to such a projection is still dishearteningly meager. Nevertheless, the supply model of Table 8.3 is presented as a first approximation. Much of the model rests on special assumptions and therefore should be interpreted with caution.

Each column except the first in Table 8.3 displays a single supply alternative. The one in the second column ("Present trend") shows what might be expected if the following conditions prevail between now and year 2020:

1. The commercial-forest-land base is reduced, by land withdrawals and conversions, to 94 percent of its present size, with consequent reductions in growing stock.

2. Timber removals for commodity use rise to approximately double their current level.

3. Forest protection, regeneration, stand improvement, and other timber-management efforts continue for the next fifty years at about the current level.

Obviously there are a great many supply programs alternative to the present trend. Two of these alternatives, representing different degrees of expanded timber-management effort, are shown in the third and fourth columns of Table 8.3. Under "Intensity I," it is assumed that land withdrawals and levels of commodity removals remain the same as under the present trend, but that 45 million acres of currently unstocked or poorly stocked land are planted during the next thirty years and that commercial-thinning programs recover and utilize 25 percent of mortality. Under "Intensity II," the planting program would be speeded up to cover the entire 45 million acres in the first decade, and the thinning program would be extended to double the salvage of mortality.

TABLE 8.3 MODEL OF LONG-TERM TIMBER SUPPLY IN THE UNITED STATES AS OF 1970, WITH TIME HORIZONS OF 30 AND 50 YEARS, AND TIMBER DEMAND IN 2020 TWICE THAT OF 1970

(Billion cubic feet unless otherwise specified)

Item	Present trend	Intensified management	
		Intensity I	Intensity II
1970: Growing stock	652	652	652
Growth per year	18.1	18.1	18.1
Removals per year	14.1	14.1	14.1
2000: Growing stock	722	796	855
Growth per year	23.8	26.8	28.0
Removals per year	22.5	22.5	22.5
2020: Growing stock	689	866	930
Growth per year	24.5	28.1	30.2
Removals per year	28.2	28.2	28.2
Management activities	Present programs continued	Plant 1.5 million acres per year for 30 years; thin to recover 25 percent of tree mortality.	Plant 4.5 million acres per year for 10 years; thin to recover 50 percent of tree mortality.
Additional costs	Present real cost levels continued	Invest in expanded planting and road construction at following annual rates: 1970–1980: $484 million; 1980–1990: $358 million; 1990–2000: $158 million	Invest in expanded planting and road construction at following annual rates: 1970–1980: $1,125 million; 1980–1990: $ 400 million
		Total cost: $10,000 million	Total cost: $15,250 million
Average cost of additional yields (4-percent discount rate)		$76.80 per M cu. ft.	$75.60 per M cu. ft.

For each alternative supply program, Table 8.3 also shows the estimated levels of investment that would be required and the average costs of the additional yields produced by the programs, assuming a 4-percent discount rate.

Despite their speculative basis, these projections provide some useful insight into the long-term timber supply. Continuation of the present trend would result in a peaking of inventories about year 2000. The excess of removals over growth would begin in about that year and would accelerate rapidly thereafter. Before this could take place, however, market supply of timber would very probably be restricted by the sustained-production policies of public, industrial, and other owners. Substantial and lasting increases in stumpage price would thus be likely to occur considerably before the year 2000. One of the long-term responses to such increases would be a shift in demand, as substitutes took advantage of higher wood prices to claim a larger share of the market. The outlook for 2020 under the present-trend supply policy would be stabilization of consumption at about 24 billion cubic feet per year at levels of stumpage price 30 percent or more above the present. Consumption would fall about 15 percent short of the level projected in Table 8.3 and would be only about 70 percent above 1970 levels.

The long-term supply program, "Intensity I," would result in substantial increases in net growth and would defer until about 2020 the moment when supply expansion would no longer keep pace with the projected expansion of demand. However, from the long-term viewpoint, this supply program is still "too little too late." By 2020, timber inventories would be dwindling, actual consumption would probably be falling somewhat short of that projected in Table 8.3, and substantial price increases accompanied by substitution of other materials would have begun an increasingly precipitate reordering of the market.

The third alternative supply program, "Intensity II," would come close to achieving a sustained-yield objective during the long term. By 2020, inventories would have increased more than 40 percent above 1970 levels, the growing stock would be more evenly distributed age-wise, and market supplies would approximate those necessary to sustain the projected doubling of demand without significant stumpage-price increases. Growth would have been raised about 66 percent above 1970 levels.

The model of Table 8.3 thus suggests that it is perfectly feasible to maintain timber supply at levels adequate to meet a doubling of demand between now and 2020 without a significant further rise in the long-term stumpage price trend and at costs for additional output which average less than current stumpage values. But it also indicates that any program for increased timber supply which does not achieve the impact of the "Intensity II" program will commit us irrevocably to a long-term future of continually rising timber prices and levels of wood consumption significantly lower than we might realize with more aggressive efforts. Indeed, the model suggests that if we fail to adopt a supply program with an impact approaching that of "Intensity II," long-term consumption will be unable to double. As an important side effect, timber-growing policies could in the future be subject to severe and proper censure as shortsighted and as failing to capitalize on evident economic opportunities of important social significance.

To say that a long-term supply program is both urgent and feasible does not mean that such a program is either easy or likely. The cost of "Intensity II" is estimated at $15 billion during the first twenty years, over and above recent levels of expenditure. More than 70 percent of the total would be needed during the first ten years. Comparison of the expenditure pattern of "Intensity I" with that of "Intensity II" indicates that either significant delay or significant reduction in scale of effort will result in abortion of the present opportunity to keep timber supply expanding in step with demand.

One of the limitations of the present model is that it is based on an extremely crude idea of how timber growth is affected by such things as site quality, tree age and stocking, and cultural measures. Although the programs are based on considered judgments, they are probably not the most efficient ones that could be developed. A detailed understanding of timber growth relationships would be needed in order to determine how far these programs miss the mark. To the extent that they fail to represent highest efficiency, the cost estimates of Table 8.3 overstate both the required timber-growing investment and the average cost of additional yields. The costs suggested for an adequate supply program are probably of the proper order of magnitude. But since we are talking about supply opportunities with price tags in the tens of billions of dollars, careful exploration and evaluation of the most efficient ways of expanding timber output in the long term becomes high-priority business for forestry.

IMPLICATIONS FOR THE LONG-TERM TREND IN WOOD CONSUMPTION

In light of the supply prospects, we can now reconsider some of the questions about trends in long-term wood consumption which were unanswered in the discussion of trends in demand. If present levels of forest-management effort are simply continued for another twenty years, we can confidently expect a sustained rise in wood prices, accelerated substitution of other materials for wood, a peaking of wood consumption about the year 2000 at perhaps 60 to 70 percent above 1970 levels, and a subsequent decline in total consumption, the magnitude and duration of which would depend on how sluggish we are in responding to it.

On the other hand, if an unprecedentedly massive effort to grow more wood is undertaken now, we appear to have the capability of at least doubling consumption in fifty years.

It seems clear that, for the long term, the supply factors emphasized here will be the dominant ones in determining the trend of wood consumption. The potential demand will emerge if we provide a sufficient supply. However, if we fail to do this, so that commodity withdrawals from the forest once again exceed growth, new and serious economic difficulties will arise to harass the nation. We will face an extended period during which supply will steadily decline while demand will continue to increase. Thus we will enter a stage of both rising wood-product prices and dwindling consumption. To reverse such trends at that time would take truly Herculean efforts and require time which is not purchasable at any cost. Consumptive needs would automatically be directed more and more toward products from nonrenewable resources which, at that stage in economic development, we could ill afford.

It should be emphasized that the evaluation of timber supply and consumption prospects presented here assumes a mere doubling of demand. A doubling of demand by 2020 lies between the low and midrange projections made by the Forest Service in 1967. It is only moderately above the low projection for 2000 made by Resources for the Future—a figure regarded as "almost the lowest of future timber-consumption possibilities."[12]

In the present model, growth is projected at rates significantly above those reflected in the "Timber Trends Study."[13] By the year 2000, I have assumed annual growth about 38 percent higher than the timber-trends estimate for the same year. The data reported by Josephson and Hair in Chapter 3 indicate that growth actually realized since 1963 has been somewhat greater than that envisaged in the timber-trends projection. This is reassuring for the reasonableness of growth assumptions used here. Nevertheless, the latter remain generally optimistic. For example, Duerr has suggested long-term growth capability as probably not much above 20 billion cubic feet per year.[14]

One final comparison may be of interest. In its most recent analysis of the timber supply-demand outlook, the Forest Service has projected demand to the year 2000 over a range of possible price levels and has begun an evaluation of significant supply alternatives.[15] Direct comparison of this Forest Service analysis with the present one is not possible because a somewhat different approach was used: Supply alternatives were projected only to 1980, and only the additional federal costs of those alternatives were estimated. However, the general conclusion of the Forest Service analysis is the same: Without prompt and substantial acceleration of forest-management efforts, supplies will fall increasingly short of demand after 1980 even at relatively high wood prices. The scale of programs which this Forest Service study envisages as meeting demand for the next couple of decades without further significant price increases is about midway between "Intensity I" and "Intensity II" in Table 8.3. Although only federal costs are estimated, these amount to about $6 billion in the first decade.

The projection model which has been presented here thus appears to be based on a fairly cautious view of demand potentialities, a rather liberal view of growth potential, and a realistic though crude appraisal of costs. These characteristics of the analysis tend to emphasize the general conclusion about the long-term outlook. They sharpen the focus on what happens to forest management during the two decades just ahead as the critical determinants of longer-term supply and consumption. They reinforce the conviction that to sustain long-term demands for wood will require vastly intensified forest-management efforts, applied with all deliberate speed and based on much more thorough evaluation of timber-growing opportunities than we have yet achieved.

9 TIMBER MANAGEMENT

J. W. DUFFIELD*

DESPITE THE URGENCY of the timber-supply situation, we have grounds for optimism in the fact that we live in the New World. The comparatively favorable ratio of population to productive land area still permits some flexibility in land-use and management patterns, and meanwhile understanding of forest biology is growing rapidly. This optimism should be somewhat guarded, however, for land options are rapidly becoming restricted, and it is not at all certain that increased understanding of forest biology will lead to spectacular increases in forest productivity. Nevertheless, appropriate patterns of land use and management and effective application of the growing knowledge of forest biology should materially increase the productivity of our forest lands.

There is probably no crop that can be grown on such a wide variety of substrates as wood, ranging from the economically important mangrove forests of the tropical tidelands to innumerable alpine and tundra timberlines. Within the broad spectrum of management procedures applicable to these varied lands, it may help to recognize three bands with special characteristics: wildland silviculture, plantation silviculture, and intensive wood-fiber farming.

Wildland silviculture is essentially the silviculture of the textbooks. It may start from natural tree regeneration, direct seeding, or hand planting. It is the only option available for rough terrain or land difficult for intensive mechanization of cultural and harvesting operations. However, the term "wildland" includes what were once called "farm woodlots" as well as a large aggregate of rural forests and woodland in other classes of ownership. The terrain features which so often determine the characteristics of wildland silviculture may, in many instances, serve to enhance the recreational values of the forest. Indeed, where ruggedness and remoteness are extreme, recreational values become wilderness values and silviculture is ex-

---

* Professor of Forestry, North Carolina State University, Raleigh.

cluded. The determination of this transition point is the subject of lively controversy.

Because air masses must rise to cross mountains, and in rising are cooled, they often tend to precipitate their load of water vapor as rain or snow. Hence many wildland forests clothe important watersheds and frame winter-sports areas. They have been important summer pastures for much the same reasons, although this forest use may yield to others. In addition, big game, upland game birds, and freshwater fish are preeminently resources of the wildland forests. Even this sketchy summary would indicate that wildland forests are strong candidates for multiple use.

In the United States, plantation silviculture reaches its most intensive and extensive development in the southeastern states, the southern pine region, where easy terrain permits mechanized preparation of planting sites and an arrangement of trees in plantations that facilitates intermediate and final harvesting. The potential value of such terrain for recreational use is closely dependent on streams or bodies of water, a fact which tends to impose a sort of automatic zoning. Wildlife and game resources of such lands may be highly important and their development quite compatible with silviculture, including timber harvesting. The soil-protection values of these forests are high and consonant with timber management as well as with properly regulated grazing.

In the areas suitable for plantation silviculture, the use of the forest for timber production seems unlikely to be displaced by other forest uses. However, in parts of the southeast, it is possible that some forest lands may again revert to agricultural production as food surpluses vanish.

Intensive wood-fiber farming is not yet a reality in significant areas of the United States. Indeed, one may doubt whether the highly fertile and accessible soils required for growing poplars and sycamores on short rotations can long be withheld from food production. In the short run, these hardwoods promise extremely high yields of wood fiber in return for heavy inputs of soil preparation, planting, cultivation, fertilization, and protection from biotic enemies. The question of multiple use of such lands, in the forester's meaning of the term, appears trivial. The extensive "batture" lands between river bank and levee in the lower Mississippi Valley appear to be the largest area available for wood-fiber farming if the clean cultivation required proves to be compatible with soil stabilization.

MULTIPLE USE OF FORESTS

Even in the absence of estimates of land areas in the three categories—wildland silviculture, plantation silviculture, and intensive wood-fiber farming—it seems clear that what are termed the wildland forests offer the greatest opportunities for making the practice of multiple use serve the goal of increasing wood production.

The concept of multiple use is the subject of so much discussion these days that one is hesitant about adding to the tumult and the shouting. Davis has contributed a concise formulation of the concept and a lucid discussion of some of the difficulties in applying it.[1] Some of today's controversy results from the variety of ideas about the nature of a forest. It may be pertinent for American foresters to recall that "forest" has at least two rather different meanings. One of the older meanings is given by Hart in these words: " 'Forest' is neither a botanical nor a geographical term, but a legal one; it is not synonymous with woodland. Territory afforested, in the medieval sense, was not necessarily woodland, it could contain moorland, wastes, pastures, agricultural land, and even centres of habitation."[2] This concept carried over into the usage of such American agencies as the Forest Service. The national forests are obviously something more than biotic communities, which is what the word "forest" usually means to the biologist. This being so, it is indefensible to consider the administration of such an area for any single use. The logic of this proposition is recognized in the Multiple Use-Sustained Yield Act of 1960.

Even if "forest" is used in the more restricted sense of a biotic community or ecosystem dominated by trees, we must recognize that there often exists a basis for multiple use. This basis is inherent in the nature of the forest ecosystem which, like oceans and lakes, differs from other terrestrial ecosystems in having a significant third dimension or vertical extension. This vertical extension of the forest not only stems from its biologically diverse composition, but also accounts for its efficient trapping of energy to make wood and its strong appeal to hunter, camper, and student of nature.

Another characteristic of the forest ecosystem which supports the concept and practice of multiple use is the time dimension. The dominant members of the forest ecosystem, the trees, are relatively long-lived, with correspondingly long cycles of change. Each portion of the cycle of regeneration, growth, maturity, and harvest provides a different sort of environment favoring different visitors, inhabitants, users, or students.

The foregoing is a biologist's elaboration upon part of Davis's definition of multiple use, namely ". . . a postulate that forest lands can and do produce many goods and services and that in many circumstances they can be produced in various admixtures and combinations of land uses." Davis goes on to state, "This is a valid assumption generally accepted." The assumption is no doubt generally accepted intellectually, but often not as a basis for practice. Why this conflict?

CONSTRAINTS UPON MULTIPLE USE

The reluctance of influential segments of the public to include commodity production in the catalog of multiple uses of forest lands seems to be an essentially American problem. There appear to be both historical and economic reasons why multiple use of forest lands, although most explicitly proclaimed in the U.S., has been a fact rather than an issue in those parts of Europe which have been influential in the background of American forestry. Nash, in his *Wilderness and the American Mind,* presents one theme which appears to underlie the revulsion, on the part of a highly articulate and growing segment of the U.S. population, against commodity use of forest resources.[3] The second half of the last century saw the simultaneous and closely related eruption of the industrial revolution, opening of the American West, and articulation of social Darwinism. These movements combined to give American society a strongly materialistic cast, which domestic and foreign critics were quick to decry. The opposition of these critics to materialism and urban blight took several forms. One form, a sort of romanticism, enlisted names such as John Muir, John Burroughs, and Theodore Roosevelt and produced, among other trends, the back-to-nature movement exemplified by the Boy Scouts, the Appalachian Mountain Club, and many other organizations still pervasively influential in our thinking. Chapter 1 expands upon the themes of materialism, romanticism, and utilitarianism and upon their relation to the timber issue.

Although urban-rural antagonisms are as old as cities, the back-to-nature movement appears to have sharpened this dichotomy, which finds two of its significant current expressions in "one man-one vote" and the flight from the central cities to the suburbs. Hendee found that "recreationists raised in urban areas clearly had the most preservation-oriented and purist philosophies regarding natural resources, whereas those raised in rural or small-town settings tended to have more utilitarian and development-oriented attitudes."[4] Other studies (Harry and colleagues) have shown that the conservation movement is largely composed of upper-middle-class individuals.[5]

It may prove instructive to contrast the reaction of the articulate urban upper-middle-class conservation movement in this country against commodity production in wildland forests with the rather general acceptance of wood production as a function of central European forests. In general accounts of forestry in Europe, Hermann and Daniel sketch the following highlights: Even aged management, usually with clearcutting, is the rule, but clearcuts are strictly limited in size, at least in central Europe. Silviculture is highly labor-intensive, but rural-urban migration, as in America, is causing labor shortages and forcing increasing mechanization and the adoption of less labor-intensive silvicultural practices.[6,7] Thus trends in Europe seem to be toward conditions we have known in the U.S., but with the difference that European forest-aesthetic standards do not involve the strongly antiutilitarian attitudes often expressed in America. These anti-utilitarian attitudes are an understandable reaction to the destruction of landscape values which has characterized much of American timber harvesting. Similar reactions may be expected to follow increased mechanization in Europe.

The issue of including commodity production among the multiple uses of forest land presents itself most conspicuously on public lands, in particular, on national forests. Yet, especially in the eastern forest regions, this issue is also a part of the small-holding problem. Although many small-scale owners are not necessarily opposed to the harvesting of timber from their lands, their neglect of or incapacity for systematic timber-management programs constitutes a major obstacle to the productive potential of these lands.

To date, the mechanization of harvesting has clearly affected, in most cases adversely, the opportunities to manage wildland forests for multiple uses. Dr. Brewer's argument in Chapter 14 that it is more difficult to shift from multiple use to management primarily for recreation and landscape protection than to make the opposite shift seems to gain force with each new development in harvesting technology, and indeed with many of the developments in pre-harvest silviculture. Nevertheless, one may ask whether alternative harvesting and silvicultural techniques more compatible with recreational use and landscape protection cannot be worked out and, like Dr. Newport in Chapter 15, urge that this be done.

The large potential for wood production inherent in our wildland forests is at present limited by societal as well as biologic constraints: by meager public acceptance of the concept of multiple use and by inadequate institutional arrangements to take advantage of the productivity of small private forest holdings. European experience suggests that both these sorts of constraint are remediable by changes in timber-growing and harvesting practices coordinated with public-education efforts and through institutional arrangements to facilitate systematic forest management on small private tracts. It remains to be seen whether the costs of applying these remedies will price wood out of many of its markets.[8]

SUITING THE FOREST TO SOIL AND SITE

Not long ago, the forester who consulted a soil-survey map was likely to find that those portions of the country which interested him most were designated merely as "rough mountainous land." This he already knew! In the past two decades, the mapping of soils in forest

areas has made a promising start and offers the forester large opportunities for putting his investments in forest management where they
will yield the best returns.

Choosing tree species for particular soils is an important decision
in programs of artificial forest regeneration. Yet even in naturally
regenerated forests, the forester's decisions to favor particular species
may need to be influenced by knowledge of soils as well as by the demands of the market, which have a history of change and flexibility.
Indeed, it seems probable that as knowledge of species-soil relationships grows, the productivity of the total forest enterprise will be enhanced by growing, harvesting, and utilizing a wider variety of species.

It would be misleading to suggest that forest-soil science has
even begun to approach the capability of predicting crop response
which has been reached in agriculture. Broadfoot studied the problems of relating soil to site index in southern hardwoods and concluded that "most prediction equations are too imprecise or too restricted in areas of application to be valuable to land managers."[9]
On the other hand, the work of Coile and others on soil-site index
relationships for southern pines suggests that for some species and
soil groups, useful predictions of tree-crop performance from soil properties are attainable.[10] Increasing knowledge of forest soils, a relatively
young and quite active discipline, can be expected to provide the basis
for better forest-management decisions in the future.

PROGRESS IN SILVICULTURE

Basic and applied research in silviculture has had unprecedented
support in this country in the past two decades, and the results offer
manifold opportunities for making U.S. forests highly productive.

A continuous and integrated process such as the management of
a productive forest has no real point of beginning, nor is it possible
to assign preeminent importance to any one of its component activities. The opportunities for increasing timber production can be
grouped in three broad categories. Rapid establishment of well-
stocked stands of desired composition, genetic quality control, and
maintenance of the quality and growth of the forest growing stock. A
fourth category, which deals with a special type of land, is the intensive wood-fiber farming mentioned earlier.

RAPID ESTABLISHMENT OF STANDS

In the past few years, as we have become more fully aware of the
importance of prompt establishment of the new stand, we have developed the tools—conceptual, chemical, and mechanical—to achieve
this objective. In simplest terms, we have gained a practical under-

standing of the importance of mean annual increment and how it is affected by delayed or insufficient regeneration or both. Whether we are dealing with naturally regenerated upland hardwoods in the Northeast, with a combination of natural and artificial regeneration in the conifer forests of the Northwest, or with the intensively managed pine plantations of the Southeast, the imperatives of quick and full regeneration apply.

Site preparation in its many forms is possibly the most extensively used innovation in American forestry practice and perhaps the most productive. In the western forests, closer utilization is starting to reduce the solid-waste disposal problem that the traditional logger delighted to leave for the forester. This problem becomes less acute as harvesting shifts from old-growth forests, particularly high-graded forests with their large quantities of defective trees, to young-growth stands still increasing in sound volume. More intensive and specialized site-preparation techniques have been worked out in the Southeast, where the problem of regeneration can be summarily described as one of maintaining pine subclimax communities in a region where succession tends toward mixed hardwoods of low present value to industry. These techniques include various combinations of (1) breaking up and compacting the residues from logging, (2) brush-land clearing, and (3) burning, often followed by ridging or bedding the soil to provide planting spots with improved soil aeration and fertility, a practice peculiar to the southern pine region.

Constantly developing techniques of site preparation favor the survival and growth of newly planted seedlings or newly sown seed. In addition, each year nurseries produce planting stock better fitted to take advantage of these prepared sites, a result of extensive research and the development of a corps of professional nurserymen. Over the past decade or so, forest planting has evolved from what might be described as an effort to cover land with trees to the installation of a forest growing stock designed to produce certain quantities of timber on predetermined schedules on particular sites. The lead in this work was taken by Craib and others in South Africa more than thirty years ago, but the principles of comparatively wide initial spacings adjusted to site quality are now generally accepted in this country.[11]

GENETIC QUALITY CONTROL

Some of the plants which are the main support of our agriculture—that is to say, of our very existence—are difficult to trace back to their wild progenitors, so drastically have they been remodeled. Over the millenia, since his abandonment of hunting and gathering as the mainstays of life, man has learned almost literally to harvest figs from thistles. The wonder and the confidence which this feat has inspired are among the strong motivations of the forest-tree breeder. Given the need, the time, and the resources, it is reasonably certain that respectable commercial timber species could be made out of gray birch, vine maple, or sourwood, to name but a few forest weeds. But these are long-range targets; we have ready at hand a great wealth of species well suited to present industrial requirements which are nevertheless susceptible of substantial improvement at comparatively low cost.

From a forest-tree breeder's point of view, a commercially important timber species is one which contains a substantial majority of individual trees which are biologically acceptable to the silviculturist and technically suitable to the manufacturer. This majority of acceptable trees is what makes the species a commercial success; the minority of unsuitable trees is what makes the species interesting to the breeder, whose twofold task is to increase the relative abundance of suitable trees and to raise the limit which divides suitable from unsuitable. These general principles of genetic improvement have been applied to a number of commercially important tree species. A good example is the loblolly pine, which is the subject of some of the largest and most advanced improvement programs in this country.

Improvement goals and achievements are most often stated in percentage by which the improved forest outperforms the unimproved forest. In some of his earlier publications on improvement of loblolly pine, Zobel predicted a 10-percent improvement in wood yield in the first generation of selection. This has proven to be a rather modest forecast. Even the first step, selection of parent trees outstanding in growth and form, has resulted in this much improvement or more, even when the seed from these parent trees resulted from open, uncontrolled pollination by inferior neighbors. We do not yet have many reliable data on the improvement achieved when the parents are pollinated by other selected parents, but there are indications of at least a 15-percent gain in wood yield resulting from this first generation of selection.

The gain in resistance to fatal diseases cannot be precisely expressed in percentages but it may be even more important than gains which can be so expressed. So far, the highest degree of genetic control found in the breeding programs with loblolly pine has been in resistance to fusiform rust, a disease which has become increasingly devastating as plantation culture of loblolly and slash pines has expanded. Unlike some plant diseases, fusiform rust does not make a clean sweep of a forest, and for this reason its impact is less dramatic than that of such diseases as chestnut blight or white pine blister rust. Yet fusiform rust is a major factor in the deficient stocking of plantations over very large areas and in the substantial degrading of those infected trees which survive to harvest age. As such, it is a major handicap to systematic plantation management. The random occurrence of infected trees makes mechanized thinning impractical in many cases. Genetic quality control gives strong promise of eliminating this handicap as well as of raising the average growth rate and yield of the rust-free trees.

Genetic quality control with loblolly pine is doing more than giving the silviculturist greater certainty and higher output in plantation management, as in the examples just cited. It is promising to give the manufacturer wood and fiber closer to his specifications. For example, wall thickness of loblolly pine tracheids affects tonnage yields of pulp and strength properties of paper, and tracheid length affects important paper properties. Zobel and his coworkers have achieved genetic control over these tracheid dimensions. Their findings have been applied in seed orchards established from parents known to transmit the tracheid dimensions desired for particular types of paper.

Once a forest growing stock of suitable quality is established, it must be maintained in the same condition until harvesting operations are completed.

Fedkiw has presented the economic argument for the urgency of getting the most out of our forest growing stock and has acknowledged that "this is a tricky problem."[12] Approaching the problem largely as a biologist, Maki has termed "high production with minimum growing stock . . . our special brand of brinkmanship."[13] If these statements represent the views of forestry economists and forest biologists, there is a measure of consensus: We have a problem.

The most important new development in maintaining the efficiency of forest growing stock is undoubtedly the application of fertilizers. Many reasons could be assigned for the tardiness of foresters to make use of the knowledge of plant nutrition (as well as for their slowness to adopt plant-breeding techniques), but perhaps the effective reason has been the unearned harvest of old-growth and volunteer young-growth timber. Data are beginning to accumulate on the increases in yields of wood which can be achieved by fertilizer applications, but, as Stoltenberg and Phares point out, many of the experiments have been designed to test the hypothesis that trees respond to fertilizer applications rather than to permit financial evaluation of fertilization as a production tool. Fertilization is highly rated in predictability of results, in flexibility, and in compatibility with multiple use. In addition, the costs of fertilization are often borne by the benefits.[14] A recent summary by Tamm of European experience with forest fertilization shows this practice moving from the experimental stage to large-scale application in northern Europe, where conditions may fairly be compared with those in this country. (In 1966, one company applied 15,000 metric tons of urea—46 percent nitrogen—to 60,000 hectares of forest.)[15]

One category of fertilizer use can be roughly compared to breeding disease-resistant trees. As a consequence either of their origin or of their past use, certain soils are deficient in some nutrient essential for the survival of trees. Examples are phosphate-deficient sandy soils in Western Australia and peat soils in Scotland and coastal North Carolina, potash-deficient farmed-out soils in upstate New York, and zinc-deficient soils in Western Australia. In such cases, rather small initial applications of the deficient nutrients have sufficed to grow a usable crop of wood, and the financial justification of fertilizer has been clear.

Unlike fertilization, maintaining the quality of growing stock by intermediate cutting is scarcely a new topic. Nevertheless, some new understandings are being gained as a result of research and experience. Although the intensive precommercial thinning and cleaning which were formerly a common feature of central European silviculture seem unlikely to be adopted widely in the United States, the minimum age for commercial thinning has tended to decrease, largely as a consequence of improved wood utilization. This tendency may be reinforced by the improvement of mechanized thinning techniques. Somewhat paradoxically, thinning in the U.S. has recently gained support from overseas experience with North American tree species. In 1933, Craib published the first of a series of South African studies on the response of loblolly pine to variations in early stocking and proposed the theory that the mean annual increment of intolerant species is seriously and irretrievably impaired by early crowding.[16] Bruce has summarized a large volume of overseas literature on the potential wood production in thinned Douglas-fir plantations in which the principal lesson is that American timber-yield tables based on unmanaged forests not only overlook losses due to early crowding, but also fail to credit the forest with the wood lost by unharvested mortality.[17] The marked superiority of overseas versus North American Douglas-fir net production has led to establishment of an extensive level-of-growing-stock study in the Pacific Northwest.[18] Comparable studies are in progress for loblolly pine and yellow poplar.[19] We are developing a much better understanding of how to get the most from growing stock.

ROLE OF FOREST PROTECTION

Growing stock functions and produces wood only so long as it is alive and well. What potential gains in wood production are offered by the forester's old basic chore of forest protection? Some spectacular fires of the last few years may have tempered optimism about the American forester's ability to cope with his oldest and most dramatic enemy, but considering the fact that people today are increasingly numerous, mobile, and urban-educated, it is possible that we could have done worse. Increasingly effective tools of fire-weather prediction, communication, organization, early attack, and mechanization have been developed. The use of prescribed fire in the Southeast and in some western forests promises not only to increase the productivity of useful tree species, but also to reduce wildfire incidence. It remains to be learned how air pollution from prescribed fires weighs against that caused by wildfires.

Recognition of the role of wildlife in reducing timber productivity is relatively recent. It dates, in fact, from the last two decades of intensive tree-planting and -seeding programs and has, moreover, been one of the reasons for the adoption of even-aged management systems for eastern hardwood forests. Wildlife may be regarded either as a timber-protection problem or as a forest resource. It is increasingly clear that the latter is the view to take: Tree reproduction, other food plants, wildlife, hunters, and predators are all parts of an equilibrium to be maintained.

Insects and diseases, though less dramatic than fire, levy a higher toll on forest productivity. The ability to control these losses has been markedly reinforced by newly won knowledge, strengthened organization, and the conversion of overmature stands to young forests. Biologic control of insects and diseases, long advocated by entomologists and pathologists, is finally receiving the study it merits, thanks to the *Silent Spring* reaction to the excesses committed by control organizations. Early stages of insect and disease attacks through remote sensing are being detected so that controls may be mounted before epidemics develop. Regional pest-action councils and similar organizations that include all classes of forest-land owners are making controls more prompt, effective, and comprehensive. Finally, the conversion of old, stagnant stands to young, vigorous forests not only increases net growth, but also permits pathologists to turn their attention from cull-factor studies to diseases of present and future importance.

INTENSIVE WOOD-FIBER FARMING

The comparatively crude uses of solid wood for structures or fuel are being replaced by more refined mechanical and chemical techniques which focus on the fibers composing the solid wood and on the molecules which make up the fibers. One might suppose that this trend would shift fiber production from forest to farm. Exactly the opposite has occurred, and on a rather dramatic scale. The pulp and paper industry of southeastern United States, the largest regional segment of the world's production of wood pulp and paper, has been erected on the ruins of the cotton kingdom. Moreover, the cotton production which survives, in what is now known to economic geographers as the southern pine region, is under strict governmental acreage controls and receives governmental subsidies. Granted that the foregoing is a sweeping, simplified, and biased summary of a complex drama, this massive displacement of farm-grown by forest-grown fiber might contain some lessons worth pondering. A first look suggests two basic explanations. The biologic explanation is simply that a three-dimensional ecosystem, such as a forest functioning in a favorable climate, is a more efficient utilizer of radiant energy than a two-dimensional system such as a field crop, which leaks a significant portion of the incoming radiation to the soil. Thanks to the boll weevil rather than to human ecologic wisdom, cotton production has shifted to regions climatically unsuited to growth of forests. A crude engineering explanation of the farm-to-forest shift is that fiber in the compact form of logs or bolts is more convenient to handle, transport, and store than fiber in the less compact and less durable forms characteristic of agricultural crops and crop residues.

Despite the advantages of forests as a source of fiber, agricultural fiber production continues to have a strong appeal to the pulp and paper industry and to some foresters, as evidenced by recurrent schemes to grow and harvest woody plants by agricultural techniques. The advantages are short rotations, the possibility of a high degree of mechanization, and the virtual elimination of the bark-separation problems which beset the manufacture of pulp from roundwood. Silage sycamore is the term used to designate one such scheme, set up to take advantage of the rapid early growth and resprouting capacity of the sycamore tree on better soils in the Southeast.[20] Schreiner has sketched the concept of minirotation forestry, which involves 1 to 5 years for silage production of fiber by agricultural methods, 6 to 15 years for boltwood, and 15 to 30 years for timber.[21] In one version, Schreiner advocates combining all three lengths of minirotation on the same land, so that the 1- to 5-year rotation would correspond to precommercial thinnings under conventional practice and the 6- to 15-year boltwood rotation would correspond to present pulpwood thinnings in stands managed for saw timber production.

Great uncertainty attends any attempt to estimate the contribuion which these short-rotation agricultural or semiagricultural techniques may make to our timber-producing potential. To achieve the yields which make them attractive, they seem to require land which may soon be needed for food production. Moreover, it is uncertain whether the yield of successive crops from sprouts will continue at a high enough level to allow the manager to escape for long the cost of establishing new roots. Finally, if seedling reproduction is necessary for each crop, the advantage of quick, heavy yields will need to be balanced against the disadvantage of frequent site-preparation and stand-establishment costs. The production of a forest differs basically from that of an annual crop. In the forest, the close relationship between yield and growing stock makes early harvest much less advantageous than in the case of field crops. It is possible to be unduly impressed with the advantages of short rotations.

UTILIZING EXISTING KNOWLEDGE

The leading silvicultural possibilities for increasing timber production in the United States will remain merely interesting until we articulate programs for making them actual.

Undoubtedly the largest contribution to increasing U.S. timber production could be made by extending technologic progress (or even minimal orderly management) to the small private holdings. Recent expansion of state and consultant services to landowners on a fee basis and the development of aggregates and lease arrangements seem to be promising.

What is becoming increasingly clear about technologic developments in silviculture is that none of them can be fully effective isolated from the others. They must be coordinated into silvicultural management systems to produce maximum or near-maximum effects. Two developments, genetic improvement and fertilization, are cases in point. A tree's capacity to respond to fertilizer seems to be strongly inherited, that is, a given "improved" family of pines can be designated as fast-growing only if the nutrient level of the soil is specified; or conversely, fertilization pays only if the fertilizer is applied to a responsive family of trees. This simple illustration recognizes only two components of a very complex system which includes such other variables as inherent soil fertility, soil drainage, site-preparation methods, plantation arrangement and spacing, thinning schedules, and harvesting methods.

Another interaction that may be anticipated within this complex system takes place between the use of genetically improved planting stock and the practice of thinning. The present role of thinning in up-grading the final stand may become much less vital. Present trends toward wider spacings and toward row and mechanized thinning may well continue.

The two examples of linkage among silvicultural measures serve to reinforce the prediction made some years ago by Duerr, that forest management will increasingly become a matter of coordinating the contributions of specialists.[22] This is not an easy task. Indeed, specialization seems to increase faster than coordination. Much greater recognition ought to be given to the role of the forest manager as a contributor to knowledge, rather than simply as a user of research findings. There is a measure of justice in the complaint of many practicing foresters that professional journals are, as they phrase it, "too technical." The reason is simply that journals are largely made up of papers written by research workers. The remedy is obvious but not easily achieved. Practicing foresters and their employers must be brought to realize that the thoughtfully analyzed experiences of a forest manager can contribute to the professional literature no less valuably than the reports of specialists in research.

SOME CAUTIONS

As we look for means to increase timber production, we are inevitably urged to adopt "get-rich-quick" schemes. This label may be pinned on a majority of the proposals for introducing exotic species into the North American continent. It is true that species such as Norway spruce, Scotch pine, and European and Japanese larches show some promise as timber trees in the Northeast and that the eucalypts may make some contribution to fiber production in the Southwest and California. However, it will still take many years and careful study to realize these potentials on an appreciable scale. The North American continent is, for rather clear reasons of geology and climatic history, a net exporter of good timber to other temperate regions of the world.

Ample justification exists for the reduction of rotation lengths below those which became traditional in the days of extensive old-growth forests and the dominance of lumber in the wood-products markets. However, it is quite possible to carry this reduction to a self-defeating extreme. Maximizing timber supply may not be synonymous with maximizing mean annual increment, but the relation is close enough to suggest that proposals for drastically shortened rotations be examined carefully from the biologic as well as the economic point of view.

More complete utilization of the wood fiber produced by the forest offers obvious opportunities to extend our timber supply. Nevertheless, it is important to realize that just as forest growing stock and the wood it produces are inseparable, so the whole forest community is a closely integrated productive system. Stumps, roots, and slash may, in some forests, make a more important contribution to continued productivity of the forest if left on site than if directly utilized as wood fiber. This is a lesson already learned in Europe, one which we need not question on a large scale here.

10   TIMBER UTILIZATION AND CONVERSION

ARTHUR F. MUSCHLER*

SUBSTANTIAL OPPORTUNITIES exist for adapting timber harvesting to the needs of more intensive forest management, for extending the timber resource by increasing the recovery of logging residues, and for reducing unit costs. For example, the Forest Service estimates that 13 million acres of young timber is in condition for thinning. Disease losses amount to 35 percent of the gross annual growth. Such material would partly be salvageable under more intensive forest management. In Oregon and Washington logging residues consisting of limbs and culls larger than 3 inches in diameter and 4 feet long approach 23.5 million tons annually, and there are 15.9 million tons of smaller material. The Forest Service estimates the national total of logging residues at 2 billion cubic feet yearly. This quantity includes only material 4 inches and larger in diameter which is left on the ground. In addition, substantial amounts of rough and decayed trees are left standing after logging. Disease- and insect-killed timber not presently salvaged must also be considered in the ultimate potential for fiber savings in the course of harvesting.

What methods of timber harvesting will contribute to the fulfillment of such opportunities as these?

Some speak of using laser equipment to fell single trees two and three miles distant. Most imminent perhaps are aerial techniques to facilitate harvest, especially in the West, on steep slopes with the least possible road construction and the least possible disturbance to the soil. Aesthetic values will play an increasingly prominent role in the harvest on such sites. Estimates indicate that as much as 10 to 15 percent of the commercial forest lands in the national forests of Washington and Oregon are inoperable by conventional logging methods. These lands promise to remain completely inaccessible unless skylines, balloons, or helicopters are employed. The need for developing aerial techniques is apparent.

The harvesting operation always has been labor-intensive. Only

---

* Technical Director, Edward Hines Lumber Co., Chicago, Ill.

in relatively recent years has the logging industry been forced into keen competition with the factory for its labor. The resulting rapid mechanization has not necessarily reduced harvesting costs, because wage rates have increased steadily and the necessary capital investments have often been heavy.

Proponents claim that rising labor costs will make long-length logging necessary for the future. This technique has already been adopted in the even-aged small-timber stands of the U.S. and Canada, where formerly high labor input demanded a new method of harvest. The wheeled, articulated skidder, which has been described as the only major logging-equipment breakthrough of the past decade, characterizes the operation. However, significant opportunity still exists to reduce costs. The pure pine stands in the South offer the greatest opportunity for mechanizing felling and handling because the terrain is relatively flat and limbs are high on the stem.

The major deterrent to wider application of long-length logging appears to be lack of sufficient receiving-conversion equipment. However, increased capital investment in logging equipment and in the log station or mill will follow as long-length logging is proven to reduce unit costs. Meanwhile, additional detailed study should be given the benefits of the log station, integrated to sort sawlogs, veneer logs, poles, pulpwood, and low-grade logs for chipping.

Long-length logging can have the disadvantage of increasing damage in a selective cut or thinning. This problem is perhaps one justification for the combined longwood-shortwood operations which exist in the South and East. A scarcity of the more highly-trained labor required in the long-length logging could also dictate continuation of short-length logging or combined operations in certain areas. To facilitate short-length logging, machines have been developed to fell, buck, and stack logs at the stump, and some machines are able to prehaul short logs to the loading areas. The prehaul appears to be the key to continued use of short-length pulpwood logging. A low-cost harvester which will do a good job of preparing pulpwood for the prehaul is vitally needed.

The log station or satellite concentration yard at which low-grade logs are chipped represents an outstanding opportunity for fiber savings. In addition, a great quantity of rough logs and pieces of logs can pay their way to this point for chipping. Collection and transport systems to bring more such material to the log station are needed. Chipping at the log station suggests chipping in the woods, a practice which has seen much experimentation since the early 1960s.

The first significant amount of chipping in the woods was in the Northwest and in eastern Oregon, although the greatest number of installations exists today in the South. Both debarking and chipping of minor commercial species, rough logs, and pieces of logs are accomplished in the woods. The potential for savings in fiber is obvious as much of the material chipped would otherwise be left unused. In addition, leaving the bark residue behind increases the efficiency of transporting the usable material and lessens bark-disposal and pollution problems at the mill. Equipment maintenance and weather pose the two most bothersome obstacles to efficient chipping in the woods. These operations are generally limited to terrain suitable for the wheeled skidder.

Further exploitation of the large potential in chipping tops and limbs must await development of effective methods for separating bark from wood.

WOOD PULPING: PROSPECTS FOR CHIPS

Pulping provides the most promising means for saving the fiber in logging residues and in residues from solid wood-products manufacture. Yearly residues in pulping are estimated by the Forest Service to be equivalent to 400 million cubic feet of wood. The lignin portion of the wood, which is dissolved in pulping liquors and lost as a pulp constituent, makes up nearly all this quantity. Future process changes should provide for at least partial recovery as pulp.

Methods of removing bark from chips produced in the woods from tops and limbs must be approached as a part of the pulping process, because today's debarking equipment cannot effectively remove bark from tops and limbs prior to chipping. Several methods have been attempted, but none has proved technically adequate or economical. Studies to determine degree of bark removal needed in relation to product quality can set the stage for major savings in wood utilization. Insulation board, hardboard, saturating felts, and certain container boards, for example, are least critical in respect to bark content. Much remains to be learned about the influence of chipper type, season of the year, and storage conditions on the breaking of the bond between bark and wood.

Methods studied for segregating bark and chips have included roller compression, vacuum, air flotation, air aspiration, soaking, and centrifugal procedures. Even segregation based on dielectric properties of bark and wood has been attempted. Most investigators agree that no one method will be successful. Rather, two or more methods will be combined to reach satisfactory bark-free levels.

Residue utilization as chips for pulping has had enormous impact on the forest-products industry, especially over the past fifteen years, and should grow in importance as the chipping operation moves to the log station and to the woods. Residue chips from sawmills were first used in the Northwest in the 1920s. By 1963, 24 percent of the nation's total pulpwood consumption was represented by residue chips, with sawmills providing 81 percent of such chips and veneer mills 16 percent. Sawmill and veneer mill chips are currently estimated to provide more than 60 percent of the wood requirements of the pulp and paper industry on the West Coast. Chips received at the nation's pulp mills from sawmills and veneer mills in 1969 were equivalent to 18.9 million cords.

The use of residue chips has required extensive stockpiling, out-of-doors and unprotected. Much deterioration has resulted. Loss of wood substance caused by decay in outside storage averages 1 percent per month. Chemical treatment promises to reduce this loss. Encouraging preliminary results have been obtained with green kraft liquor, which acts both as a fungicide and as an enzyme inhibitor. Complete elimination of chip storage losses, as estimated by the Forest Service, would recover the equivalent of 100 million cubic feet of wood yearly.

WOOD PULPING: PROCESSES

Consistent with minimum quality requirements, the projected shortage in the timber resource dictates that pulping processes of the future provide high pulp yields and make full use of available fibers, including nonwood fibers. History points to remarkable progress in extending pulping to the available resource. Pulping has been adapted well to the widest range of tree species and paper qualities and properties.

New chemical processes, both acid and alkaline, have been adopted in the pulping industry. The polysulfide process promises up to 20 percent higher yields than the kraft process, along with pulp quality which is equivalent to that of kraft. The average yield of kraft pulp is less than one-half of the wood which enters the digester. About 30 percent of the wood substance lost is lignin and extractives, but cellulose is also lost. The polysulfide process is not wholly compatible with the present kraft recovery system, but new recovery systems are under study which could prove economical and could also control air pollution. Potential savings in wood costs and reductions in capital and operating costs with the polysulfide process amount to $7–12 per ton of pulp, a substantial portion of which can be applied towards a recovery system.

In recent years, the application of the disk refiner to a wide range of pulps, notably groundwood pulp, has been an interesting and valuable development. The groundwood process permits the highest attainable yield of pulp. In addition, groundwood pulp from chips furnishes substantially stronger paper than was thought possible. Such pulp therefore offers the opportunity both for utilizing sawmill and veneer mill residues and improving the utility of the product.

Investigators point to other unrealized possibilities for increasing pulp yields. They hope to make fuller use of hardwood by retaining the lignin in the end product and to recover more usable fiber from waste water. As much as 80 percent of fibers lost in conventional treatment can be returned to the paper machines.

Future pulping processes may involve entirely new concepts and the use of new and different pulping agents. Such pulping processes may go a long way towards overcoming water and air pollution.

WOOD PULPING: ADDITIONAL FIBER SOURCES

Pulp yields from tree tops and limbs and roots have been the subject of only limited study. When we learn how to separate bark from pulp chips, extensive yield studies will be needed before the potential for fiber savings can be known.

Sawdust and bark also offer significant possibilities for use in pulping. Advances in the technology of pulping sawdust have already made possible its use by many pulp mills. Groundwood pulp from sawdust and shavings is being used successfully in newsprint. More sawdust and shavings will become available for pulping as their use for fuel continues to decline. The Forest Service estimates yearly residues in sawmills and veneer mills, largely sawdust and shavings, at 900 million cubic feet. Bark is estimated at an additional 400 million cubic feet. Bark poses the greater problem in pulping. Many persons predict that little bark will be used to make paper pulp. However, the use of bark in insulation board and particleboard is a distinct possibility. Bark use may increase as pulp-quality requirements and standards are reconsidered to meet changing product needs.

The recycling of wood-fiber waste offers remarkable opportunity and challenge. In some western European countries and in Japan, between one-third and one-half of all wastepaper is recycled. But in this country, where the wastepaper total approaches 50 million tons per year, collection and sorting costs have held recycling down to 18 percent. Presorting of wastepaper in homes, offices, and plants, such as is done in many other countries, could permit substantial gains.

Solid wastes from our cities and towns have grown into a staggering disposal problem, totaling nearly 350 million tons yearly. The traditional approaches to disposal—dumps; incineration, smokeless or otherwise; compaction and burying in sanitary landfills—are proving unsatisfactory. Futhermore, they fail to provide for salvage. Recycling, not only of wastepaper, but also of wood debris from demolished buildings and other discarded wood products can ease the demands on the timber resource and reduce the pollution problem. Nearly all such wood fiber is suitable for pulping.

SAWMILL DEVELOPMENTS

For sawmills and veneer mills, the first giant step towards full log utilization began with whole-log debarking and the recovery of bark-free chips for pulping. During the 1950s rapid development of mechanical ring debarkers to handle logs varying widely in species, size, form, and condition brought significant changes to the forest-products industry.

Adaptation to small logs as raw material has been a notable development in the industry. Many of the larger sawmills on the West Coast and in the South have been redesigned in response to the decrease in the supply of large logs and the continued availability of small logs. Such redesigning has provided for maximum recovery of chips from the portions of the log which cannot produce lumber.

The chipping headsaw and chipping edger are the most important innovations in mechanical conversion since the ring debarker. Chipping headsaws are designed to produce lumber at higher speeds than the conventional circular saw or bandsaw and therefore are advantageous where small logs predominate. In the South, an integrated system of wood procurement is evolving in which tree-length logs are channeled into their highest uses through the sawmill with a chipping headsaw. Tops are processed for pulpwood; the major portion of the log is converted to dimension lumber and chips; the butt log of suitable grade is sold to the plywood plant, which, in turn, converts the veneer core to 2x4s and chips. Tree-length logs of suitable grade may be designated as poles and sent to the treating plant. Eventually, limbs, roots, and low-quality logs, normally left in the woods, can be processed for chips either at the sawmill-log station or in the woods—although, as Professor Duffield points out at the close of Chapter 9, residues may in some cases contribute most to timber productivity if left to fertilize the soil.

All participants gain from the integrated system. The quantity of raw material available to the pulp mill as pulpwood and as chips is increased, since the sawmill draws logs both from the forests of the paper company and from many farm and other small holdings. In most cases, the sawmill has been able to guarantee a weight of chips equal to twice the weight of logs taken from the paper-company lands. Furthermore, at one and the same time, the sawmill is assured of an adequate log supply, the pulp firm is relieved of the problems of logging if it so wishes, and the plywood manufacturer benefits by not having to purchase and harvest stumpage or dispose of logs unsuitable for his purposes. The system undoubtedly spread to other regions.

Another recent innovation, aimed at more efficient conversion of large, high-grade logs, involves new sawing accuracy and narrow kerf with the use of improved bandsaws, and also abrasive rather than conventional planing. Initial experience is encouraging and presages rapid development.

The sawmill of the future will be completely computerized, from log breakdown to lumber trimming and grading. The Forest Products Laboratory has already produced a computer program for hardwood lumber grading. Further improvements which lie ahead include (1) computerizing the control of lumber edging and trimming and improving technology for the processes themselves; (2) devising a system for sensing log defects and thus providing the sawyer with the information he will need for increasing the grade yield of lumber at the headsaw; and (3) creating a computerized system for dividing tree-length logs into short sections of optimum value. Computerized guides to the remanufacturing of lumber remain to be worked out. The necessary system for sensing lumber defects is already in process of development with the use of ultrasonic scanning.

Other, less dramatic, sawmill developments are currently extending the timber resource. Lumber of small-diameter tree species has not been well accepted in the market except as boards which have more and more been replaced in construction by plywood and other panel products. A major potential use for the small log—in the manufacture of dimension lumber, especially studs—has awaited refinements in manufacturing method. Now, sizable modern sawmills, geared almost totally to production of studs, have been built in the Rocky Mountain region and in the South. Furthermore, the feasibility of producing studs from the large and underdeveloped aspen resources of northern Lake States is being considered.

A new circular saw, the "taper-tension" saw, has been devised by the Forest Products Laboratory to reduce kerf by about 3/32 inch. The invention is important because half of our lumber still comes from mills with circular headsaws. The kerf of the average circular saw is about double that of a bandsaw or sash-gang saw. Accordingly, two-thirds of the nation's sawdust is produced by mills with circular saws. Any small reduction of kerf for such mills represents substantial wood savings.

VENEER, PLYWOOD, AND PARTICLEBOARD

Softwood plywood manufacture has increased sixfold in the last twenty years and has been extended to a number of tree species, including southern pines. However, more important from the standpoint of improved utilization has been the use of small logs for producing construction plywood. Plywood plants in the Rocky Mountain region are equipped to process tree species and log sizes previously unutilized because of cost. A plant has been built at Ironwood, Michigan, to produce aspen construction plywood. Studies are in progress to determine the feasibility of using eastern spruce.

These developments are made possible by new equipment specifically suited to the conversion of small logs and capable of nearly complete utilization. New veneer lathes allow blocks to be turned down to diameters of less than five inches. New lathe chargers handle small logs efficiently. Clippers have been speeded up. Veneer drying has been improved. An automated lay-up system remains the most vital need in plywood manufacturing.

From the standpoint of improved residue utilization, particleboard is the glamour product of the years since World War II. Residues unattractive or unusable for pulping are readily accepted as raw material for particleboard: dry and green planer shavings, lumber trim, dry veneer clippings, plywood panel trim, sawdust—even bark. The particleboard industry is growing faster than any other forest industry, and a further doubling of its output is anticipated over the next few years.

Researchers have been working on a method for obtaining wood flakes as a by-product of dimension lumber. Particleboard made from the experimental flakes is strong and stable. Fine dust produced in the abrasive planing of lumber would be used to give the board a smooth surface. These developments could open up new markets—specifically, particleboard could invade the plywood field more deeply. Thus a residue-based product would be substituted for one dependent on logs—and often the premium portions of the logs.

REMANUFACTURED WOOD PRODUCTS

The Forest Service estimates that producers of millwork, flooring, furniture and furniture parts, containers, pallets, and other remanufactured lumber products create about 700 million cubic feet of residues yearly. Some 70 percent of such residues result from sawing, planing, sanding, and similar operations. The rest comes largely from defects associated with drying.

The diversity of remanufacturing operations makes it difficult to estimate their wood-saving potential. As in the sawmill, improved thin saws and abrasive planers can reduce remanufacturing residues substantially. So can the end-joining of lumber and millwork by means of finger joints. Studs are being finger-jointed, but the lack of suitable product standards prevents full market acceptance. The laminating industry made an abrupt change from scarf-jointing to finger-jointing of its highly engineered members. Unique methods of forming the finger joints substantially reduce the wood lost in cutting the fingers, reduce the adhesive required, and develop almost the full strength of solid wood.

New methods under study for drying lumber and its products show promise of speeding the process and reducing the loss from warp. One such method involves drying 2x4s under restraint at high temperatures. Ten-percent moisture content is reached in one-fourth the usual time, with one-half the energy, and with 50 percent less crook and twist.

Another study concerns automation of conventional kilns for continual surveillance of drying conditions and progress. Investigators at the Forest Products Laboratory have hopes of doubling kiln capacity by reducing drying time up to 50 percent. The cost of equipping a conventional kiln is estimated at approximately $5,000, a low sum in view of the benefits expected.

Wood savings through residue reduction may be offset to some extent by significant new wood products. For example, fire-retardant treatments have brought wood into use where untreated wood was previously prohibited by building codes or insurance costs. The preservative treatment of wood with water-borne salts makes for a clean, paintable, odor-free product which is durable even in contact with the ground. A pressure-preservative-treated wood foundation system has been worked out jointly by industry and the Forest Service which entirely replaces poured concrete or concrete block. The system allows for all-weather construction and significant cost savings. The Federal Housing Administration has accepted the foundation system for homes offered as security for insured mortgages. In addition, wider use of pressure-preservative-treated lumber and plywood can increase the timber supply by lengthening its service life. The full potential of the system will be determined only in time, but this example serves to emphasize that reduction and utilization of residues are not the only results of a developing technology.

EFFICIENCY IN THE USE OF LUMBER

Concern is often expressed, especially within the design profession, that some of the construction procedures recommended by the forest-products industry or required by the regulatory agencies make inefficient use of wood. Outstanding achievements have been made over the years in amassing data on wood performance, and we now have the basis for confirming that opportunity does exist for savings in wooden structures.

For example, recent findings indicate that the stiffness of wood-joist floors is 24 percent higher than predicted by calculations which consider only the individual joists, as required by the Federal Housing Administration and by building codes. The contribution made to floor stiffness by the interactions among all the elements of the structure receives no consideration from the regulatory agencies. Partitions are shown to reduce significantly both deflection and vibrations of floors, and yet most building codes require doubling of joists below partitions. Studies in Norway several years ago indicated that traditional bridging between joists contributes little or nothing to floor stiffness. Subsequent studies by the National Association of Home Builders Research Foundation confirmed the findings. Bridging had been required by all the codes. Now the requirement has been removed from many, with consequent savings in materials and in the labor of cutting, fitting, and installing the bridges.

There are still other causes of overdesign in wood structures and consequent waste. Regulatory agencies commonly require that floors for living areas be able to support 40 pounds per square foot. Such a rule anticipates wall-to-wall refrigerators!

The question of a revised softwood lumber-size standard faced the industry for years. In 1965, several firms started to make lumber that was drier than then required and also a little thinner: 1½ inches instead of 1⅝ for 2x4s, 2x6s, etc. The traditional widths were retained. The effect of the change was to reduce thickness only slightly (less than the apparent ⅛ inch) and to increase width—since the new dimensions related to drier (more shrunken) lumber. Because width is particularly important for a member loaded on edge, such as a joist or rafter, the 1½-inch dry product was accepted in the four model building codes and by the Federal Housing Administration as the technical equivalent of the 1⅝-inch green product.

Thereafter, a revised lumber-size standard was put through under U.S. Department of Commerce procedures and made effective in 1970. In this standard, sizes for green and for dry products are related so as to become the same at any given moisture content. However, in the course of the compromising which led to the standard, some engineering efficiency was lost, whereas there could have been gains if attention had been paid to optimum thickness-to-width ratios. The implication for the timber supply is clear: The question of the most efficient lumber sizes is still an issue.

EFFICIENCY IN THE USE OF PLYWOOD

The softwood-plywood industry is undertaking a simple but basic change in the combination and thickness of veneers to improve the performance of its widely used ½-inch product. Plywood stiffness is a particularly important consideration in designing structures. Moreover, strength and stiffness along the length of the panel are more important than across the width, although some balance is necessary to satisfy structural needs and to keep panels flat. Traditional ½-inch plywood comprises five layers of veneer. The alternative adopted by many producers is a panel of four ⅛-inch veneers, the grain of the two face veneers running the length of the panel and that of the two center veneers running across. The resulting plywood has 14 percent greater stiffness along the length of the panel, but of course stiffness is lost across the width.

Similarly, the American Plywood Association has found that on-the-job gluing of plywood subflooring to wood joists greatly increases the stiffness of the assembly over that of the joists alone. Further improvement in stiffness is obtained by gluing the tongue-and-groove joints between panels. With obvious savings in material, the National Association of Home Builders, in one of its highly publicized research houses, employed one layer of ⅝-inch plywood glued over 2x6 joists instead of the conventional nailed application of separate layers of ½-inch and ⅜-inch plywood over 2x8 joists. Floor stiffness was increased 10 percent. Furthermore, floor stiffness was shown to exceed the Federal Housing Administration minimum requirement by 61 percent.

Technical data on wood properties is constantly being expanded and refined through studies by the trade associations, universities, and public laboratories. Such research must certainly be encouraged. However, the researchers have a concomitant responsibility to help the regulatory agencies appreciate the wealth of existing knowledge of wood properties and establish more realistic design criteria. Continued neglect wastes the timber resource.

POTENTIAL GAINS IN REVIEW

This discussion suggests that the opportunities to increase timber supply through better utilization and conversion are of three sorts: (1) opportunities to reduce the quantity of unused residues, (2) opportunities to recycle products, and (3) opportunities to use wood more efficiently in manufacture and construction.

The Forest Service has estimated the current annual quantities of residues: logging, 2 billion cubic feet; sawmills and veneer mills, 0.9 billion; pulp mills, 0.4 billion; bark, 0.4 billion; secondary manufacturing, 0.7 billion. The total of 4.4 billion cubic feet represents one-third of the timber harvested each year. Still, the total is not a complete accounting. The estimate of logging residues does not include material less than 4 inches in diameter left on the ground, the substantial quantities of rough and decayed trees left standing, or the disease- and insect-killed trees. All such material is potentially usable. Moreover, additional residues now used as fuel, some 2.8 billion cubic feet annually, can become available for higher uses.

Lassen and Hair, in close collaboration with members of the Forest Service and other professionals, have made quantitative estimates of potential gains in wood supplies through better conversion and use (Table 10.1). Their figures, totaling 4.7 billion cubic feet per year, are probably the most realistic available. The estimates recognize that only part of the 4.4 billion cubic feet of logging and manufacturing residues is presently available for utilization. Logging residues are often remote from potential users and scattered over forest land in a manner which precludes their becoming accessible in the foreseeable future. Likewise, some of the manufacturing residues are remote from potential users or occur in small quantities. But con-

TABLE 10.1 ESTIMATED POTENTIAL ANNUAL GAINS IN WOOD SUPPLIES THROUGH HARVESTING AND UTILIZATION IMPROVEMENTS (AS COMPARED WITH THE 1968 HARVEST)

Source of potential gain	Quantity (Billion cubic feet)	
1. Reduced quantity of unused residues:		
Logging	1.4	
Manufacturing:		
Sawmills and veneer mills	0.6	
Pulp mills:		
Chemical pulping	0.3*	
Mechanical and groundwood pulping	0.2*	
Elimination of pulp-chip storage losses	0.1	
Remanufacturing:		
Greater use of machining residues and improved drying practices	0.5	
Total potential gains from residues		3.1
2. Reuse of paper, fiberboard, and wooden debris		1.3
3. Increased efficiency in manufacturing and construction		0.3
Total potential gains		4.7

SOURCE: L. E. Lassen and Dwight Hair, "Potential Gains in Wood Supplies through Improved Technology," *Journal of Forestry,* July 1970, pp. 404–7.
* The realization of this potential would involve some shift in use of residues from fuel to pulp.

tinued increases in the price of roundwood relative to the price of residues can create rapid changes in utilization. Technologic improvements to reduce residues or to reduce the cost of using them can also result in rapid changes.

It is important to note that Lassen and Hair's estimates are of gains judged to be economically and technically feasible by 1980. The body of new fundamental knowledge which can be created and applied by such a date is possibly quite small. In other words, the industry already appears to have the knowledge for accomplishing 1980 goals. Adequately funded development is needed.

Progress beyond 1980 will depend on fundamental studies, which must be encouraged. The long-term future offers the exciting possibility that the wood-based industry can enhance the timber resource by virtually eliminating unused residues.

11   WOOD PRODUCTS AND SUBSTITUTES

ROBERT J. SEIDL*

IT IS APPROPRIATE and timely to reassess the problems of the U.S. timber supply and to evaluate present and future needs with the objective of modernizing forest policy. The problems are vastly more complicated than in the past, when they revolved around increasing the forest growth and yield, providing simple products for use, the simple extrapolation of statistics, and possibly a few lively exchanges of opinion on the merits of government versus private operations. What is done and what is left undone in the management of forest resources now affects more people in more ways than ever before and affects them more urgently. The formulation of sound forest policy is correspondingly more important and more urgent.

Timber supply is only one, although a highly important one, of the objectives of forest management, and the timber subject cannot be adequately treated without reference to the total environment. On the other hand, striking developments in new materials and technology question the future importance of wood in its traditional uses. Of course, there is nothing new about change except, perhaps, the dramatic rate of it.

How is wood viewed by consumers, who do not necessarily share in the romance or benefits of its growth as a commodity? In the form of houses, apartments, pallets, paper, rayon, furniture, fences, chemicals, and many other well-accepted items, wood grew to vast importance because it was functional, available, satisfying, low in cost, versatile, and, through the centuries, deeply rooted in our culture.

Thinking on future forest policy requires a bold look at what lies ahead. There is so much tradition in the managing of timberland, the harvesting of trees, and the manufacture of lumber, plywood, and paper that it is very difficult to make mental adjustment to the quantum jumps in use patterns that could occur. For example, it is commonly assumed that lumber is needed for housing, that the amount

---

* Vice-President and Resident Manager, Simpson-Lee Paper Company, Anderson, Calif.

135

needed is related to the number of housing starts, and that planning for future tree growth need not go much beyond such rudimentary concepts. On the contrary, forest policy makers, dealing as they must with long periods of time, should allow for radical changes in products and their use. Some trends are clear enough at present to affect basic assumptions relative to tree growing. There is no need to apologize for uncertainties about the end use of wood in the future. Even though some predicted changes may not fully materialize, it is "better to be vaguely right than precisely wrong," as someone has said. It is certain that major changes in wood-use patterns will occur. Clues to such changes are:

1. There is a "materials revolution" resulting from massive technical programs, mostly outside the wood industry.

2. Traditional methods of converting wood to structures cannot survive, because the cost of labor is too high.

3. The builder has become a businessman with the usual businessman's interest in cost, performance, schedules, and market acceptance of his products. His only interest in timber versus nontimber products lies in the degree to which the choice affects his success.

4. The end user is losing much of his basic interest in wood except for aesthetic applications. Apart from a few specialized uses, the new generation accepts substitutes and often demands them.

5. The instability of wood prices relative to those of other products drives some users to nonwood materials on each price upswing, and many of these product substitutions are irreversible.

6. Much of the forest-products industry is disadvantaged because it is dependent on small lots of timber, particularly government timber, with its high prices and uncertain supply. Firms fail to achieve economies of scale, and their efficiency in the use of raw material suffers.

7. Urbanization, high-rise buildings, and mobile and modular units invite nontimber materials and changing methods. The wood industry may find it difficult to meet this competition.

8. Particle and fiber processes can be expected to increase relative to solid-wood products, and this trend will have an important bearing on future tree-quality requirements. Particle and sheet commodities will increasingly displace lumber.

9. Cellulose-fiber products such as pulp are relatively safe from displacement, and their increasing output will probably require an expanding volume of suitable wood. Fiber use will provide great economic strength for the wood-products industry.

The total effect of these circumstances on the future of wood is not known, but reflection may provide considerable guidance to the future and will probably reveal genuine opportunity for more rational use of materials.

SHORT-TERM OUTLOOK

A brief consideration of a few ordinary timber products and their competition may be helpful. Structural lumber, for example, has been rated high in terms of performance in relation to cost, yet both steel studs and rolled steel joists are taking more of the market. Compared to wood, they are lighter in weight, straighter, do not burn, have punched holes for passage of utilities, and may involve lower in-place cost.

Lumber siding has significantly declined in importance, while aluminum, steel, concrete, plastic, and fiber products have gained. These materials promise ease of application, better paint performance, strength, and moderate cost, and most of the products are easily adapted to the so-called systems approach: They can be delivered to the erection site complete with fasteners, gutters, fascia, and downspouts.

The wood entrance door is feeling competition from metal and plastics. Some of the new doors have exceptional thermal properties by virtue of foam cores, and most are characterized by straightness and freedom from splitting.

The warmth and beauty of natural wood paneling have always been much esteemed. However, this advantage is being eroded by facsimile grain, often done so well that only an expert can distinguish the counterfeit from the genuine article. Meanwhile, natural wood becomes scarcer, and prints become better and more abundant. New generations may simply cease to discern the charm of natural wood paneling. A similar trend may be seen in furniture where, for example, carved effects can be achieved in plastic foam at relatively low cost compared to wood.

Wood-fiber insulation board has a prominent position in structural, acoustical, and decorative uses. Yet this product is under heavy assault from mineral fibers, with their seemingly inexhaustible raw material and high fire resistance.

Plastic film, foil, chemical coating, and synthetic fiber are greatly affecting the paper industry. However, their advance appears to contain more promise than threat to paper producers who, with their more highly developed technology, are able to combine the competing products with wood fiber and thus avoid displacement of wood by the competitors.

The message is clear that nontimber commodities can take and are taking traditional markets from timber. In some cases, the substitution is predictable and appropriate, and the wood-using industry might well accept the trend. In other cases, markets are being lost through the industry's failure to improve its products or adapt them to factory systems.

Analysis of competitive forces is basic to forest-policy discussion and action. The long-term demand for timber depends to a large extent on how the industry meets its competition. If the industry's efforts are not successful, projections of housing starts, gross national product, and population growth may be fairly inaccurate.

It is important to understand the potential of timber, relative to its competitors, for meeting the wants of consumers. Trends in both solid lumber and fiber clearly presage great change, but also great potential, for wood. The many instances of substitution for wood and paper suggest that the producing companies must do what is necessary to serve their markets regardless of raw material and must not pass into oblivion by stubbornly promoting wood when its usefulness has passed. A constructive market policy will reveal new potentials for wood.

CHANGING CONSUMER POSTURE

The exposure of individuals to timber products has changed considerably in recent years. Low-cost wood is no longer easily available at a local lumber yard, and skilled craftsmen can no longer readily be found to work with it. More and more, the consumer is choosing pre-manufactured items, from fencing to dwellings. The items he buys come from factories that must achieve ever-increasing efficiency—and do it without the craftsmen of earlier years.

A major influence on wood-use patterns is the expanding industrialization of the construction process. Although factory-built housing has been developing for many years with only modest success, it now appears that numerous forces are combining to stimulate the expansion of industrialized housing. Indeed, the mobile-home industry already has an impressive record for the efficient building of shelter, and its effect on wood-product use is considerable. Mobile shelters are distinguished by their low cost and high efficiency. Because of their mobility, they enjoy a special position with respect to building codes and taxes. Conventional house construction suffers increasingly from high labor costs, shortage of labor, unskilled labor, over-use of material (see Chapter 10), and shortage and high cost of land. The projected demand for housing could not conceivably be met by the old methods. What is happening, therefore, is rapid concentration of effort in factories, involving everything from precutting and fabricating components to completing modules for transport and assembly at the site. Factory operations sharpen competition of materials on the basis of cost, performance, availability, and stability of price. The traditional loyalty to wood in the construction industry is in jeopardy as craft gives way to factory work. If the forest-products industry fails to stay competitive, the so-called timber crisis may come to exist only for the producer, as the consumer grows accustomed to using much less wood.

An indication of trends in the building business is found in the response of American industry to the government's housing and urban development program. Although the program was modest in scope, it prompted the formation of a large number of consortia representing various talents and interests. Most of the names were relative strangers to conventional building and certainly to the wood industry. Dozens of groups competed for a few awards. Although most of these rapidly formulated groups will probably fail or fall short of their immediate objectives, it is likely that many business, financial, and creative groups will become committed beyond the point of return and will enter housing construction successfully, introducing innovative methods that may or may not include wood. Some of the house-construction materials described by the 22 winners include: cement asbestos board with polyurethane core and aluminum extrusions; factory-cast concrete floor and wall panels; shop-fabricated wood with polyester fiberglass facings; prestressed concrete cast on site with "dry" mechanical joints; rigid honeycomb plywood-faced floor panels with metal stud wall panel; structural wood or alternate, as cost and availability dictate; permanently colored resin-filled fiber products; stressed-skin plywood construction; steel components for quick on-site assembly; and mandrel-wrapped, fiber-shell plastic modules. Of the material proposed, 49 percent is concrete, 26 percent is wood, 15 percent is metal, and 10 percent is plastic. Some of the winners did propose wood, but it is noteworthy that awards were for total systems and environment, independent of any material, and there was certainly no obvious sentiment for tradition. The burden is on wood to hold its place, and if wood products are to hold or expand their position, producers will necessarily progress from commodities to special products, to components, to systems.

The recent history of the forest-products industry has shown more price fluctuations, irregular output, and unsatisfactory manufacture than is acceptable with modern factory methods. Unacceptable performance calls into play what may be termed the irreversibility of product substitution: Although wood has operated from a base of ready acceptance and modest cost, a single cycle of failure on one of the above counts might result in its permanent displacement.

Consider the possible forces for product substitution in the factory production of houses. Costs must be minimized and controlled, and flow of units not interrupted. Rapid price changes, change of product mix, or inadequate inventories could result in a quick shift from natural wood walls to printed grain and plastic film, or from wood to metal structures. Once substitution takes place, it is difficult for wood, with its natural variability, to recover its earlier position.

In general, the lumber industry sells its output in an auction-type market, in which each carload is traded for the most it will bring at the moment. This market procedure could hardly indicate either interest in or obligation to the lumber user, and thus it is not surprising that the user favors materials that are free of lumber's hazards. The more the building industry evolves toward factory operation, the more essential it becomes for the industry to find material suppliers who will respond to its needs. This consideration has led to the advocacy of a futures market in lumber as well as in plywood.

IMPACT OF TECHNOLOGY

Although great advances in research and development have been made in recent years by the leading forest-products firms and some of their associations, the industry in general is at a considerable disadvantage in technology and in development of products. Largely because of its fragmentation and lack of technical sophistication, the industry has not supported research on a scale even close to that of the large chemical and plastics companies aiming at traditional markets for wood and paper. On the other hand, the inherent properties of wood, together with traditional acceptance of wood and fiber, give timber a substantial advantage over competing raw materials. Furthermore, much of the "fall-out" from nontimber research, particularly that in plastics and chemicals, has direct application to wood. Two immensely important examples are permanent resin bonding and the remarkable wet-strength resins which need only to be put to use (for lumber-plywood and for paper, respectively). Both these materials were developed elsewhere. The hydraulics of papermaking, the chemistry of rayon and explosives, the science of graphics such as xerox, the physics of latices or coatings, the engineering of devices for testing, and many other developments in the forest-products industry have grown out of other industries' research.

Because many timber-processing firms must remain small in relation to firms in competing industries, a practical policy for the little company appears to be to adapt research results or available technology to its specific needs in wood conversion. The transfer and use of others' findings require a staff with an appreciation of technology and research and with enough competence and creativity to sense what is useful and to adapt it to wood products and processes. A promising aspect of research and technology in wood and paper is that much of the ground is still relatively unplowed, which makes commercial success more probable than it might be, for example, in the case of a new oil derivative.

Paper and solid wood are both sensitive to competition from noncellulose materials, but the paper industry is better able to turn such competition to its advantage. The higher levels of technology in the industry are partly responsible, but largely it is because of the relative homogeneity of pulp and its consequent adaptability to a variety of products. Already, there is scarcely a major paper company that is not also a plastics company. The combination of paper with resins, plastics, films, and foils is burgeoning, to the advantage of everyone except possibly the wastepaper dealer. While coatings and films have been prevalent for decades, noncellulose materials have been converted to fibers more recently. Thus "paper" is formed in either air or water from long and special fibers such as nylon, glass, acrylic, and polyester. The fibers are bonded chemically or sometimes thermally, as in so-called spun-bonded products.

While paper is usually thought of as fibrous, some new, promising paper substitutes are essentially plastic films coated to provide the feel and printability of quality paper. The substitutes have excellent resistance to chemicals and good dimensional stability. The manufacturing plant, which should be near a gas source, is totally independent of the forest. Of course, the new paper substitutes involve a host of other problems, such as disposability and raw-material supply.

Rayon, a chemical wood product, illustrates the hazards and opportunities that lie ahead. It began its checkered career as "artificial silk," which led in turn to its use in tire cord, carpet yarn, and now absorbent fibers for nonwoven fabrics. It is periodically displaced by plastics.

To be effective, modern technology must be employed in a large and continuously operated manufacturing plant. In the competition between wood and nonwood manufacturers, scale of operation is a serious problem to the former. Only a few are blessed with dependable supplies of raw material. From the vast government landholdings, timber is sold in small lots, which precludes the economies of scale that could support good utilization, product development, and progressive marketing. Thus wood is at a disadvantage compared to nonwood materials. That government timber is made available to all on an equal basis is understandable, but this policy forces shortterm action by the successful bidders. Forestry operations need concentration as a means of survival just as farm operations do.

WOOD QUALITY FOR FUTURE PRODUCTS

Because trees grow slowly and technologic growth tends to accelerate, more consideration must be given to defining the quality of wood that will be needed at the time a new crop of trees is harvested. No factor will be of more significance to forest management and therefore to policy than the product spectrum made possible through the use of wood fiber and subdivided wood. Tree growers, wood-products producers, and fiber-products manufacturers have been too far apart in their interests and in their communication for the common good of the forest industry. Until recently, the lumber industry has seemed indifferent to fiber, the paper industry interested only in pulpwood or fiber, and the tree-growing fraternity to be thinking of wood quality in terms of sawlogs measured in dubious units such as board feet. The industry's painfully slow modernization is evidenced in such inadequate categories of raw material as "peeler logs for sawmills," "sawlogs for peeling," "cull logs," "wood logs," "peelable pulp logs," and so forth—all these terms coined in the search for a meaningful classification.

It is difficult to predict what use patterns will exist when today's new forests are harvested. Yet some characteristics of end use are almost certainly in prospect: Plywood processes will be automated. Manufacturers will produce composite wood-nonwood materials. Industry will employ chemical patching, electronic defect scanning, automated gluing, better preservative treatments. Softwood-plywood plants will utilize uniform small logs, and the product will survive over particleboard only when high structural strength is needed or when overlays are used to give high-performance surfaces coupled with high strength. (But note that particleboard as strong as plywood may be possible if flakes are oriented.) The use of particleboard will continue to expand because of its versatility as a raw material and its relative economy. Particle products will be widely accepted for exterior use (laboratory products with engineered flakes of wood now show more potential than products currently in commercial use). Indeed, it is not unreasonable to suggest that an entire house could be made with fiber and resin, with no solid wood at all. If such developments materialize, the growing of what are now termed quality sawlogs will be rendered obsolete. Forest management will aim toward a high yield of wood substance, with new and more appropriate definitions of quality.

Paper and particle products will continue to outpace solid-wood products. Although pulp for paper is subject to increasing competition from nonforest materials, the bulk of paper must come from wood cellulose for many years. Chemicals from low-grade wood and bark will continue to enter commerce slowly, but time is in their favor. With increases in cost of raw material and transportation, integrated wood utilization will gain in importance, which will encourage the production of solid wood, fiber, and chemicals in the same operations.

All these trends indicate that earlier concepts of wood quality expressed in the classic terminology of the lumber industry are inadequate for the future. The economy cannot wait for nor afford to grow what once was freely available. At the same time, to grow only a heavy tonnage per acre may be too risky. The necessary compromise is between high weight of wood substance and low number of tree stems. The versatility of wood and its response to technology assure industrial adaptation to any reasonable formula.

The central point for policy consideration on wood quality is the need for a much clearer view of future commodities. It is especially important to clarify the prospects of solid-wood products compared to fiber and chemical goods, in the light of prospective competition from nontimber materials. Although estimates of future wants are bound to be imprecise, the implications for forest management are great and cannot be ignored.

DESIGN AND AESTHETICS

As an article of commerce in a competitive society, most wood is viewed in terms of cost, structure, and quantity. The immense industry based on timber and its derivatives is testimony to its importance as a material. Yet wood in solid form is being sorely pressed in major product areas which are dominated by the need for low labor cost and repetitive manufacturing processes. As a result, much wood is hidden in the structure or covered by plastics, metals, and other substances that often are less satisfying aesthetically and no better in performance.

Reflection suggests that wood is being maneuvered out of its strongest position, which is beauty combined with function. Multiple functions are essential and easy to achieve with wood, especially when combined with other materials. In their struggle to become competitive with wood, other producers are always trying to improve on the nonuniformity of wood so as to achieve low-cost and functional structures. Variability is undesirable in manufacturing, but advantageous in producing aesthetic value. The best balance between function and aesthetics in design is a controversial question, but to the extent that the answer dips toward the aesthetic, it appears to favor wood.

The need for design is human and basic to the quality of life. Because people will pay for something that stirs their senses, design also has a material value thus far only inadequately exploited in large-scale wood use. It is true, of course, that nonstructural wood and plywood paneling have brought great satisfaction to millions, but too often such paneling has been designed for "book matches" and mirror images that only paved the way for printed wood figures and plastic surfaces.

Although the relationship between design and function seems obscure to some, there probably is such a relationship, and a maturing wood industry has much to gain in trying to discover it. In a practical way, the extremes of mass production and pure art can well be tempered by application of industrial design. Here is a disciplined way of bringing sensitivity to a structure or a product, contributing equally to aesthetic values and performance, with apologies for neither. Industrial design, as distinguished from art, attempts to provide an appearance of "visual spontaneity" under fixed practical constraints. Where wood is treated purely as a commodity, with insensitivity to visual aspects, low product price can be expected to follow. This, in turn, affects the producer's ability to support the forest programs necessary to sustain the resource.

The surface of wood is universally accepted as beautiful; the number of other materials of which this can be said is very small. Split rock and water are other examples. Designers have upgraded concrete visually by combining special aggregate surfaces with freedom of form. A type of steel that retains its rust is another illustration of surface beauty. With respect to wood the point is simple enough: There should always be a conscious effort to seek out, by disciplined means, the best combination of aesthetic and functional values at acceptable cost.

These comments on design and function are included in an attempt to sharpen the sensitivity of wood producers to the needs and opportunities to contribute the most to society. Considering society's emphasis on environment and life quality, and considering how deeply wood use is embedded in the culture, it would be unfortunate if wood were maneuvered into a primarily functional or structural role. We know how to combine design and function in the use of wood which may give it a singular advantage over other materials.

WOOD PRODUCTS AND THE ENVIRONMENT

Proper appreciation of the aesthetic values of wood is a direct contribution to a good environment. In contrast to the defensive position the forest industries have sometimes inherited as cutters of trees and despoilers of land, a new case might be advanced for the importance of wood in helping man cope with the ever-increasing complexity of his environment. Indeed, instead of making apologies for upset ecologies, the industries can stress that, whatever other factors may be changing the planet, the growth of trees for fiber and shelter and the pleasure of man is a good manipulation of the surroundings for the benefit of the human body and soul.

Discussion of the mass use of wood usually focuses on its function, with only passing reference to the satisfaction it can bring to a person in his environment. Perhaps more could be done to invite greater participation in fashioning wood into objects that are beautiful and useful. Such participation builds individual satisfaction through creative work. Skill in these creative arts might be taught in the schools as a means for improving the quality of life; the teaching would also build kinship with and respect for wood far beyond our usual preoccupation with board feet and costs. The end result would be a contribution to the quality of life and a greater respect for wood. Fashioning of wood in the traditional sense is not retrogression when viewed broadly. In Japan, for example, carefully and artistically used wood is a product at once traditional and modern and is complementary to a good environment.

All the pressure, the logic, and the illogic of contemporary discussions of the environment create a new vector in forest policy. The return-to-nature idea implies the dignity of wood in the creation of habitat for man. The rush to metals, concrete, factory systems, blacktop, plastics, excess decibels, and sterile surfaces should make welcome a fuller return to the warm, friendly, organic, and aesthetically satisfying surfaces of wood. While the needs of man are more and more difficult to identify, the honest surfaces of wood seem a safe candidate for acceptance.

WOOD VERSUS NONWOOD MATERIALS, LONG-TERM VIEW

Looking toward the long future, the interrelationships between wood and other materials form a collage of multiple problems and opportunities that defy rational planning. Analysis of the intrinsic attributes of various substances, beginning with wood, might be useful.

Among the numerous features which make wood truly distinctive are warmth, beauty, light weight, strength, toughness, thermal insulation, versatility, and wide acceptance in the culture. However, wood is a variable substance and is subject to attack by fire, organisms, and moisture.

Concrete is strong, durable, fire-resistant, and moldable into free forms. The emergence of concrete for architectural use is of special interest. Its old function has been enhanced by pleasing shapes and sculptured surface features that clearly make it a most important material for the future. The technology for precasting is well developed, and new methods for the use of cellular aggregates or foam are impressive.

Steel features strength, stiffness, economy, and a vast, well-organized producing industry and product line, well keyed to the needs of engineers and designers. Its limitations include rusting, quick deformation with heat, and limitations in aesthetic use, except in special cases such as a controlled-rust "natural finish." Steel joined with concrete utilizes the best features of each.

Aluminum is an important competitor with wood for such uses as sash, siding, and trim, featuring ease of fabrication and promising long life of applied finishes. Its light weight and reflective surfaces are often advantageous. Thus far, cost has limited its structural use. Its shortcomings include easy denting, quick heat distortion, poor thermal properties, and an appearance which is not particularly appealing.

Plastics provide stimulating competition for wood. The versatility of plastics is enormous, ranging from structural to nonstructural uses. Like wood, plastics are organic. Unlike wood, they form easily into compound shapes. They can be inert to chemical attack. When reinforced with fiber, they can behave differently along each of their dimensions, as wood does. Indeed, wood itself can be described as a fiber-reinforced plastic, lignin bonded. The disadvantages of plastics include high cost, fire susceptibility, uncertain durability, limited aesthetic appeal, and resistance to natural recycling. However, the use of plastics with wood provides great advantages to both and thus holds much promise.

SOME PHILOSOPHY

What follows is conceptual, not documented, and intended only to stimulate thought.

It might be argued that wood is needed to sustain future generations for many reasons not connected with its performance, and that this need transcends its competition with other materials.

Steel, for example, is derived from mines that can be used up. As the prime-quality ores in Minnesota were depleted, the technology of converting taconite pellets provided a great new ore supply in the United States. Yet the grinding of ore to very fine mesh for pellets requires enormous power and thus leads to the use of more coal, another depletable resource. In addition, coal mining often damages land surfaces and streams far more than tree cutting does. More energy implies more oxygen use and more air and thermal pollution, needing regeneration by growing plants. The silt disposal from ore processing is a serious problem. Steel can be recycled, but not without great expenditure of energy. If the old auto is a good example, progress is not impressive.

Steel is an immense industry, and some people expect its products to fill any gap arising from wood shortage. However, these people fail to realize how much steel this might take and how great the environmental disruption would be. Today the tonnage output of wood greatly exceeds that of steel, and wood's volumetric output is a multiple of steel's. A relatively small percentage boost in wood production through intensified resource management and utilization is an easier and less disruptive means for closing a gap.

Oil and gas are wonderful building blocks for both chemical products and energy, and they support the age of plastics. Such products seem to have the potential to displace wood and metals in infinite quantity. Yet obtaining oil requires ever deeper probing, greater distances, more cost, and more energy, until in some far-off year oil exists no more. The peak development in the United States may already be here. The "life" of oil is sometimes expressed in decades, as is that of shale and coal. Certainly planners dealing with wood have no such close-in terminal point.

A prevalent economic theory has it that as resources become scarce, people work harder to create new sources, and all continues well. However, it is certain that the absolute physical supply of a resource will not be increased by economic theory. Endless energy is presumed to be available in nuclear form. Yet again, the twin problems of thermal pollution and radioactive waste set limits to the use of nuclear energy. Recent generations have had a splendid opportunity of harvesting incredible riches, but have not had much appreciation or concern for future limitations upon their efforts.

One conclusion from the preceding philosophy is that we grossly underrate the ultimate importance of timber and that something akin to evangelism is needed to elevate timber to its proper place in the life of man. Man's very survival may, in fact, depend on the growing and cutting of trees. Stated bluntly, eventually there will not be enough energy or material to leave much choice. It is often said that nonwood products will "fill the gap" in presumed shortages of wood. But in this context, there is no gap: There is only a "trade-off" of properties and cost at one moment in history.

Such reflections reveal timber as a grossly unappreciated material. It is processed by a fragmented industry, presumably non-progressive, buffeted by the sophisticated technology of competing materials. An important new consideration must, in the long run, support timber as a basic resource. Not only is it nondepleting, but also, quite possibly, its production and use could increase severalfold with techniques already employed in agriculture, except on a compressed time schedule. Trees are a vast sponge for solar energy and bestow attendant benefits of air purification and oxygen generation. They produce products for shelter, for fiber, for energy, and, if one can forego gourmet considerations, for food. When wood has served man, it disappears into the soil as a biologically degradable substance, to begin a cycle for new generations. In a sentence, wood can be generated, processed, used, reused if necessary, and returned to the soil with minimal use of energy and not much damage to the environment.

Unless the foregoing predictions are grossly erroneous, timber must emerge as an exceedingly important resource, not yet fully appreciated in the spectrum of resources that sustain life. This chapter has attempted to portray the future of wood in two contexts. One is relatively short-term, involving business aspects of the competition between wood and nonwood materials. The other is long-term and concerns the need to grow trees to meet the broad needs of mankind for air, water, shelter, fiber, food, and recreation, through the permanent application of the solar conversion process.

Deliberations on national forest policy must consider the reasonably near future, but they cannot avoid the longer view, concerned as they must be with the time required to produce new forest crops.

12   IMPORTS

HENRY S. KERNAN*

THE VALUE OF TRADE in timber products, fourth largest commodity group in shipments among the countries of the world, has more than doubled since 1960. In 1969, the value was $12.7 billion, a 13-percent increase over 1968. Exchanges of this magnitude indicate wide disparities among nations in the domestic supply-demand ratio for wood products. In general, the trade is also evidence of strong economic and other social incentives in both underdeveloped and developed countries.

In 1969, the United States imported about one-fifth of its consumption of wood products, the roundwood equivalent of 2.5 billion cubic feet. At the same time, the U.S. exported about 1.2 billion cubic feet. Most imports were softwood lumber, woodpulp, and newsprint paper from Canada and hardwood plywood from east Asia. Most exports were softwood logs to Japan and woodpulp, paper, and paperboard to Japan and western Europe.

To what extent and under what circumstances will the United States be able to avoid timber scarcity and satisfy its market preferences by importing timber products? The country's desire for wood may outrun its capabilities of producing it, especially under the constraints which society may impose upon the use of U.S. forest resources. If imports can fill the gap, society need not overdraw upon the available forest for wood or modify such priorities as it may wish to give to nonwood uses of the forest. The United States can import timber if importation holds enough net advantage, if marketable resources exist abroad, and if the nations possessing these resources have the necessary production technology and the incentives to produce wood for export.

UNITED STATES AS AN IMPORTER

The United States is in an excellent position to benefit from wood importation. Although the U.S. forest resource is extensive and di-

* Consultant in international forestry, Worcester, N.Y.

verse, it cannot always yield the products in demand. For example, domestic stocks of pulpwood are ample, but those of veneer-quality hardwood logs are low. Furthermore, while the country's affluence generates wants, it also places some lines of timber production at a disadvantage compared to alternative activities.

The American people make heavy use of wood products, especially paper and plywood. Per-capita consumption of paper reached 573 pounds in 1970, from 385 pounds in 1955. The country's 842 pulp and paper mills cannot keep up with such a demand (half the world total). In round figures, U.S. mills turn out 53 million tons a year while consumption is 60 million tons.

The comparative disadvantage of the U.S. in some lines of timber production is reflected in the rates of return in wood-using enterprise. In North America, these rates have slipped in the last few years from an average of about 8 percent to about 4 percent. Meanwhile, in the United States, an advanced technologic society seeks, and normally finds, business and industrial investment opportunities that promise relatively high rates of return. Activities such as sawmilling are less suitable in a society with many alternatives than in one with few. The United States would tend to be an importer of sawmill products even if its domestic supplies of sawtimber made importation physically unnecessary.

It is easily conceivable that by the year 2000, the United States would want to buy from abroad about twice today's annual imports of wood products: a roundwood equivalent of 5–5.5 billion cubic feet, of which as much as eight- or nine-tenths would be softwood.

POTENTIAL SOURCES: SOFTWOOD

Where, then, will the United States look for wood?

The sources can be either natural forests or plantations. Increasing worldwide by several million acres a year, plantations have created exportable surpluses in Chile, South Africa, New Zealand, and Morocco: The products of forest plantations are indeed capable of competing in international markets although their quantities will be relatively small for the next 30 years. Therefore, the source of wood imports for at least this period will be almost entirely primeval natural forests.

The world has five large reserves of timber. Softwood forests are found in Siberia and Canada, two regions with similar forests but very different economic systems and export incentives. Large hardwood reserves are located in the Amazon basin, west and central Africa, and southeast Asia—underdeveloped tropical regions.

Of the world's five large reserves, the softwood reserve in the U.S.S.R. is the most extensive. It is nearly three times the forest area

of the United States and has more than four times U.S. timber growing stock. The largest part of this reserve is larch and pine, in a
belt that broadens eastward from the Urals between the Arctic tundra
and the steppes of central Asia.

Several major difficulties hinder utilization of the Siberian forests,
either for domestic use or for export. Even the largest rivers, the
Lena and the Yenisei, are unsuitable for transport because ice blocks
their channels much of the year and because they flow north, away
from the centers of population and the trans-Siberian railway.
In addition, the larch does not float well and hence must be moved
overland if at all. The climate is severe and labor is scarce. The
chronic deficit of wood products in European Russia indicates the
difficulty of exploiting the Siberian reserve.

Another obstacle to exploitation is Soviet economic policy. Although meeting domestic needs requires a large and continuous investment in timber industries and transport, policies give priority
to heavy industries and defense.

Nor do Soviet policies favor response to world markets. Foreign
trade is controlled by political considerations and the needs for foreign currency. In general, the Soviet Union offers wood products for
sale to two categories of nations: those from whom she intends to
import capital goods and those with whom she is cultivating economic
and political ties. Since the United States falls in neither category,
the prospects of Siberia becoming a source of wood for the U.S. are
not promising.

Canada presents a striking contrast to the U.S.S.R. In 1969, with
43 percent less forested land, Canada exported nearly four times the
value of forest products exported by the Soviets. Indeed, Canada's
forest-product exports regularly earn nearly one-quarter of her foreign exchange, and over three-quarters of these exports go to the
United States. The dominant incentives underlying Canada's policies
toward her forest resources are not political, but financial: They are
responsive to markets and prices as Soviet incentives are not. Moreover, the Kennedy-Round Agreements reached in 1967 strongly bene-
fited Canadian export trade in wood products to the United States.
Thus Canada is the likeliest source of U.S. softwood imports in both
the short and the long run. The chief question is whether Canada
can continue to offer wood products for export to the United States
at competitive prices.

The Canadian Council of Resource Ministers met in November
1970 to study their country's forest resources and timber industries
and to discuss ways of developing them for domestic use and export.
The figures the ministers considered were large enough to encourage
Canadians who look forward to larger foreign sales of wood products

and Americans who hope to buy more Canadian lumber, pulp, and paper. These figures indicated an exportable yearly surplus of 2.5 billion cubic feet by 1980 and of 5 billion cubic feet by 2000. The huge volume of shipments forecast for 2000 was thought to be compatible with domestic demands of 5.7 billion cubic feet. This level of continuous output would be backed by 400 billion cubic feet of timber growing on 800 million acres of forest land. Certainly lack of wood will not force Canada out of her position as the world's leading exporter of wood products.

The wood-output prediction supposes that Canada will be able to manage problems of forest development. Nearly one-quarter of all Canadian forests, 190 million acres, presently falls outside the operative forest area for reasons of remoteness, rigorous climate, scarcity of labor, or scant quantities of wood per acre. Canada cannot increase the operative forest area merely by raising prices. Production costs, at least in southern United States, compare favorably with those in Canada. Efficient logging and manufacturing can help keep prices competitive. Also helpful will be restraint in the demands made upon wood industry for wages by labor, for dividends by stockholders, and for stumpage and assessments by the provincial governments, which own 90 percent of Canadian forests.

In spite of the problems of accessibility and competition, the Canadian expectation is that by the year 2000, Canada will export to the United States the roundwood equivalent of 4 billion cubic feet of wood annually. Included will be 8,675 thousand tons of newsprint, 5,545 thousand tons of woodpulp, and 10,100 billion board feet of softwood lumber. These estimates assume an 80-percent increase in demand for forest products in the United States during the next thirty years.

The Canadian expectations also suppose that at least until the year 2000, primeval forests will supply most of the timber. The shift to young-growth forests will take place at a gradually accelerating rate, until at some point such growth will become the most significant and ultimately the only source of wood. Whether the young-growth forest will be able to sustain removals as high as those anticipated depends upon how effectively the Canadians deal now with related silvicultural problems: the 80 million acres inadequately stocked with young trees; the high annual incidence of fire, insects, and disease; and the uneven matching of resources to markets. (For example, Douglas fir is the tree most in demand, whereas poplar is abundant but less in demand. Again, the largest markets for Canadian wood exports are in eastern United States, whereas the largest potential for expanding exports is in British Columbia.) The outcome of these long-run problems is unpredictable.

POTENTIAL SOURCES: HARDWOOD

For hardwood products, the United States will turn to the primeval tropical rain forest in underdeveloped countries. In assessing export potential, both the forest itself and the underdeveloped state of the countries must be considered.

No more than a rough estimate of the tropical rain forest area is possible, partly because this type of forest has not been studied as thoroughly as the temperate forest and partly because the area of tropical rain forest is changing all the time. Recent figures show that the largest and least disturbed belt is the Amazonian forest of 1,088 million acres. Next is the Asian Pacific region, with 768 million acres. Africa has 640 million acres, and outlying areas of Central and South America have another 384 million. The total area of tropical rain forest is close to three billion acres, an expanse roughly comparable to the softwood forests of Russia, Canada, and Scandinavia combined.

Tropical rain forests are not only extensive but they include a very large number of tree species. They are far more heterogeneous than forests of the temperate zones. The richest forest is in southeast Asia; Malaya has a sample acre with 143 species. The next richest forest in number of species is the Amazonian, and the least is that of Africa.

The nonuniformity of the rain forest has a profound influence upon the proportion of usable wood. Estimates of the total quantity of stemwood on a fully stocked acre, varying little among regions, are on the order of 500 cubic feet. But much of this is unusable. Many trees are rotten, poorly shaped, or both. A number of species occur so rarely as to make their marketing difficult. Others have poor or unknown technical qualities. The rain forests richest in usable wood are probably the dipterocarp forests of the Philippines and adjacent Borneo. These forests are the main sources of the lauan panels becoming so common in American houses. One reason for the panels' relatively low price is that often half of the standing timber is of export quality. In contrast, a 1967 study of 4.7 million acres in southwest Ivory Coast showed an average of 1,500 cubic feet of timber per acre, of which 210 cubic feet were of exportable quality. In that year, the average removals per acre were 71 cubic feet. By and large, logging in the tropical rain forest must seek out the trees of top quality and size, which can bear the high cost of extraction.

Demand is increasing for sawlogs and veneer logs of high quality and well-established species such as the dipterocarps and mahoganies. In the future, large investments will have to be made by the exporting countries to regenerate the favored species or else the importing countries will have to accept a greater number of species. The exporting countries are making regeneration efforts, but have many demands upon their investment funds. The Forest Products Laboratory at Madison, Wisconsin, is studying the lesser known tropical woods which may have uses within the United States for lumber and plywood.

The Forest Products Laboratory is also studying the potential of the tropical rain forest for woodpulp products. Because of formidable marketing and financing problems, woodpulp manufactured from tropical hardwoods will not be a significant factor in international trade, at least not for the next several decades.

HARDWOOD TRADE TRENDS

A notable feature of the hardwood trade has been its rapid rise in percentage of all exports from underdeveloped countries. From 1960 through 1968, the proportion of total export value accounted for by forest products rose from 1.8 percent to 3.2 percent. Underdeveloped countries with timber resources have incentives to exploit them and export their products, thus improving the prospects of the United States drawing upon tropical rain forests.

The single most powerful incentive for tropical nations to promote exports is probably the need to finance rapidly rising imports of capital and consumer goods. The annual cost of pulp and paper imports alone offsets by more than half the annual earnings of these countries from the export of forest products. In 1969, Brazil, with the largest hardwood reserves in the world, exported $115 million of forest products and imported $52 million worth, largely woodpulp products. Rather than restrict imports, which most lower-income countries regard as the key to their development, these countries prefer to promote exports.

To foster exports, countries with surplus timber work out policies toward their resources. Where resources are plentiful and local use of industrial wood is small, the economy benefits by shifting from fuelwood to industrial wood and from future use (conservation) to present use (depletion). In underdeveloped countries, conservation and depletion do not have the moral and emotional connotations they have in the United States.

TRADE, CONSERVATION, AND DEVELOPMENT

Nondevelopment favors rapid depletion of natural resources. The poorer the country, the enterprise, the agency, or the individual, the higher the rates of interest which obtain: Rates of interest are inversely related to wealth. In underdeveloped countries, wealth is scarce. Attendant high interest rates represent a low present value of future net revenue. Time preferences are redistributed toward the present, away from the future.

A depletion policy has several advantages for a country in which rates of interest are high and forests are in primeval condition, showing little net growth. It is more economical for planning agencies to reduce capital immobilized in timber than to borrow more money and carry debts at high rates of interest. In depleting the forest, planners see a way to generate domestic currency for social programs and foreign exchange for imports. The greater a country's needs, the more likely it is to seek markets for its timber and thereby reduce the urgency of its fiscal problems. Two results of such a policy will be an increase in the nation's standard of living and a reduction of timber capital. The amount of timber capital retained has an inverse relation both to the nation's productivity goals and to the intensity of its timber management. The best prospects for U.S. hardwood imports will lie in countries with tropical rain forests which seek high timber productivity and intensive management.

Rapid depletion of natural resources is furthered, not only by underdevelopment, but also by fluctuations in the markets for primary materials. Unprocessed wood, which earns half of the timber-product foreign exchange for underdeveloped countries, is a primary material subject to extreme market instability. For poor nations, income has a powerful influence upon the choice between present and future resource use. When markets are rising, the rate of natural-resource depletion diminishes (the industry wants to hold off in expectation of higher prices and is able to do so since its income is up); but when markets are falling, the rate of depletion increases, for the industry is striving to sell before prices drop still further and also to sustain its income. The falling-market phase is the more influential. As a result, market instability has the net effect of drawing timber resources away from future uses into those of the present.

Political instability has effects comparable to those of the fluctuating market. Governments change, and so do policies toward land tenure, taxation, foreign capital, and industry. The greater the consequent uncertainty, the higher the discount of the future and the more rapid the timber removals. Thus, in the short run, fluctuating markets and politics make timber available for export to the United States. In the long run, the U.S. import market will depend upon the degree to which the exporting nations grasp their opportunities to build productive young forests through intensive management.

AGENTS OF TRADE

In an underdeveloped country, three agents of trade respond to high interest rates, fluctuating markets, and political instability by influencing the removal and export of forest products. One is the wood-using industry, which operates at least in part with foreign capital and management and with little long-term commitment to the replenishment of the resource. Its primary concerns are profit and the flexibility to guard against the uncertainties of politics and markets. The industry finds that extraction and export of logs yield the highest profits obtainable from timber enterprise and respond most readily to foreign market demands. The largest relative increase of 1969 over 1968 wood export figures was in hardwood logs: 27 percent. The United States is exceptional in that its import of logs has steadily decreased. Instead, the United States has imported veneer and plywood manufactured from hardwood logs, largely in Japan, Taiwan, Korea, and the Philippines. It has thereby avoided direct competition with the major log importers and product consumers, who are in western Europe.

The Ministry of Finance is a second agent of trade. Its revenue comes from the sale of public timber and from taxing the profits of enterprises which exploit timber. To the extent that these enterprises export their products, the Ministry of Finance has assurance of foreign exchange. Present-day concepts of justice require that public funds be spent for social services and infrastructure to encourage industry. To the Ministry of Finance, an over-capitalized timber reserve is a logical source of public funds and foreign exchange.

The public body administering the forest lands is the third agent of trade. Its officials are likely to have conservative commitments to unvarying rates of annual removals and cautious views regarding the forest's response to demands for increased productivity. With such commitments and views, officials find their leadership undermined when markets for exports are expanding and government funding of imports and social services is urgent. Then their chief concerns too often become overseeing concession agreements and collecting revenue. The long-range prospects for exports are best in countries where forestry officials can give major attention to replenishing resources in anticipation of demands several decades ahead.

HARDWOOD OUTLOOK

Incentives and attitudes in the tropical hardwood nations are based upon an estimated exportable timber reserve of 630 billion cubic feet of suitable species and quality. The countries most likely to supply the United States directly are the Philippines, Indonesia, and Malaysia; indirectly as middlemen, Japan, Korea, and Taiwan. The forests of the former countries have the world's highest proportion of exportable wood; the processing facilities and trade channels of the latter are best adapted to supplying markets in the United States.

Prospects of forest exploitation are less favorable in the Amazon region because of the relative scarcity of labor, transport, and exportable wood. Exports of wood products from the Amazon could be increased rapidly if sufficient investments were made. However, the costs of both investments and the products thereof would be higher than they are in southeast Asia.

For wood products from west and central Africa, the United States must compete principally with the common market of western Europe, which has strong economic and cultural ties with former African colonies and a growing hardwood deficit. The result is a rapidly increasing flow of logs from Africa to Europe. The best prospects for U.S. imports of African wood and wood products lie with species, grades, and forms of use not now in competitive demand.

PART 3   POLICIES AND PROGRAMS

13 FORESTRY POLICIES AND PROGRAMS

SAMUEL T. DANA*

Policies are courses of action adopted by groups or individuals for the attainment of objectives. For example, the Multiple Use-Sustained Yield Act of 1960 (74 Stat. 215) declared that "it is the policy of the Congress that the national forests are established and shall be administered for outdoor recreation, range, timber, watershed, and wildlife and fish purposes" and proceeded to specify in broad terms some of the means for attaining that objective. Implementation of this policy required the development by officials of the Department of Agriculture, from the Secretary to the forest ranger, of specific courses of action which may be regarded from the national point of view as subpolicies.

The ramifications of policy created by an act dealing with a single agency (the Department of Agriculture) and a single subject (establishment and administration of the national forests) are impressive. They become almost endless in relation to so broad a subject as the timber supply, for timber-supply policies are influenced not only by large numbers of timber owners with widely varying interests, but also by the regulatory and cooperative activities of public agencies at all levels. Furthermore, timber-supply policies are inevitably influenced by policies for the ownership, management, and utilization of the forest of which timber is an integral part. Forestry policies, in turn, are influenced by still broader policies such as those relating to national defense, housing, pollution, and population. For instance, Stewart L. Udall remarked that he considered "the movement in this country for very liberal abortion laws a part of the environment movement."[1]

GOVERNMENTAL POLICIES: LAND OWNERSHIP

As the owner of the original public domain, the federal government has always exercised a strong influence on land and water poli-

* Dean Emeritus, School of Natural Resources, University of Michigan, Ann Arbor.

cies. With enactment of the Ordinance of 1785, it adopted the policy of selling the public lands. The immediate objectives were to promote settlement and obtain revenue, but underlying these objectives was the basic philosophy that, in general, private ownership is preferable to public ownership. The settlement motive became dominant with passage of the Homestead Act in 1862 (12 Stat. 392) and abolition of auction sales in 1891 (26 Stat. 1095). Sales were supplemented by large grants to states and railroad corporations for various purposes.

For about a century, none of the federal government sales or grants dealt specifically with forest lands or with timber. Then, in 1878, the Timber and Stone Act (20 Stat. 89) provided for the sale of timber in tracts of 160 acres in the Pacific Coast States; in the same year, the Free Timber Act (20 Stat. 88) provided for the use of timber, under certain restrictions, in the Rocky Mountain States. Both acts were subject to serious abuse, and the Timber and Stone Act was repealed in 1955 (69 Stat. 434). Timber trespass on the public lands was forbidden in acts of 1807 (2 Stat. 445) and 1831 (4 Stat. 472), but the acts were never effectively enforced.

An act of 1817 (3 Stat. 347) authorized the reservation from sale of public lands containing live oak and red cedar for the use of the Navy. Altogether, some 264,000 acres of reservations were established under this act, but they were never extensively used and were eventually abandoned.

The first permanent reservation of forest land in the public domain came in 1872 with the creation of Yellowstone National Park (17 Stat. 32)—not for the protection of the timber supply, but "as a public park or pleasuring ground." This action served as the first step toward evolution of the policy of withdrawing extensive areas of forest land for national-park purposes. The second step came in 1890 with the setting aside of Yosemite, Sequoia, and General Grant National Parks as "reserved forest lands" (26 Stat. 478, 650). Preservation of the forests was a major objective in each of these cases—again, not for commercial use as timber, but for aesthetic enjoyment.

Meanwhile, a movement had developed for the permanent reservation of sizable areas of the public domain for watershed protection and timber production. This movement was led by the American Association for the Advancement of Science and the American Forestry Association in the belief that such reservation would result in better protection and management of the forests and in continuing receipt of substantial revenues by the government. This view was not universally shared. Commissioner Burdett of the General Land Office, for example, stated that the sale of timber without the land would, under careful supervision, be the ideal method, but that he feared it would be ruinously expensive and would afford "opportunities for fraudulent collusion and unjust exactions" on the part of corrupt public servants. He consequently came to the conclusion that "the greatest protection to the timber of the country, now rapidly decreasing, will be found in placing it under private ownership."

Undiscouraged, supporters of the reservation policy continued their efforts until they were rewarded by passage of the forest reserve acts of 1891 (26 Stat. 1905) and 1897 (30 Stat. 11, 34). Reservations under these acts constitute the great bulk of the lands now in national forests.

The next step in the development of federal forest-land policy— from reservation to acquisition—came in 1911 with passage of the Weeks Act (36 Stat. 971). This act, which authorized the purchase of lands at the headwaters of navigable streams, was extended by the Clarke-McNary Act of 1924 (43 Stat. 653) to authorize the purchase of lands for timber production as well as for streamflow protection. Under these acts, the government has acquired some 26 million acres of forest land, mostly commercial (see definition in Chapter 3). Funds for these purchases have come from the General Fund of the U.S. Treasury and from the Land and Water Conservation Fund established in 1964. Under the latter, acquisition is limited to lands primarily of value for recreational use, but may include land valuable also for other purposes.

OWNERSHIP BY STATE AND LOCAL GOVERNMENTS

The states have followed somewhat the same cycle: forest land acquisition, disposal, reservation, and acquisition again, but with significant differences and on a smaller scale. In the East, the states' original holdings came mainly by inheritance from their colonial predecessors and from the Republic of Texas; in the West they came from federal grants. Both regions followed the basic policy of sale, with no distinction between forest lands and other lands.

No specific reservations of forest land were made by the states until 1885, when New York established a "forest preserve" in the Adirondack and Catskill regions. A proviso in the state constitution of 1894 that state lands in the forest preserve be kept "forever wild" is still in effect in spite of repeated efforts to obtain its repeal. Washington has established some 2 million acres of its grant lands as state forests.

In addition to their original holdings, many states have acquired, and retained, considerable areas of forest land through purchase and as a result of tax delinquency. Foremost in the group of purchasers is Pennsylvania, which has acquired nearly 3 million acres of forest land since 1900. Only two states have set aside large areas acquired through tax delinquency as permanent forest reserves. These are Michigan, with a total of 3,700,000 acres, and Minnesota, with a total of 3,300,000 acres.

Altogether, the states own about 21 million acres of commercial forest land, a considerable amount of which is not included in forest reservations. This area is about one-sixth of that in federal ownership and one-third of that in industrial ownership. Timber is the main product, but the prominence of recreation is rapidly increasing. Many state parks, with a much smaller total area, also contain forest land, which is classed as noncommercial because the timber is not available for commercial utilization.

County and municipal ownership of commercial forest land totals about 8 million acres, with smaller amounts of noncommercial forest land. Only in Minnesota and Wisconsin, where county ownership comprises about 3,500,000 acres and 2,600,000 acres respectively, is the production of timber for commercial use a major objective.

MANAGEMENT OBJECTIVES AND PRACTICES

Watershed protection and timber production were specified by the Act of 1897 as the objectives for which forest reserves could be established, and the Secretary of the Interior was authorized to regulate the occupancy and use of these reserves. Acting under this authority, Secretary Wilson of the Department of Agriculture (to which administration of the reserves had just been transferred) instructed the Chief of the Bureau of Forestry in 1905 that "all land is to be devoted to its most productive use for the permanent good of the whole people," and referred specifically to conservation of the water, wood, and forage of the reserves.

Secretary Wilson's early statement of the principle of multiple use received legislative endorsement by passage of the Multiple Use-Sustained Yield Act of 1960. In the intervening period, emphasis on the different resources of the national forests varied. For many years, grazing was predominant in terms of number of users and their payments into the federal treasury. Timber and water were, however, consistently regarded as the major products of the national forests and received special attention in the managerial practices adopted. Since the depression of the 1930s, the demand for timber has increased so greatly that in recent years receipts from timber sales have averaged around 95 percent of total treasury receipts from the national forests.

Compared to water, wood, and forage, wildlife and recreation were relatively slow to receive attention. Curiously enough, a writer in the February 11, 1925, issue of the influential magazine *Outlook* accused the Forest Service of having abandoned timber production, fire control, watershed maintenance, pest and disease control, and grazing administration in the forests, and of having completely turned to promoting forest recreation.

Although the charge was so exaggerated as to be absurd, it is true that the Forest Service, in theory at least, had started to recognize recreation as an important use of the national forests. The Gila Wilderness Area had been established in 1924, and in the same year Chief Forester Greeley had stated in his annual report: "Outdoor recreation ranks today as one of the major resources, or utilities of the national forests, not because of anything the Government has done to facilitate or increase this form of use, but because of the demonstrated belief of several millions of people that the forests offer a broad and varied field of recreational opportunities."

In 1932, in a letter of instructions to regional foresters, Chief Forester Stuart stated that recreation "will in many situations constitute a use of natural resources coordinate and occasionally paramount to their industrial conversion into commercial commodities," and that "it deserves and should receive the same relative degree of technical attention and administrative planning that is now given to the other forms of utilization."

MULTIPLE USE AND SUSTAINED YIELD

The policy of giving managerial attention to all forest values received legislative endorsement by Congress in the Multiple Use-Sustained Yield Act of 1960. Statement and application of a policy are, however, horses of a different color. The objective is clear: to promote the "national interest." But what constitutes the national interest and what combination of uses will best promote this interest in specific situations? Two recent controversies illustrate the difficulty in securing agreement among groups with different interests and points of view.

The proposed National Forest Timber Conservation and Management Act of 1969 (H.R. 12025) would have created a "high timber yield fund" consisting of 65 percent of all receipts from the sale of timber and other forest products from the national forests. This fund would then be available, when appropriated, for managerial practices aimed at increasing timber yields. The proposed act was supported by the Department of Agriculture and the forest-products industry as an effective means of meeting the urgent need for increased timber supplies. It was opposed by many conservation organizations such as the Sierra Club, the Wilderness Society, and others, as a threat to to the development of recreational and other resources of the national forests. The question was also raised whether it would be wise to jeopardize the best allocation of available funds among the various forest products and services. Both groups favored the principle of multiple use, but disagreed violently on its application in this specific case. Although the bill was favorably reported by the House Committee on Agriculture, it was not considered by the House as a whole.

Similar disagreement existed about a proposed timber sale on the East Meadow Creek watershed in the White River National Forest in Colorado. Opponents of the sale claimed that the area should be studied by the Forest Service for possible preservation as a wilderness area. This view was upheld by the U.S. District Court in Denver, which issued an injunction of indefinite duration against proceeding with the sale. Here again, disagreement centered around the application of general policies. The fundamental difficulty was expressed by the regional forester at Denver when he said that "there are no criteria for the national interest."

Multiple use is subject to such varied interpretation that its application to specific situations often leads to sharp controversy. Identification, measurement, and comparison of the benefits and costs of different courses of action (policies) to determine which is the "best" is extremely difficult. The difficulty is enhanced when such incommensurables as financial, social, aesthetic, and spiritual benefits and costs are involved, as is now usually the case. More and more, the assumption that maximization of the timber supply has top priority is being questioned, with the certainty that increasing attention will be paid to the relative values of *all* forest products and services in the determination of future forestry policies.

The 1960 Act adds to multiple use another basic policy of national forest administration—"to produce a sustained yield of products and services." More specifically, it provides for "achievement and maintenance in perpetuity of of a high-level annual or regular periodic output of the various renewable resources of the national forests without impairment of the productivity of the land." The policy is clear, but its application is difficult.

Two questions are inescapable: Sustained yield of what, and at what level? Maximum production of all potential goods and services, which at first blush might appear to be the goal, is impossible, and even if possible, might not always be desirable. Secretary Wilson's oft-quoted instructions to Pinchot to seek "the greatest good of the greatest number in the long run" overlooked the stubborn fact that three interrelated variables cannot be maximized simultaneously. Whether the area involved is a 40-acre tract or a million-acre national forest, a choice must be made of the levels at which the production of the various goods and services to be favored under a multiple-use policy will be sustained. With timber, for example, the goal can be set at any level from zero to the maximum productivity of the site. In addition, the quantitative level must be chosen with specific reference to the species and the product to be grown.

Attainment of the joint objectives of multiple use and sustained yield requires the wise choice and skillful application of the appropriate techniques of managment. These techniques involve use of all the knowledge at the disposal of professional foresters, who may not always see eye to eye about the best courses of action (policies) to be followed in specific situations.

Sharp differences of opinion on managerial policies may also exist between professionals and laymen. A conspicuous example, with important implications for the timber supply, is the use of clearcutting in certain types of forest, a practice defended by most foresters as ecologically and economically sound and attacked by many environmentalists as aesthetically unsound. Connaughton has pointed out that if foresters abandon clearcutting, they lose a sound practice, while if they reject the critics completely, they may be overwhelmed by public opinion. He believes that the resolution of this clash of views lies in a compromise: to modify current clearcutting practices so as to meet both silvicultural requirements and public opinion as well as possible.[2] Compromises are never entirely satisfactory to everyone, but they have been, and will doubtless continue to be, common in settling the disagreements that always arise in the development and application of forest policies.

Most of the forest lands under the jurisdiction of federal agencies other than the Forest Service and the National Park Service are managed under the general principles of multiple use and sustained yield. In 1937 Congress (50 Stat. 874) provided specifically for sustained-yield management of revested Oregon and California railroad lands administered by the Bureau of Land Management. In the Classification Act of 1964 (78 Stat. 986), it provided for the interim management (pending classification) for multiple use and sustained yield of most of the forest lands under the jurisdiction of the Bureau. Although recreation is receiving increasing attention both on these lands and on the forest lands administered by the Bureau of Indian Affairs and the Department of Defense, the lands also contribute substantially to the timber supply of the country.

Lands in the national park system, on the other hand, are managed on a principle of "dominant use," which may involve the preservation of nature, recreation, or historical purposes. Lands may also provide such services as watershed protection and amelioration of the climate, but these are not among the major purposes for their establishment or management. Consequently, the national parks do not contribute to the timber supply of the country, but, on the contrary, remove some 5.25 million acres of productive forest land from commercial utilization. Of this total, some 2.8 million acres consist of lands transferred from the national forests.

With the exception of the state of New York, where the forest lands in the Adirondacks and Catskills are to be kept "forever wild," most commercial forest lands in state ownership are managed for multiple use, with recreation playing an increasingly important role. Although they may provide a valuable supply of timber for the local forest-products industries, their contribution to the national timber supply is relatively small. This is even truer of the few million acres of commercial forest land in county and municipal ownership on which, except for Minnesota and Wisconsin, recreational uses are commonly dominant. As pointed out in Chapter 6, less than a tenth of our national timber harvest is taken from state- and local-government forests.

REGULATION OF CUTTING ON PRIVATE LANDS

From about 1919 to 1953, federal regulation of cutting on privately owned forest lands was a live issue. First advocated by a committee of the Society of American Foresters headed by Pinchot, the proposal subsequently received the support of three chiefs of the Forest Service. It was vigorously opposed by leaders in the forest-products industry and by many others. Although the movement resulted in no federal legislation, it is commonly thought to have had considerable influence on the forest practices of many private owners and to have led to some state legislation on the subject.

Some 17 states have "forest practice" acts, all of which aim to perpetuate the timber supply on private lands through some form of state regulation or encouragement. Oregon, in 1941, was the first state to adopt and enforce a regulatory law with real teeth. Oregon's law requires the leaving of all immature pondersosa pine trees less than 16 inches in diameter east of the Cascade Mountains, and the leaving uncut and well-stocked of 5 percent of each quarter-section west of the Cascades. In 1945, Washington passed a similar law. The act was declared constitutional by the state supreme court, which emphasized that "we do not think that the state is required to stand idly by while its natural resources are depleted." In both states, passage of the legislation was supported by timberland owners.

Most other states with regulatory legislation specify in the law itself the measures that must be taken to perpetuate the timber supply, a practice commonly known as legislative silviculture. A few leave the formulation or approval of forest-practice rules to a designated agency such as the state conservation commission or department of forestry. A California law, for example, provided that rules of forest practice be formulated by district boards composed of forest landowners and be subject to approval by the state board of forestry. Here, as in several other states, flexibility was promoted by authorizing owners to substitute for forest-practice rules specific plans of management approved by appropriate authority. Flexibility seems to be attainable only within limits. The California law has been judged unconstitutional because (1) it provided no standards for the district boards and (2) it put approval in the hands of timber owners and thus involved them in conflict of interests.

Still another approach is to prescribe rules of forest practice, compliance with which is optional with the individual owners. In New York, the state extends management and marketing services to owners who sign agreements to comply with the state's forest-practice act.

In general, the objective of timber-cutting rules is to maintain or to provide for reasonably prompt establishment of at least a minimum stand of desirable commercial tree species. The rules do not attempt the impossible task of enforcing the practice of intensive forest management, and they either do not apply to, or have little influence with, the small-woodlot owner. Perhaps for these reasons, plus a steadily increasing intensity of management by industrial forest owners, the passage of state regulatory laws seems to have gone out of fashion: None has been enacted for the last twenty years. Should the states resume the policy of regulating timber cutting on private lands, either through the amendment of existing legislation or through new legislation, the prospects indicate that they would aim to protect aesthetic and recreational values rather than timber values.

COOPERATION

Since 1911, when the Weeks Act authorized federal cooperation with the states in fire control for forests on the watersheds of navigable streams, the federal government has followed a steadily expanding policy of cooperation. In 1924, the Clarke-McNary Act extended cooperation in fire control to all forest lands, irrespective of their location, and also authorized cooperation with the states in the promotion of reforestation and forest management on private lands.

The next forestry legislations were the Cooperative Farm Forestry Act of 1937 (50 Stat. 188) and the much broader Cooperative Forest Management Act of 1950 (64 Stat. 473). The latter authorized federal cooperation with state foresters in providing technical services to private forest landowners and operators and to processors of roundwood. Combined federal and state help in forest management is also offered through the state-federal Cooperative Extension Services. This help is primarily educational in nature and is chiefly limited to relatively small owners.

Federal cooperation in the control of insects and diseases, which had previously been spotty, became inclusive with passage of the Forest Pest Control Act of 1947 (61 Stat. 177). The act is so broad in scope that it authorizes the federal government, both independently and in cooperation with states and private timber owners, to take steps to prevent or control outbreaks of destructive insects and diseases on all forest lands irrespective of ownership.

The policy of cooperation with private owners on the part of both the federal government and the states has long been established, but has seldom been adequately financed. Although its major objective has been to perpetuate and to augment timber supply, it has also served to safeguard other forest values, which will probably receive increasing attention in the future.

TAXATION

The general property tax has long been regarded as a major, and at times as even an insuperable, obstacle to the practice of sustained-yield forestry by private owners. Special legislation on the subject has been enacted by 34 states. Of the 61 laws on the statute books, nearly 40 percent provide for a modified property tax, and nearly 30 percent provide for a yield tax.

Excluding the severance tax, which is an addition to rather than a modification of the property tax, only 31 percent of the laws are mandatory in their application. The optional laws actually affect 5,600,000 acres, or 3.3 percent of the area of commercial forest land in private ownership in the states involved. In view of the emphasis that has been placed on the yield tax, it is perhaps not surprising that nearly four-fifths of the area on which the special tax laws are in effect is subject to the yield tax. What is surprising is that forest owners have taken advantage of the yield tax on only 3.7 percent of the area eligible for its application. In no state does the area reach 10 percent.[3]

A significant development in the modification of the property tax is the recent tendency to provide for assessment of rural lands, including those devoted to timber production, on the basis of present use. This provision has been accompanied by growing interest in long-range, rural land-use planning and land-use controls, including zoning. The older movement for enactment of special forest-tax legislation is thus giving way to a broader outlook in which farm, timber, recreation, and "open space" interests find common ground.

Although the federal government does not use the property tax, the Clarke-McNary Act of 1924 recognized its influence on forest management by authorizing the Secretary of Agriculture to undertake a study "to devise tax laws designed to encourage the conservation and growing of timber." The exhaustive report that resulted brought together an enormous amount of valuable information. It also made several suggestions for modification of the property tax, which have not been generally adopted.

One of the important contributions of the taxation report was its thorough consideration of means of improving the administration of the property tax. Among these was the improvement of assessment practices, on which much progress has subsequently been made. In 1966, 36 states had property-assessment guides in which the assessment of forest land and timber received specific coverage, with the treatment varying from very brief to extended. Four states issued separate timber manuals; the California manual runs to 160 pages. In Oregon, where great attention is paid to the taxation of forest land, the State Tax Commission has 33 professional foresters on its staff.[4]

Two significant and hopeful trends in the critical field of forest taxation are (1) the tendency to center on state organizations' responsibility for improved administration and (2) the increasing emphasis on site productivity as a major factor in valuation. Williams, in an article in the *Assessors Journal* for January 1968, came to this encouraging conclusion: "Administered with resourcefulness, it would seem that the real property tax as applied to forest land and timber can continue to meet the revenue needs of local governments and at the same time meet the resource conservation needs of the broader community."[5]

An important change in policy with respect to application of federal income tax to timberland owners came in 1944, when Congress broadened the long-term capital-gains provision to cover timber harvested by the owner for sale or for use in his business, and also to cover certain sales of stumpage not previously eligible for such treatment. A subsequent attempt to repeal this provision, supported by the Administration but opposed by the forest-products industry and others, was unsuccessful.

The Tax Reform Act of 1969 made no change in the provisions of the Internal Revenue Code relating specifically to timber, but it made a number of changes in the treatment of capital gains and losses in general. The net effect was to reduce somewhat the advantages of capital-gains treatment for both individual and corporate taxpayers.

INSURANCE AND CREDIT

From time to time, considerable attention has been paid by both public and private agencies to the subjects of forest-fire insurance and forest credit. Comprehensive studies in both fields have been made by the Forest Service and the Farm Credit Administration, with little apparent result. In 1944, the Federal Crop Insurance Corporation was authorized to insure timber and forests, but took no steps in this direction. Several states have considered the subject, but have taken no action.

Limited credit has been extended by several of the federal reserve banks and by the Farmers Home Administration. National banks were not allowed to make loans secured by forest lands until 1953, when Congress authorized the banks to make such loans for not more than ten years, with amortization at the rate of 10 percent a year.

In general, other measures for securing adequate timber supplies appear to have been regarded by both government and industry as having a higher priority than insurance and credit.

INTERNATIONAL TRADE

Tariffs on lumber, pulpwood, and manufactured products have varied from time to time, but have seldom been high. Rates of duty were revised downward over a five-year period under the General Agreement on Tariffs and Trade (GATT). The United States will apparently continue, in a minor way so far as total consumption is concerned, to be a net importer of roundwood products.

Imports of timber from Canada have long been substantial, but since 1950 they have increased greatly. This situation has led to attempts, spearheaded by the National Forest Products Association (formerly National Lumber Manufacturers Association), to restrict Canadian imports. Explaining its failure to do so, the Tariff Commission in 1963 found that the U.S. softwood industry was not suffering "major injury" as a direct result of trade-agreement concessions.

In the late 1960s, a significant part of the logs exported from the Pacific Northwest to Japan came from federal lands. This situation caused serious hardships to many companies and communities which were unable to purchase needed supplies of logs in competition with exporters. To improve the situation, the Secretary of Agriculture and the Secretary of the Interior issued an order requiring domestic manufacture of federal timber in western Washington and Oregon, with the exception of 350 million board feet, which was made available for export as logs. In 1968, Congress went somewhat further by providing that not more than 350 million board feet of unprocessed timber be sold annually for export from federal lands west of the 100th meridian during the calendar years 1969 through 1971.

Tariffs on forest products have generally been advocated on the ground that they are essential to assure reasonable profits, which in turn enables timberland owners to practice more intensive forestry than would otherwise be possible. Congress has sometimes reacted favorably to this argument, but not to the extent of imposing excessively high tariffs. So many factors are involved that the exact relation between tariffs and forest management is difficult to determine. However, it is clear that international trade has not been a major factor in the development of forestry policy in the United States.

RESEARCH

Conducting research as a basis for improved forest practice has been a definite federal policy ever since Hough's appointment as the first commissioner of forestry in 1876. Marked advances were made with the establishment of the Forest Service's first regional experiment station in 1908, the Forest Products Laboratory in 1910, and the Branch of Research in 1915. Research came of age with passage of the comprehensive McSweeney-McNary Act in 1928 (45 Stat. 699).

Several aspects of Forest Service research policy are worthy of note. Organizationally, research is coordinate with administration: Experiment station directors, like regional foresters, report directly to the Chief of the Forest Service. Research deals with problems of concern to all forest owners, both public and private. Timber production and utilization, range management, and watershed protection have received major attention, and emphasis on recreation has increased steadily and markedly in recent years. Of much interest from the policy standpoint is the stress being given problems created by the complex biologic, economic, and social ramifications of multiple use and sustained yield.

Compared to that of the federal government, forestry research by state agencies is relatively minor, both in scope and in quantity. Most of it is conducted at agricultural experiment stations and at educational institutions, including those privately as well as publicly financed. The activities of the latter were strengthened by passage of the McIntire-Stennis Act in 1962 (76 Stat. 806), which initiated a new policy of providing federal financial aid to schools of forestry for research.

POLICIES OF THE WOOD-USING INDUSTRIES

With 72 percent of the commercial forest lands of the country in private ownership, the policies of their owners have a strong influence on the timber supply. Although only 18 percent of the area in private ownership is held by wood-using industries, the policies of these owners are of particular significance because of the greater intensity of forest management on the industrial holdings.

The practice of intensive forest management is a relatively recent development. For many years, the myths that the forests are inexhaustible and that most forest land is suitable for agriculture led to the practice of cut-and-get-out. This practice strengthened current fears of an impending timber famine and was largely responsible for the movement to bring about federal regulation of cutting on forest lands in industrial ownership.

Lack of progress in the practice of forestry by industrial owners was due largely to economic factors. A Forest Service study published in 1917 showed that in the West, industry had acquired some 700 billion board feet more timber than the existing mills could afford to carry as an investment. Carrying charges in the form of interest and taxes on this surplus constituted a heavy burden. As a result of this situation, Greeley saw a "sick industry" where Pinchot saw a "willful industry."[6]

Conditions did not improve during the 1920s, when the timber industry suffered a severe depression nearly a decade before any industries but agriculture were seriously affected. In his annual report for 1927, Chief Forester Greeley listed among the obstacles to better forest practice "the current depression in lumber markets, the financial obligations imposed by existing investments in plants or timberlands, the uncertainty as to the future course of taxation in respect both to merchantable timber and young forest growth, and the burden of raw-material waste still carried by the forest industries in the United States."

Two years later, Chief Forester Stuart stated that "economic conditions have not yet reached the point at which the remaining stands are being sufficiently husbanded. . . . The pressure to liquidate holdings of virgin timber is operating as a powerful deterrent to the reorganization of our forest economy on the basis of timber growing in place of forest exploitation."

Private and public agencies attempted to meet both the economic and the silvicultural crisis through the calling by the Chamber of Commerce of the United States in 1927 of a Conference on Commercial Forests and the appointment by President Hoover in 1930 of a Timber Conservation Board. The latter endorsed expansion of federal and state acquisition of timberlands as sound public policy. In some quarters, it was even suggested that private owners should be allowed to donate their timberlands to the government, with retention of cutting rights.

Then came the short-lived National Industrial Recovery Act of 1933, one of whose declared purposes was "to conserve natural resources." Article X of the Code of Fair Competition for the Lumber and Timber Products Industries provided, among other things, for the establishment by industry of regional rules of forest practice which would have the force of law. Little progress was made in the adoption and application of such rules prior to invalidation of the act by the Supreme Court, but the Code had a strong influence in hastening the evolution of forestry as a voluntary private enterprise.

ROLE OF THE WOOD-INDUSTRY ASSOCIATIONS

In April 1937, a national conference called by the lumber industry accepted "the continuous production, sustained yield, of forest resources as the ultimate objective of our industries" and favored the voluntary formulation of rules of forest practice. A month later, representatives of a majority of pulpwood-using companies in the South adopted a statement of policy which provided that "all land, including noncompany land, must be cut over in a manner which will maintain and build up the forest growing stock." Rules of forest practice were later prepared for each of three sub-regions, and the Southern Pulpwood Conservation Association (later renamed Southern Forest Institute) was organized (1939) to direct their enforcement. In July 1937, The National Lumber Manufacturers Association (now National Forest Products Association) urged each of its regional affiliates to continue the development of suitable forest-practice rules which, when confirmed by experience to be effective, should be considered as matters for state legislation.

Industrial acceptance of the policy of sustained yield, however difficult its application in practice, was symbolized by the establishment in 1941 of the Clemons Tree Farm in western Washington. This action led to a national tree-farm movement which has been fostered and directed by American Forest Products Industries (now American Forest Institute) organized in the same year. A tree farm was defined by AFPI as "an area of privately owned forest land devoted primarily to the continuous growth of merchantable forest products under good forest practices." Land in any ownership which meets the specified standards of forest management is eligible for classification, but the great bulk of the area certified is in industrial ownership. The total tree-farm area has grown to about 75 million acres in the 48 contiguous states.

The National Forest Products Association has long been interested in policies and programs affecting the forest lands of the country. Major statements of policy were adopted in 1937 and 1953. Among many other items, the latter opposed federal regulation of private forest-management practices and federal control of state forestry policies; expressed the belief that "only those lands which private ownership cannot keep productive should be taken into public ownership, primarily by the states and secondarily by the federal government;" and favored the transfer of public forest lands to private ownership wherever the public interest would be served. At the same time, the 1953 policy statement recognized industry's obligation to maintain its forest lands in productive condition and invited support by all organizations and individuals of the Tree Farm, Keep America Green, and More Trees for America programs operated by American Forest Products Industries.

As far back as 1954, the National Forest Products Association stated that "the lumber industry has long recognized the multiple-use principle in the management of its forest lands. . . . Our industry emphasizes that good forest management includes the maintenance of forest soils, the production of wildlife, and the development of resource values comparable with forest production. Private forest landowners should seek to develop further use of their lands for hunting and fishing which would not be detrimental to the major purposes of management. . . . In the management of forested lands, it is recognized that the harvesting of timber according to tree-farm principles provides substantially greater supplies of usable water than will a program of management which eliminates timber harvesting."

More recently, American Forest Products Industries stated: "The industry supports and practices multiple-use management with forest lands with the primary objective of growing and harvesting timber. By growing continuous timber crops through effective tree-farm management on its own lands, the forest-products industry is protecting watersheds and soils, providing grazing where feasible, favorable wildlife habitat, and abundant opportunities for outdoor recreation."

This optimistic appraisal of the compatibility of different uses was at least partially confirmed by a 1968 survey by the American Forest Institute, which showed that most of the forest land in industrial ownership is open to and widely used for hunting, fishing, and camping and that large areas are also open for other recreational uses.

While all these statements definitely endorse multiple use, they make it clear that industry gives priority to timber production, which it believes can be so managed as to provide adequate amounts of other desired good and services. The industry emphasis on timber stems from two considerations: the need to meet the burgeoning and prospectively enormous wants of the country for wood for housing and innumerable other uses, and the need to increase profits by growing and marketing more of the chief commercial product of the forest.

The American Forest Institute objectives are also sought, often even more aggressively, by the pulp and paper industry, whose products continue to be in great demand. This industry expresses its policies through its two major national organizations, the American Paper Institute (formerly American Paper and Pulp Association) and the American Pulpwood Association. The latter, for example, aims "to guide and help the pulpwood industry to grow and harvest pulpwood of the highest quality in sufficient amounts now and for future generations at a reasonable cost." Land-owning companies in the pulp and paper industry have been among the leaders in attempting to safeguard the future supply of their basic raw material. They have practiced increasingly intensive forest management and have relied heavily on research, both that by public agencies and that by the industry itself. Notable examples of industry research are provided by Weyerhaeuser Company and International Paper Company, with their research stations at Centralia, Washington, and Bainbridge, Georgia, where both basic and applied research is conducted in such fields as soil science; genetics; tree physiology; control of fire, insects, and disease; silvicultural systems of cutting; timber-stand improvement; and artificial forestation.

POLICIES OF FARMERS AND MISCELLANEOUS OWNERS

The policies of farmers and other nonindustry private owners, each with about 30 percent of the commercial forest area of the country, obviously have a major influence on the timber supply. On the whole, their policies have failed to bring about the kind of management that would enable the lands to make the contribution to timber supply of which they are capable. The major activities of both groups of owners have apparently been devoted to more pressing interests and problems, and both groups have lacked adequate knowledge of the techniques of timber production, harvesting, and marketing.

The problem of the nonindustry forest owner has long been recognized by public agencies and by the forest-products industry, which have attempted in various ways to provide the motivation and the knowledge needed for improvement. State forestry departments and state extension services, with the cooperation of appropriate federal agencies, have been increasingly active in general educational programs and in specific on-the-ground advice.

The forest-products industry has offered similar assistance, partly for altruistic reasons and partly because it is dependent on nonindustry forest owners for a considerable part of its timber supply. Three regional organizations that are doing significant work in this area are the Southern Forest Institute in the South, Trees for Tomorrow in Wisconsin, and the Industrial Forestry Association (formerly the Forest Conservation Committee of the Pacific Northwest Forest Industries) in the Pacific Northwest, organized in 1939, 1944, and 1949, respectively. Individual companies, particularly in the South, also provide assistance to individual owners, who are sometimes grouped into "tree-farm families."

The policies of both public and private agencies agree on the importance of increasing the timber supply from nonindustrial privately owned forest land as an essential element in the production of adequate supplies to meet future demands. A recent promising development is the formation, with the support of the American Forestry Association and the National Association of Soil and Water Conservation Districts, of a task force calling itself "Trees for People—A National Task Force for Private Forest Management" to investigate and recommend solutions to timber-management problems on nonindustrial private forest lands. In doing this, the task force will be helped by the findings and proposals of the industry-sponsored Southern Forest Resource Analysis Committee and its successor, the Southern Forest Resource Council.

POLICIES OF BUSINESS, PROFESSIONAL, AND OTHER ORGANIZATIONS

The United States has a multiplicity of private organizations interested in one way or another in almost every conceivable aspect of the management of natural resources. Some organizations are concerned primarily with timber, while many more concentrate on other resource products and services. All of them take positions respecting the policies which they believe should be followed by governmental agencies and resource owners, and whose adoption they attempt to obtain. Either directly or indirectly, the activities of these organizations have an influence—sometimes weak, sometimes strong—on the emphasis that will be placed by legislators, administrators, owners, and managers on the timber supply as compared with other resources.

In addition to the industrial organizations mentioned, there are numerous national and regional associations which deal with various segments of the forest-products industry. Whether their main concern is with lumber, plywood, pulpwood, or other products, they are all interested in the adoption and execution of policies that will maintain the supply of their basic raw material—wood.

Many other national organizations with primary interests in different fields have played, and continue to play, an important part in the formulation of forestry policies. Prominent among these are the Chamber of Commerce of the United States, the National Association of Manufacturers, labor organizations, garden organizations, women's organizations, and farm organizations.

Two prestigious scientific organizations have had an influential part in the development of forestry policies. The American Association for the Advancement of Science was instrumental in obtaining the legislation resulting in the appointment of the country's first commissioner of forestry and in passage of the Forest Reserve Act of 1891. The National Academy of Sciences sponsored the forestry commission whose study and report preceded the Forest Reserve Act of 1897, and has stimulated comprehensive surveys of forestry research and forestry education. Its affiliate, the National Research Council, has been active in a wide variety of forestry research programs.

Of the professional organizations, the Society of American Foresters has taken the lead in developing policies for many aspects of forestry. Other groups that have taken a less direct but nonetheless important interest in forestry policies include the Ecological Society of America, the American Society of Range Management, The Wildlife Society, and the Soil Conservation Society of America.

Among the many organizations composed primarily of laymen, The American Forestry Association has been a leader in the development of forestry policies ever since its formation in 1875. Although it is committed to "the advancement of intelligent management and use of our forests, soil, water, wildlife, and all other natural resources necessary for an environment of high quality and the well-being of all citizens," its major interest has always been in the forests, with strong but by no means exclusive emphasis on timber supply. Of special significance are the five national forestry congresses which the Association has held and the three comprehensive Programs for American Forestry which it has promulgated. At the state level, numerous forestry associations are influential in local policies.

Many conservation organizations, some with broad and some with restricted interests, have policies which often impinge directly or indirectly on the management of forest resources. A partial list will give some idea of their diversity and of the possibilities for conflict: Izaak Walton League of America, National Audubon Society, National Parks Association, The Wilderness Society, National Wildlife Federation, Camp Fire Club of America, the Conservation Foundation, Sierra Club, Appalachian Mountain Club, National Recreation and Park Association, Keep America Beautiful, The Nature Conservancy, Friends of Nature, Boone and Crockett Club, Defenders of Wildlife, Wildlife Restoration, National Waterfowl Council, Ducks Unlimited, and Trout Unlimited.

Many of these organizations are having a steadily growing impact on natural-resource policy. In forestry, they tend to divert emphasis from the timber supply to other values. The same tendency is evident in the nationwide campaign for a better environment.

The Natural Resources Council of America is a group of 44 professional and lay organizations with more or less common interests in natural-resource matters. It was founded in 1947 for the purpose of maintaining contacts and exchanging information and views. Although not an action agency, it occasionally takes positions on questions of policy and through its deliberations influences the stands taken by its individual members. On the question of timber supply there will doubtless be universal agreement that substantial amounts of wood should be produced and harvested, but wide disagreement as to how much, where, and how.

POLICIES OF EDUCATIONAL INSTITUTIONS

Institutions of higher education do not formulate or execute forestry policies except for such forest properties as they may happen to own, but they do exercise an indirect, though strong, influence on the policies of both public and private agencies through the attitudes, knowledge, and skills which they impart to their graduates, whether the latter are looking forward to careers in resource management or in other fields. The influence is particularly strong upon foresters and other resource professionals whose future activities will be directly concerned with resource management.

Early instruction at schools of forestry recognized the broad scope of goods and services produced by forests, but laid special stress on the protection, production, and harvesting of timber. Graduates were often dubbed "sawlog foresters" by persons whose primary interests were in water, wildlife, or recreation. This situation gradually changed as the whole profession broadened its sights. The Society of American Foresters, for instance, which had previously tended to identify "forest production" with "timber production," recently adopted a new definition of forestry as "the science, the art, and the practice of managing and using for human benefit the natural resources that occur on or in association with forest lands."

This change in emphasis has long been apparent at schools of forestry, many of which have steadily broadened their curricula in forestry and introduced new curricula in related fields. The implications and ramifications of multiple use have been more clearly recognized and stressed. Forestry schools taught integrated management of all forest resources on sound biologic and economic principles long before "ecology" and "total environment" came into vogue. Simultaneously, schools stressed a firm grounding in the social and behavioral sciences, the humanities, and the communication arts as valuable assets for the resource manager both as a professional man and as a citizen. (The president of Resources for the Future, Inc. has suggested that some knowledge of aesthetics would be helpful to the forester.)

Forestry educators have also made progress in the quantity and quality of training provided for technicians in forestry and related fields. Some fifty schools now offer such training, which may lead to an associate's degree. Although graduates are not likely to have a strong influence on policy, they will add greatly to the effectiveness of professionals in carrying out approved policies.

Another recent development of great significance is the sudden awareness on the part of both educators and the general public that what happens to natural resources is a matter of concern, not only to their owners and managers, but to everyone. Nearly every institution of higher learning seems to have become convinced that national salvation lies in the maintenance of harmony between man and nature, and that the institution must offer courses and programs that make this apparent to its students, whatever their particular field of interest. Students, fully as much as faculties, have reacted strongly to the new concern for man's relation to his environment. It is no accident that the national celebrations of Earth Day have centered on the college campuses of the country.

The same concern for natural resources is being manifested in elementary and secondary schools, where efforts are being made to find ways of instilling an appreciation for the environment in students from kindergarten through high school.

The effect of developments in the educational field has been twofold. In the professional sphere, they have tended to place relatively less emphasis on timber as the forest's major contribution to the well-being of the nation and to promote the concept and practice of integrated management of all resources, with full recognition of the importance of social and cultural as well as financial values. In the broader sphere of the community at large, there is for the first time an almost universal appreciation of the fact that in the long run man's prosperity, and even his existence, depends on his use of natural resources in conformity with nature's laws. Educational institutions have a responsibility to (1) raise the quality of professional and semi-professional training and (2) equip the laity, particularly the younger generation, with the ideals and the knowledge needed to exercise intelligently and constructively their ability as voters, as members of organizations, and in other ways to promote sound legislative and managerial policies and programs.

14   POLICIES, PROGRAMS, AND CONSUMERS

MICHAEL F. BREWER*

MORE THAN ONE-FOURTH of U.S. forest land is in public ownership. This public acreage contains more than half the country's standing commercial sawtimber and contributes about one-third of commercial sawtimber sales. Through their programs of timber sales and information, the Forest Service and other public agencies influence the market on which private stumpage is sold. Their policies and programs affect private owners of forest land, the country's wood-using industries, and the consuming public. Each of these constituencies has different objectives and often quite different perceptions of the forest-land resources that provide the goods and services they seek. The job at hand is to sketch out a context within which forestry policies can be assessed in terms of their impact upon the welfare of the consuming public.

One must cope at the outset with the elusive notion of a "public." Several publics can be readily identified, each of which consumes goods and services produced from forest lands. First is the group which consumes wood products. While virtually everyone uses wood, there are identifiable groups for which wood is especially important. Those involved in construction activities, for instance, are understandably concerned with the current adequacy and future dependability of timber supply and will be sensitive to the way public policies affect the price of lumber, plywood, and other wood products.

Another "public"—those who fish, hunt, or derive value from the amenities forest lands afford—is primarily concerned with the physical availability of recreational facilities and with their quality. Since national custom has assumed the provision of such facilities to be a public responsibility, these types of forest-land services are usually supplied independently of the market system and rarely bear a price. The recreating public is very aware of and responsive to policies which affect the physical characteristics of forest lands or which change their accessibility.

---

* President, Population Reference Bureau, Washington, D.C.

A third "public" consists of general consumers, who spend their income to acquire those goods and services that provide maximum utility. This group, the largest of the publics thus far considered, is concerned with wood products, fishing, recreation, and other forest and nonforest items. This group is concerned with the prices it must pay for the goods and services it decides to buy.

Although the general consumer would prefer lower prices for wood products, his economic interests may not be served by a reduction in the price of wood products if this entails price increases for other products in his market basket. In short, he is best served when all the contents of his basket are produced efficiently—that is, at least cost—and are available on a competitive market. His welfare will be affected by public forestry policies to the extent that they facilitate or impede general economic efficiency. When forest-land resources are utilized efficiently, the economic rent they generate for society is a maximum.

EFFICIENCY AS A POLICY CRITERION

When the objectives of these three publics are not consistent, economic efficiency is the most appropriate criterion for assessing public forestry policies. Desirable policy encourages the production of goods and services the value of which exceeds by a maximum their real costs of production. Thus, the instruments of public policy should favor that mix of "forest products" that is most highly valued (evidenced by the public's willingness to pay for them) and the most efficient (least-cost methods of producing them). This principle is embodied in the benefit-cost analyses which are used to evaluate public investments in land and water development. It can also serve as a point of departure in assessing forestry policies.

The question is sometimes debated as to the appropriate geographic context within which costs and benefits are to be calculated: Are we concerned with forest policy from the standpoint of the immediate community, the region, or the country as a whole? Reflecting a point of view that has characterized discussion of federal agricultural programs, there has been a tendency in the past to consider forestry policies primarily from the standpoint of subnational regions or communities for which forestry constitutes a major source of employment and income. However, a national accounting is more appropriate for viewing alternative federal forestry policies. Analysis of regional economic consequences may be useful, but the impacts of policies upon a particular region may be offset elsewhere in the nation.

As tastes and consumption patterns change, efficient policy facilitates responsive change in the mix of forest goods and services. Desirable policy also encourages changes in production processes that will take advantage of new technology and thereby keep real cost minimized.

It is useful to think of three sectors to which forest-land resources are allocated: (1) timber products; (2) fish, wildlife, and recreation; and (3) landscape protection. Within each sector, resources are combined with other productive factors (labor and capital) and are made to yield various products which may be consumed directly or used as raw material in subsequent production. Each sector has a consuming public for whom its products have value.

The timber-products sector is a familiar one which requires no elaboration.

Within the recreation sector, forest-land resources are allocated to the creation and maintenance of an environment that can yield various recreational experiences. This involves developing areas for this purpose, maintaining and policing them, and providing other managerial activities. In a real sense, the land is being combined with labor and capital to yield an array of recreational opportunities.

The protection and maintenance of landscape presents a somewhat different economic situation. Watershed protection, soil stabilization, or the maintenance of certain desired ecologic conditions do not increase the existing stock of goods and services as would the creation of new recreation areas. Rather, these actions serve to maintain certain desirable attributes of the forest-land resource beyond the point in time when they would otherwise have been extinguished. In essence, forest-landscape protection claims a social value not so much by adding an item to the consumer's market basket as by sustaining the quality of his natural environment.

EFFICIENCY CONDITIONS

Within the foregoing framework, it is possible to describe the type of efficiency which best serves the public interest and toward which forest policies should contribute. Ultimately, the array of products yielded by each of the three sectors should be produced at lowest real cost and supplied to the consumer in quantities that equate the value he places upon them with their cost of production at the margin. When the economic universe just outlined is performing efficiently, the following conditions will hold:

1. To assure efficient (least-cost) production of each product, the ratio of price to physical productivity must be the same for all productive factors.

2. To assure efficient levels of output of each type of product, its marginal cost of production must equal the marginal revenue generated by its sales (or by consumers' willingness to pay, which would be reflected in market transactions if a market existed).

3. To assure efficient allocation of forest land among the three sectors, the value of the land's marginal product must be the same within all three lines of production.

4. To assure long-range efficiency in forest-land allocation, the present value of the time stream of social returns which would be lost by reallocating forest land from one sector to another must not exceed the present value of the new time stream of social returns which would be generated through such a reallocation.

In a perfectly functioning, competitive market, characterized by full employment and mobile factors of production, efficient patterns of production would tend to occur as a result of economic incentives associated with decentralized private production and consumption decisions. With individual economic behavior motivated by profit, the system would respond efficiently to such changes as consumer tastes and productive techniques. Adam Smith's invisible hand would massage the system into reallocating factors of production so that the necessary marginal conditions would be reestablished. In short, such a system would be self-equilibrating: Its performance would be efficient.

This fiction departs from reality in several respects: some of the products derived from forests lack a price. Much forest land is within the public domain, and allocation decisions are made by administrative fiat rather than within a competitive market.

We cannot assume a priori that market forces will automatically establish an efficient equilibrium of products, quantities, and prices. Price changes and alleged shortages in supply must be interpreted against the realities of the timber economy rather than against the abstraction of a perfectly competitive market. It is also necessary to assess the extent to which the structure of the timber economy permits decentralized decisions and efficient response to changes in consumer demand and in innovations in production technology.

We must identify inefficiencies in the allocation of forest-land resources to the three sectors and determine the extent to which these inefficiencies might be reduced through public policy. Another area of concern is the efficiency of production within each sector and the possibilities of increasing it through policy. Finally, the capacity of existing forest policies and programs to accommodate changes in allocation that appear likely to be needed in order to remain efficient in the future should be gauged.

ALLOCATION BIASES

Certain attributes of the U.S. forest economy appear to introduce biases into its decisions:

1. Prices are not competitively established. Although there is a

semblance of competition in the timber sector on which to base the value of timber and wood products, the social values of recreation and landscape-protection services are not established in a market. Markets for recreation service have been simulated in some cases, from which a "price" can be deduced and used as a basis for evaluating recreation sites, but this has not been done for landscape protection. In any case, the validity of the results would be questionable. It is difficult to determine if the net effect of our uncertainty about values is to put a systematic bias into resource decisions. The possibility of bias does suggest that the problem of establishing values for the significant forest-land services merits relatively high priority for research.

2. Prices do not reflect full costs of production. Timber conversion has often been referred to as a "dirty activity." Indeed, it does entail substantial environmental disruption and pollution, particularly with pulp and paper production and timber harvesting. Any degradation of environmental quality associated with production can appropriately be considered as a real production cost. Of course, this social cost will not be taken fully into account in private production decisions until it is imposed upon the producing enterprise. Thus, as long as industrial wastes can be disposed of through streams or the atmosphere at no cost to the firm, this essentially free disposal service will be fully used as a factor of production by the firm. Its price-productivity ratio will be effectively zero from the private standpoint. Only if the firm is charged for the service will there be incentive to pursue less polluting modes of production. Ideally, this charge should be in an amount equivalent to the environmental damage.

It may be difficult to conceive of production costs being redefined in this manner, but public interest, including the efficient use of forest resources, clearly requires this be done once we have exhausted the capacity of the environment to assimilate production wastes without some sort of associated social damage. Such damage may be either direct (polluting water so that downstream users are required to construct and operate water-treatment facilities) or indirect (extinguishing environmental amenities enjoyed by others and thereby depriving them of a previously enjoyed service). Only as long as waste can be disposed of without exceeding the assimilative capacity of the river system is it valid to consider the productive service freely available.

The assimilative capability of the environment has been surpassed in many instances, either because it has been misgauged or because of the lack of a system of rules or incentives to limit waste disposal. Under these circumstances, the cost of preventing production residuals from degrading the environment is a valid and proper cost of production. Failure to charge this environmental input to the production process simply subsidizes production. More important, ignoring this input destroys the important system of cost signals which guides production into patterns that are efficient from the national standpoint. Including the cost of environmental degradation as a production cost through an effluent charge or similar device would provide a positive incentive for industries to be alert to opportunities for technologic change that would reduce the toxicity or amount of wastes discharged. Another result would be an increase in product prices and a corresponding reduction in consumption from the levels which had prevailed previously.

3. Government timber rotations are typically too long. The most efficient length of timber rotations for various commercial species has been widely discussed. As a growing tree increases in value, its maintenance and management involve a cost. Some of the cost is incurred as direct outlays, some is in the form of revenues forgone by preempting the site for this tree. The amount of forgone revenue depends upon the suitability of the site for other uses. If there is an active demand for the site for development purposes, the revenue forgone may be high—for example, interest on the site's value for development purposes. If the site is suitable only for timber production, the revenue forgone is relatively small—the discounted value of the new tree which could take the place of an existing tree. Revenue forgone because of site preemption is a very real cost of extending a timber rotation. Since present public-forestry practice seldom takes this cost into consideration, timber rotations on public lands are typically longer than economic efficiency dictates.

4. Differential tax incidence bends the directions of capital investment. Both the income tax and the property tax introduce biases into the system for forest-resource allocation. As a prime example, the federal income-tax provisions allow most income from timber harvesting to be counted as long-term capital gains rather than ordinary income, and thus to enjoy a marked tax reduction. Special advantages are also given to firms in which timber ownership, management, harvesting, and processing are integrated. Thus the prevailing tax structure influences the direction and timing of investments in private forestry.

5. Financial arrangements are inadequate. Financial arrangements for private harvesting of public timber lead to misallocations. In particular, the method of financing road construction, whereby the private bidder must construct his own access roads during his harvesting operation, fails to realize economies of scale and often results in roads of low quality, which cause substantial environmental disruption. Furthermore, a given area harvested over a period of time under the present contractual arrangements will yield less com-

mercial timber than if the entire road system for an area were to be constructed at one time and permitted harvesting of the overmature trees wherever they were accessible from that system.

RECREATION AND LANDSCAPE PROTECTION

The outlook for timber resources and their management and for the demand for timber products is discussed in other chapters. Far less is known about these same dimensions of the often competing nontimber uses of forest lands.

Americans are, increasingly, recreationists. Although the product is difficult to classify and there are rarely prices available for ascribing value, a wide variety of indices indicate a rapid growth in consumption of recreational services. Recreation expenditures as a percent of personal disposable income almost trebled between 1945 and 1959. Visits to national parks rose from 9,000 in 1946 to 34,000 in 1964, and those to improved national-forest lands rose by about the same magnitude.[1] We do not have as clear a picture of the demand for landscape protection in recent years but it, too, has appeared to increase substantially.

The value of recreation and landscape protection to the people of the United States validly can be expected to increase more rapidly than the value of wood products. This is suggested not only by the extension of past trends in consumption, but also by the fact that landscape protection and wilderness-based recreation will have fewer and fewer substitutes in future years.

Substitute materials for timber and plywood have been developed in relatively recent times, and others can be expected to be developed in coming years. For some types of outdoor recreation there are substitute areas which can support similar types of recreation activities; however, the range of substitution may well prove to be a good deal narrower than it is for construction materials. There seems to be no suitable substitute for landscape protection. If future demands for wood products expand relatively more rapidly than the demand for unique landscape features, it may be possible through management to substitute timber production for preservation. The reverse is not often possible. In short, some flexibility is afforded future planning by initiating policies which provide generous protection to recreation and landscape-preservation uses of forest lands.

GUIDELINES FOR POLICY

The foregoing holds several implications for public forestry policies:

1. Public policy should facilitate an allocation of forest lands

in favor of landscape-protection and recreation uses. The multiple-use concept is important in securing recreation and landscape protection where they can be achieved simultaneously with timber production. Where timber harvesting is incompatible with other uses of forest land, public policy should reserve the right to classify lands for recreation or landscape-protection use and to restrict timber cutting on those lands. A budget to fund the necessary surveys should be a part of such policy.

2. One method of making timber products available at least cost is an increase in imports from other countries. A reduction of barriers to Canada-United States trade is especially important, as the composition and location of the timber resources of the two countries argue strongly that they be considered a common resource to be jointly managed in response to future demands.

3. Policies permitting more intensive timber management—shorter rotations, advance roading, and other measures—may be justified on areas now designated for cutting. Such justification should be specified and supported by appropriate empirical analysis. For example, a careful forecasting of wood consumption by the construction industry should include analysis of the future size and age structure of the population, the future composition of new housing, and the role of substitutes for wood.

4. The timber rotations employed for most public softwood forests should be recalculated on the basis of appropriate considerations, and the new rotations should be used as the basis for timber management.

Any discussion of policy guidelines for forest-land allocation should emphasize the need for flexibility in reallocating land resources in the future. Efforts to project future supply and demand are confounded by uncertainty. Allowance must be made for the allocative adjustments that become appropriate as we move into the future. The three types of forest-land use—timber, recreation, and landscape protection—severely limit the direction in which reallocations can occur. Basically there is relative flexibility in shifting uses from landscape protection to recreation or to timber use. There is also some flexibility in shifting recreational lands to timber use, and possibly to landscape protection. Because of the physical consequences of timbering operations, the greatest difficulty is in effecting a shift from timber or other extractive uses to recreation or to landscape protection. Such transfers can occur, and they become increasingly feasible as one thinks of longer and longer periods of time before reallocation is required. Since we operate in the face of uncertainty, prudent policy should build safeguards so that when allocative errors occur, they occur in the direction that favors recreation and landscape protection.

15   POLICIES, PROGRAMS, AND THE INDUSTRY

CARL A. NEWPORT*

BECAUSE THE WOOD-PRODUCTS INDUSTRY consists of many individuals and firms, it is difficult to find explicit statements of industry objectives. However, three objectives which are probably common to most firms are profit, growth, and continued existence. These objectives are neither independent of nor complementary to each other. In many instances, profit is sacrificed in order to achieve growth in the sense of total sales or asset value or some other measure. Likewise, short-run profit may be sacrificed by a firm in order to assure its long-run existence.

Numerous other objectives are sought by the industry because it is made up of people and therefore has social objectives, explicit and implied. Stockholders of firms are people and often take it upon themselves to inject their thinking as consumers into the policies of wood-products firms. Social objectives or man's desires for the amenities or other aspects of the good life sometimes conflict with the growth and profit objectives of industry firms. In brief, the industry is concerned not only with itself, but also with the goals of those other two segments of the public, consumers and forest owners.

Industry plays a dual role in the problems of timber supply: It processes wood in order to meet the demands for end products and it provides a supply of standing timber.

INDUSTRY AS TIMBER PROCESSOR

Industry is a purchaser of timber on the one hand and a producer of timber products on the other. It is therefore within the structure of the industry that prices are established and serve to equate demand and supply. This is probably why the industry is so highly criticized for timber-demand and timber-supply problems. This aspect of industry is not commonly considered or understood, even by industry

---
* Partner; Mason, Bruce, and Girard, Portland, Oregon.

itself. The industry does view itself, however, as a processor, not a consumer, of wood.

The consumer of wood products generally makes no distinction between timber on the one hand and lumber and plywood on the other. In the pulp and paper segment of the industry, the substance is usually so modified in processing that the consumer doesn't relate "timber supply" to the end product. Until recently, there was little evidence that the consumer felt he had anything in common with the industry on problems of national timber supply. That the timber supply is a problem common both to industry and to consumers was recognized in controversies over log exports and over the proposed National Forest Timber Conservation and Management Act of 1969. In these two examples, certain groups representing the consumer, such as home builders' associations, joined with the wood-products industry in supporting policies deemed beneficial to their common objective of supplying the demands for wood products. A failure to clarify its own role as a processor of timber rather than as a source of all timber has been a weakness of some recent efforts on the part of the industry to accomplish changes in public timber policy.

Public and private timber owners and growers tend to view industry as a profit-making consumer of wood. Public officials who manage forest lands may act as though they think the industry is really the ultimate consumer of the wood products rather than simply the processor. This has significantly inhibited negotiations between the industry and public agencies on methods of timber disposal, timber appraisal, and timber management. In periods when timber was in short supply on the national markets, some high-level public officials said that if the allowable cut from public lands were increased, it would only serve to let the industry make more profit. Here was failure to recognize that the real source of demand was the end-product consumer, and that the industry, as processor, was attempting only to respond to demand. It would be ridiculous to deny that a profit might be made by industry in this process. However, to approach timber-supply problems on the premise that profit would be the only result of an increase in the availability of public timber does not create a climate for improving policies whose objective is providing the nation with an adequate timber supply.

The private nonindustrial timber owners' view of the industry is more difficult to clarify. Some private owners have entered into mutually beneficial long-term leases and agreements with the industry with the specific intent of supplying timber. Many other private owners, and they are probably the most numerous, can ignore the wood-using industry because these owners are only infrequent or intermittent suppliers of timber. In some cases, private owners view the industry as a benefactor because it provides a market for their timber.

Other private owners undoubtedly view the industry as a profit seeker which is forcing them to sell their timber at much too low a price.

A poor image of the wood-using industry was established in the minds of the general public in the past and has tended to persist. Industry was the despoiler of the natural resources of the West. Industry people were the "cut-out-and-get-out" people. They were characterized as leaving acres of hillside stumps and fire-blackened forest land. They have often been shown as villains in the movies and literature, even before the days of "The Perils of Pauline." The image of the timber barons in the movies, who were shown to be cheating the homesteaders out of their timber and land, is still held in the minds of more people than we realize. Unfavorable public opinion developed to some degree from actual instances of poor performance on the part of industry and its associates. Much improvement in performance and in public relations is needed to change the public mind.

Those who are interested in improving public timber-supply policy would do well to view the industry as a processor of timber for the use of consumers, as the arena in which wood-product demand and supply are equated.

INDUSTRY AS TIMBER GROWER

As mentioned in Chapter 6, wood-using firms own and manage a sizeable portion of the total available timber-producing land in the United States. Although each firm's supply of standing timber is primarily for its own needs, many firms supply others with raw material (see Chapter 10).

In its role as timber grower, the industry has profit as an objective. However, holding timberland or making efforts to grow timber is not necessarily profitable as a separate venture. That segment of the industry which provides as well as processes standing timber generally operates the growing and processing as a single, integrated enterprise. Under such circumstances, it is difficult to distinguish the source of profit, if any, in the operation. Growing timber may simply be a procedure for providing security for a profit opportunity which exists in the conversion processes.

Firms in the industry which both grow and process timber may sometimes find themselves hard put to reach internal agreement on certain timber policies. The trend toward mergers and concentration has increased the proportion of firms which play the dual role of growing and processing. These firms hold views on some policies and programs that are not quite the same as those of the balance of the industry.

The industry has a major interest in policies and programs designed to encourage other private owners to grow more timber. Individual timber-industry firms may often have special programs to assist other private owners in their management. Sometimes assistance is provided with a specific agreement as to who will get the harvest when it is available.

Industry associations also have major programs for encouraging nonindustry private timber owners to grow more timber. The industry also has a considerable interest in convincing public landowners to produce timber. The interest, in this case, is generally expressed through the associations which assist public agencies in obtaining appropriations for timber programs or in supporting legislation to establish programs that favorably affect timber growing.

GENERAL ECONOMIC POLICIES AFFECTING INDUSTRY

Of the broad spectrum of policies and programs which affect the wood-using industry, four categories are of special interest:

1. Public policies on consumption and economic activity in the broadest sense.
2. Public policies on public forest lands.
3. Public policies on private forest lands.
4. Industry policies and programs.

The first category, public policies on consumption and economic activity, includes such items as housing programs and public policies on investment funds, interest rates, inflation, and world trade. One item can be disposed of easily. No one wants inflation: neither the industry, the federal government, the consumer, nor the private forest owner. Therefore, public policies designed to halt or lessen inflation are certainly going to contribute to the objectives of industry.

Federal housing policies are of particular concern since housing is the major destination of wood products. The industry has strongly supported federal housing programs because a strong housing market not only strengthens wood-products markets, but is also generally accompanied by a strong total economy. However, many individuals and groups in the industry have recognized that a program goal as high as 2.6 million housing starts per year by 1975 cannot possibly be met even with a great effort to make additional timber available for harvesting.

The short-run problems of high timber demand and high wood-products prices brought to national attention the fact that it is the demand for end products that puts the pressure on timber supply, not just the industry demand for additional timber. Because of its dual role as processor and grower, industry may experience internal conflicts about the wisdom of supporting certain short-run programs aimed at increasing timber supply.

Federal programs to regulate the economy through controls on money and interest rates generally have their greatest impact on the industry through the housing market. To industry, one of the disconcerting things about federal policies is that they are so often found to be in conflict with each other. For example, the common action of controlling the availability of mortgage funds conflicts with the government's program to meet housing needs.

If timber supply becomes a limiting factor, the federal government has proposed an increased use of substitutes for timber products in order to bring about adequate housing for all the people of the nation. The industry has cooperated in public programs such as Operation Breakthrough, in which new housing methods and materials are being developed. In general, the industry does not favor an all-out federal program for the development of substitute materials for wood products. Mr. Seidl, in Chapter 11, points out the problems that may be created by long-run effort to provide substitute materials made from nonrenewable resources. He presents a strong case for the advantages of wood because of its beneficial environmental effects and its renewability.

One wonders why federal programs are not also aimed at providing substitutes for some of the wilderness and outdoor-recreation needs of the nation. For example, in Chapter 2, Dr. Saul Nelson points out that additional wood imports from Canada could provide an important part of the timber supply in the near future. Using the economically marginal Canadian timber is obviously going to increase costs to the citizens of the United States. The question can be raised: Why not recreate in Canada and grow the additional timber in our South and Pacific Northwest, particularly where recreational uses are now being given priority over the growing of timber on highly productive lands?

POLICIES FOR PUBLIC TIMBER MANAGEMENT

The industry's concern about policies for public forests is particularly great in western United States, where public forest lands provide such a large portion of timber supply. Intensive timber management has always been the goal of foresters for the public forests. For many years, much of the industry looked upon this silvicultural goal as something to be humored and borne, because the real business at hand was the harvesting of the already overmature standing timber. But during the past ten years, the industry has clearly recognized the effects of intensive timber management, not only upon the production of timber in the distant future, but also upon short-term yields. In carrying out the policies of even flow and sustained yield on the public forests, the manager who can expect higher future yields can harvest more timber in the present: By increasing his cut of trees currently mature and overmature, he can draw in advance upon the timber bank account which he knows will be ample if intended silvicultural measures are followed.

Although public agencies want to practice intensive forestry, they have been reluctant to include the expected results of intensive management in the allowable timber harvest because they lack assurance of adequate funds for intensive management in the future. Industry has joined with public agencies in seeking appropriations and other assurance of future levels of funds and manpower sufficient to carry out such intensive management programs as thinning, using genetically improved stock, and fertilizing. Such joint effort could accomplish a great deal; much of the nation still has a confused picture of the meaning of even flow and sustained yield.

Another complication is the currently prevalent notion that increases in the allowable cut result in deterioration of the environment. Such an attitude makes it exceedingly difficult for either industry or public agencies to institute effective programs for intensive forest management. The extreme positions against timber culture and timber cutting taken by some groups have thus far tended to prevent the industry from joining with the less extreme groups of users of other public forest benefits to support policies and programs for intensive management.

POLICIES FOR PUBLIC TIMBER SALES

After a public agency has set the allowable cut for its forests, there remains the problem of meting out this supply. The market for wood products is highly variable, particularly in the short run. Thus, policies that fix the allowable cut over periods such as ten years or longer neglect the additional problem of response to short-run increases and decreases in demand. Most public timber sales are of relatively short duration and involve fairly rigid requirements concerning the length of time for harvesting a particular timber tract. Such rigidity on the supply side of the market tends to widen the fluctuations in timber and product prices.

In former years, when there was little pressure on public timber supply and when local community development was considered important, many public agencies made long-term timber sales. Although these sales permitted the industry to respond to fluctuations in market demand, this result was not intended. The intent was to develop local industry, to harvest and process the timber, and to manage the lands more effectively.

Because harvesting mature timber is an integral part of the total management program, the contracts under which public timber is sold often specify services to be performed by the buyer during or after logging. Agency officials justify these requirements on the basis that timber harvesting creates a need for other services, such as road building, erosion control, and snag removal. Some of the requirements are related to nontimber uses of the forest, and some are related to the establishment and protection of a new timber crop. A troublesome situation is created. The industry enters into the contract of sale primarily in order to obtain raw material to serve the nation's needs at least cost. On the other hand, the public agency's primary interest is in the terms of the contract other than quantity, price, and time, which, from one viewpoint, are its only essential elements. This difference in interests between the parties to the timber-sale contract is almost certainly the cause of their almost constant lack of agreement.

PUBLIC LOG-EXPORT POLICIES

Public policies for log exports provide an area of conflict between the national interest in the balance of trade and the local interest in the survival and stability of industry.

Log exports affect local communities and regions which are dependent upon a limited source of raw material. Alaska is a particularly interesting example. Although log exports from Alaskan national forests are restricted, most of the end products manufactured from Alaskan timber are exported, principally to Japan. The restriction on log exports from Alaska is a policy aimed at supporting the development of local industry and related activity. The Jones Act, an entirely separate part of our federal policies, serves to hamper shipments from Alaska to the lower 48 states. It is this act, together with the proximity of Alaska to Japan, which is responsible for the processed-wood shipments to Japan. If restrictions were not placed on log exports from Alaska, the logs would no doubt also go to Japan. The tests of the policy of restricting log exports from Alaska, then, are the desirability of stimulating Alaskan development, the effectiveness of the stimulation policy, and the importance of this policy relative to others, such as meeting national housing needs.

Further complications in Alaskan forest policies are revealed by the lawsuit brought by the Sierra Club against the Forest Service, attempting to halt economic development by preventing the harvesting of the timber crop. If the supply of timber to the U.S. is the sole subject of this discussion, an important question has been raised by those who want to restrict timber harvesting in Alaska, where the bulk of the end products are merely serving the needs of Japan and other nations. But remember Dr. Nelson's point (Chapter 2): the U.S. wood-product position is a function of net imports, not just of the magnitude of exports nor of the magnitude of imports.

POLICIES FOR MULTIPLE USE OF PUBLIC FORESTS

The wood-using industry is concerned about policies and programs on public forest lands for the production of values other than timber which are increasingly in real or imagined conflict with timber-production programs. The industry has become deeply involved, primarily because of the impact that these other programs have on timber supply from the public lands. Dr. Brewer (Chapter 14) points out the difficulty of balancing public policies for production of timber with policies for protection of other values. He shows that the lack of a pricing system to help regulate the supply and demand of nontimber uses makes it impossible to weigh these uses objectively against priced commodities such as timber.

A great deal of emotion comes into the discussion of forest uses. People who never have and never will use outdoor-recreation opportunities on the public forests voice strong opinions and contribute to the total apparent demand for outdoor recreation. Similarly, citizens who spend a great deal of their time in undesirable environments in New York, Washington, Pittsburgh, and Los Angeles make strong pleas for the protection of the environment on the public forest lands—protection, that is, from timber harvesting. They apparently believe that an increased supply of desirable forest environment will benefit them and that timber harvesting has an undesirable effect on the environment. Although there have been too many cases of improper timber harvesting in the past, there is ample evidence that today's harvesting can be done in a way that avoids degrading the environment or other forest values.

The suggestion has been made that some system of establishing prices for nontimber forest uses be effected so that the benefit and costs of the entire forest production, including timber, can be weighed. This would certainly assist public managers in achieving a better balance among uses. However, how does one exclude from the calculation (if exclusion is desirable) the strongly expressed wishes of many people who would be unwilling or unable to pay for wilderness, outdoor recreation, and improved environment? And similarly, how does one include the wishes of those who would be willing to give up something, in the form of price or of wood products or of something else of value, in order to gain the unpriced benefits?

A great deal of foresight was exhibited by those who established multiple-use policies for the public forests. They apparently realized that as time went on, the emphasis would switch from one use or product to another, and that they should be prepared to accommodate these changes. They probably didn't realize, however, the extent to which emotions, broad public sentiment, and organized group campaigns would come to bear upon decisions. Industry finds itself in the front line of controversies regarding policies and programs for the production of forest values in real or imagined conflict with timber values. Industry's weapons in this battle are very ineffective and out-of-date: the profit motive and desire for economic growth.

PUBLIC POLICIES FOR PRIVATE FORESTS

The forest-products industry feels that incentive programs, sub-sidies, and other devices for increasing timber supply from private forests have not been very successful, nor do they appear to be very promising for the future. The most effective of the assistance programs has probably been the cooperative program of forest protection from fire, insects, and disease. Industry has been a major participant in this program, not only as private forest owners, but as a group inter-ested in stimulating additional timber output from nonindustrial forest lands. Policies and programs for private forest lands are par-ticularly important to the industry in the South, where private forest holdings are a major source of timber supply. The southern wood-using industry is currently making great efforts to bring these lands into higher production.

Another policy area for private forest lands is taxation. Changes in tax policy resulting in heavier property-tax burdens on private for-est land might possibly bring short-run benefits to that portion of the industry whose role is simply the processing of forest products. The changes would exert pressure on owners to liquidate their timber to avoid the tax. However, that portion of the industry which is also a timberland owner would undoubtedly suffer, particularly if it were involved in a program of stretching out the cutting of timber which it owned.

The major problem in forest property taxation is the increasing cost of local government. The principal local tax on timber and forest land, the ad valorem tax, is an increasingly inadequate source of rev-enue. There is growing pressure on local governments to raise prop-erty taxes because of the shortage of other sources of local revenue. These problems have become so acute that there has been serious talk of sharing federal income-tax revenues with local government. Although a reduction of the general property tax on forest lands might not greatly increase timber output, increases in the property tax on standing timber might significantly reduce timber supply in the longer run by causing reductions in growing stock.

Zoning and burning regulations are two currently important re-strictions on private lands that can affect timber supply and the in-dustry. The recent emphasis on both these types of regulation stems from attempts to improve the environment. A major cause for con-cern in the industry is that these environment-oriented limitations are being enforced by those who don't bear the cost or recognize the effects on timber supply. In Oregon, for example, logging slash must be burned or otherwise disposed of in order to protect adjacent timberlands and improve conditions for growing future crops. This long-standing requirement is now confounded by regulations against burning, enforced by an environmental agency which is not concerned with the problems of forest fire or of timber supply. Attempts are being made to place the enforcement of all regulations for private forests with the state forestry agency, which is more likely to seek a balance among the various policies. This may have the weakness, of course, of putting too much power in the hands of one agency. However, it does seem important to industry that the enforcement of such limitations as may be necessary on private lands be carried out in such a way that those who seek the benefits will appreciate the attendant burdens.

INDUSTRY POLICIES AND PROGRAMS

The fourth category of policies and programs in which the industry is concerned includes those of the industry itself. The policies of individual firms in the industry are likely to be oriented toward profit, growth, or continued existence. Public attitudes about affluence and the possession of physical goods, along with increasing concern for the environment, are causing the industry to adopt additional policies that, in effect, modify the extent to which they will pursue their other objectives. For example, industry's policy has been not to go to court to avoid the imposition of environmental limitations on mills or forestry operations. Industry policy has been, in general, to devise methods of reducing or eliminating undesirable effects on the environment. Those members of the industry who have been doing a good job are attempting to get credit for it through a public-relations program. Those who have not been doing such a good job are generally making a genuine effort to improve their performance.

Much concern has been expressed about effects on the environment of timber-harvesting operations, although foresters agree that the impact on the environment is not as great as some people believe. The most vociferous objectors to timber harvesting because of its influence on the environment would be greatly surprised if they carefully examined forested areas cut over more than five years ago. There are many acres of forest land from which timber crops have been removed and on which any visitor would be hard put to complain about the forest environment. Jules Billard, Assistant Editor of *National Geographic,* speaks appreciatively of newly logged hillsides on Vancouver Island showing their "green underwear of new growth."[1]

When forestry for timber production is practiced carefully and intensively, there is every reason to believe that impacts on the environment will be minimal. Undesirable effects in the past have resulted from a lack of concern for a future timber crop. The public should be informed that policies and programs which are undertaken today in order to increase the timber supply are not likely to affect the environment adversely.

Industry's policies are reflected to a great extent through the policies of its associations. Policies on processing timber products have been most emphasized by industry associations. They have been concerned with such aspects as marketing practices, prices, transportation problems, wages, technology, and manufacturing. These issues are related to timber supply in that they quite often affect either the degree of utilization of timber or the cost of conversion.

Industry associations also have policies related to industry's role in growing timber on its own lands. Industry's profit motive seems to work rather effectively toward achieving national timber-supply objectives. Although all industry lands are certainly not up to their maximum productivity level, these lands are some of the best-managed in the nation. New or special policies or programs aimed at industrial forest management are not as promising, in terms of increased timber supply, as other types of policies and programs.

POLICY CHANGES FOR PUBLIC LANDS: BACKGROUND

All future formulation of public policies for the public lands should involve greater public participation. Although forest lands cover a large portion of continental United States, forestry and timber production are really not significant activities on the national scene as a whole. The Public Land Law Review Commission reports that public lands make up one-third of the area of the United States, but their importance in terms of value and in terms of their contribution to economic and social activities is much smaller than that. The public tends to have a poor understanding of the relationship between public forestry policies and housing needs, printing-paper needs, environmental needs, and recreational needs.

Although forest lands are not significant in the total U.S. scene, they are nevertheless important in many localities. Industry has frequently found itself standing alone in dealing with the federal agencies on matters of timber supply. Public agencies have sometimes dealt with industry as if the latter were the sole beneficiary of any improvement in timber supply, disregarding the fact that consumers of wood products are really the ultimate beneficiaries. The industry can stand to gain only by great public participation in the formulation of forestry policies. This line of thought is, of course, predicated on the assumption that greater public understanding will accompany greater public participation. Public participation has increased recently, but a good portion of it has been emotionally based and inadequately supported by an understanding of the facts and of the interrelationships among various policies and programs.

POLICY CHANGES: SALES OF FOREST GOODS AND SERVICES

Changes are needed in the system of paying for management and use of public forest lands. If all the desires of the nation's people for outdoor recreation and wilderness are to be fulfilled, a comprehensive program of manpower and expenditures to protect and manage the resources used for this purpose will be needed. Already, the levels of recreational use in many places are such that neither the resources nor the managers will long be able to bear the burden. Similarly, increased support is needed in timber production. Policies are needed which will set allowable levels of each use of public lands, similar to the allowable cut of timber. These allowances would help relate the benefits received from each use to the costs thereof. If this were done, the industry would be more willing to accept restrictions in timber production resulting from conflict with other uses. If it is bad practice to harvest timber at a rate dependent upon expected future levels of management that will not materialize, certainly it is bad practice to aim for future levels of recreational use which cannot be financed. The proposed National Forest Timber Conservation and Management Act of 1969 would have provided for a system of paying for timber production on public lands and would have given a degree of assured financing to the intensification of both harvest and production of new crops. Future attempts to pass such a bill will probably require broadening to include the use of some portion of all receipts from the public lands to service all uses, including recreation. If this is done, a policy will still be needed to provide for establishing allowable amounts of recreational and other uses.

A change in policy and program is needed to separate timber harvesting from the performance of services on the public forests. At the same time, increasing emphasis should be placed on intensive management for timber production and on the enhancement of the environment and other forest values. The separation of timber harvesting from the performance of services may have to be accomplished through the letting of contracts for performance of services on portions of the public forest over periods of time—for instance, up to ten years. The timber harvested from serviced areas would have a value which could be used to offset the cost of performing the services. One objective of such a policy should be the development of an attitude on the part of both industry and public agencies that when services are to be performed in conjunction with timber harvest, or for any other purpose, there should be a meeting of minds regarding these services and a measuring of contractual performance in terms of the required services. Currently, agencies and purchasers are entering into contractual agreements without clearly specifying their objectives.

The contribution made by public forests to the payment of local-government costs are of concern to the industry. Recent proposals that the contribution be based on tax equivalency should be carefully examined. With increasing costs of local government and with property taxes the primary source of local-government revenue, one would expect the industry to be taxed increasingly through this method. Furthermore, if the public agency pays tax equivalency, conflicts will soon arise between the public agency and local government. In fact, local government may have a strong tendency to raise property taxes in order to get its hand deeper into the pocket of the public agency.

The industry should support a policy directed toward some form of revenue sharing from public lands. This would tend to avoid the problems of a tax-equivalency scheme and bring about a much closer and more widely held local interest in the management of public forests. Revenue sharing is a form of income tax, which has proven to be more equitable than the property tax as applied to forestry.

POLICY CHANGES: TIMBER HARVESTING

The industry has and should continue to have a policy of supporting the long-term capital-gains treatment of timber-harvest income. Modifications, if any, should be directed toward further timber-growth incentives based on the premise that the environmental benefits will parallel the benefits of increased timber growth. Capital-gains taxation has helped to make timber growing profitable, and this profit has been an incentive to further production of timber crops by the industry. Policies concerned with national timber supply should therefore provide for a continuation of long-term capital-gains treatment.

Policy changes are needed to enable industry to respond to the wood-products market during short-run price fluctuations. This is particularly true for that important segment of industry which is dependent on public timber, not having access to its own timber supply or to private open-market timber supplies. This segment feels the major stress during the equating of timber supply to end-products market demand. It needs not only to have timber on hand under contract in order to be responsive to demand, but also to have it at a price which is reasonable with respect to the time periods involved and with respect to the market being served. Removing the fluctuations in the end-products market would be desirable, but there is no evidence that this is possible.

The industry should favor policies for increased research and development in the methods of harvesting, particularly those needed to protect the environment. Although a good start has been made in this direction, supported by both the public agencies and the industry, a much greater effort is needed. Industry has not wholeheartedly attempted to develop and improve harvesting methods because such systems are generally believed to cost more than conventional methods, even when they have been perfected. Thus incentive for research and development is lacking, even though public agencies have a policy of appraising timber value in recognition of all the costs of special harvesting.

The public forestry agency is somewhat inclined to take this attitude: Here is the timber for sale and here are the requirements for harvesting it, including protection of the environment. If the industry wants the timber, they'll just have to figure out some way to harvest it.

One might expect the equipment industry to make an effort in the development of special methods of harvesting, since this could result in sales of equipment. However, two factors are limiting. First, the equipment industry is not well informed about the needs for special types of logging. Second, special logging equipment is often very expensive, and the equipment industry needs firm commitments on several orders to invest safely the engineering and development time and effort.

Each of the three groups devising improved harvesting methods has made substantial progress in recent years. Greater efforts seem to be needed on the part of the public agencies. If protection of the environment and production of nontimber benefits are important to public agencies and to the nation, the agencies can take an approach similar to that of the Defense Department. In the case of national defense, the agency, in effect, underwrites the development of the necessary pieces of equipment. For example, it has underwritten the development of improved aircraft and nuclear power sources. If the agencies interested in special harvesting systems were to do this, the industry would take up the subsequent challenge of putting these systems into effect.

POLICY CHANGES: MANAGEMENT PLANNING

The industry would greatly benefit from policies, programs, and procedures resulting in better-integrated planning on the public lands. Planning in the recent past for such things as transportation systems, recreational use, watershed development, improvement of wildlife habitat, and timber production has been done a piece at a time, with little coordination. Plans for the management and use of public lands should be made so that all management activities and all uses are considered simultaneously. The trade-offs required among the uses and different alternative levels of use should be thoroughly considered at a fairly high level, and knowledgeable local people should be involved prior to the final decision.

In the case of public forest lands, timber-management planning has generally been the most sophisticated and well-developed of all the functional planning. Although the continuation of this trend would at first appear to be of benefit to the industry, this is probably not the case. Planning for nontimber functions lacks adequate evaluation of the impacts on timber management and harvesting. The industry's interest is in good, integrated planning which means strengthening the nontimber side of the work.

Integrated planning would help avoid a common difficulty in planning for single functions. For example, once a transportation plan has been made and part or all of it carried out, the prior approval of this plan may limit the possibilities of logging an area in such a way as to protect the environment. A policy requiring integrated planning would also avoid the current situation in which those concerned with timber voice their opinion about the timber-management plan and those concerned with recreation voice their opinion about the recreational plan. If the planning for these and other uses were done together, those concerned with timber would also find themselves participating in the planning for the other uses.

16   POLICIES, PROGRAMS, AND FOREST OWNERS

JAMES G. YOHO*

FORESTRY POLICIES which significantly influence the behavior of the forest owner are of two types, direct and indirect. Direct policies have been in the majority historically and hence have been more significant than indirect policies. Direct policies include cooperative state and federal programs, public regulation, insurance, credit, research, and education.

Historically, perhaps the most important indirect public policy influencing private forest landowners has been taxation. As Ciriacy-Wantrup has observed, the tax system often has significant but unintended impact on the conservation decisions of private planners.[1] Other policies indirectly affecting forest owners include tariffs, import and export quotas, and other restraints on international trade.

In contrast with the price impact of import-export policies (indirect policies), a subsidy paid to a forest owner in the form of a price support for timber products is classified as a direct policy measure.

Although direct public-policy measures have probably been the most significant in the United States in the past, or at least have attracted prime attention, the future may see a change, a change which is already underway: Indirect measures will be receiving more attention.

Consider for a moment the multitude of public environmental-policy measures which are likely to bear on the forest owner in such a way as to influence his decisions about timber supply. Environmental quality is as much a product of the forest as timber and, in this respect, environmental policy is direct. Nevertheless, seen from the timber viewpoint, the policy is indirect.

Housing is another area of indirect policy in which a great deal of new activity will affect wood-products demand and, secondarily, timber price which, in turn, will influence forest landowners' decisions.

* Director, Natural Resource Planning, Overseas Division, International Paper Company, New York, N.Y.

Forestry policies influencing landowners may also be conveniently classified according to the means they employ to achieve their objectives: (1) Educational or technical assistance; (2) Use of the police or regulatory power; (3) Cost sharing, subsidy, or price supports; and (4) Taxation.

This classification system, based as it is on means of implementation, is more straightforward, and hence easier to visualize, than the direct-indirect system. Its simplicity, however, can be a disadvantage: One should carefully consider where he wants to go and why, before becoming preoccupied with how to get moving.

GOALS OF INDUSTRIAL FOREST OWNERS

Understanding the goals of private forest owners in respect to their holdings is basic to understanding their policies. And, of course, understanding both goals and policies of private forest owners is fundamental to considering public policies for the private sector. On the surface of it, this may not appear to be difficult. However, in many respects, the more we learn about the roughly 4 million private forest owners in the United States, the less we find we actually know about their goals and policies. The problem has been further complicated by the fact that private owners' goals have changed over the years while we have been striving to learn more about them.

The holders of large industrial forests are the easiest to understand, because their goals seem to fit nicely into the profit-maximization assumptions of classical economics and of our private-enterprise philosophy: They manage their lands for the purpose of growing timber for a profit or as raw material for a manufacturing process pursued for a profit—and, as Dr. Newport adds in Chapter 15, they also seek growth and continued existence. Ordinarily their aim is to produce from the forest a high value of wood at low cost.

Timber growing per se is not an extremely profitable venture unless one is able to realize a windfall from inflation in land and timber values. Most industrial owners view tree farming as a less profitable place to invest scarce capital than manufacturing or marketing. They seldom plan to supply all their raw materials from their own forests. Accordingly, industrial owners' goals and ensuing policies involve viewing the forest as a raw-material contingency reserve as well as a profit source.

As with any profit-seeking private enterprisers, industrial forest owners realize that their forestry policies must recognize the non-market wants of society in order to minimize profit-negating harassment and regulation. Unfortunately for the industrial owner, he often faces a difficult dilemma in formulating policies for managing his forest, because of the cost of satisfying society's nonmarket wants.

He finds himself face to face with real constraints in the formation of his policy no matter how sympathetic he may be toward the desires of society.

Between the extremes of profit-seeking timber-growing forest enterprise and profit-negating forestry to satisfy nonmarket wants of society, there is a spectrum of combinations involving nontimber products which conflicts with, rather than complements, timber. The industrial landowner's policy necessarily strikes a compromise among the alternatives.

GOALS OF NONINDUSTRIAL PRIVATE OWNERS

The goals of nonindustrial forest owners, who control most of our private forest land and account for all but a small portion of the number of holdings, are far from clear-cut. A minority, whose holdings are generally larger than average, pursue profit-oriented goals. In fact, these so-called investment owners often have policies which are more clearly profit-oriented than those of industrial forest owners.

Beyond industrial forest owners and investment owners lies the great heterogeneous mass of forest owners who control the major part of U.S. forest lands, generally in small parcels. The lands of these owners have long been recognized as falling far short of their potential for timber production and hence as holding the key to increasing timber supplies. As a result, the owners—farmers, wage earners, widows—have been subjected to a great deal of study in an effort to ascertain their goals of ownership. They have also been the recipients of much public aid predicated on naive assumptions about their goals. In these studies, it is always implicitly hoped that goals can be related to easily-defined categories of owners. It would be flattering to say that such efforts are even partially successful. What they do succeed in establishing is that the forestry objectives of these owners are varied and complex.

Although nonindustrial, noninvestment private forest owners have been thought to seek profit-maximization for their forest land, this hypothesis defies verification. Their imperfect knowledge of timber-management possibilities is an obstacle to such a goal. A clear picture of their objectives is difficult to obtain because of the fact that they vary greatly in the amount of capital available to them, in their propensities to consume, and in their planning horizons.

Perhaps the most disconcerting result of the studies seeking to establish objectives of ownership is the revelation that a large share of nonindustrial private owners have no particular goals. Many acquired forest land by default and continue to exhibit a passive attitude toward their property.

To timber-oriented persons in forestry circles, it has always been somewhat disturbing to learn that many persons who deliberately acquire forest land have nontimber objectives which often conflict with timber production. It is, of course, even more disturbing, in terms of developing a rationale for analyzing the future timber supply, to realize that more and more forest properties are being acquired by persons who have nonmarket objectives. Here is one of the manifestations of a society which continues to behave in an ever more affluent fashion without regard to whether it may be overextending itself.

ALTERNATIVE POLICY NORMS

The establishment of goals, or norms, for public policy related to private landowners must, in the final analysis, be based on one or both of two fundamental precepts. In the language of Rainer Schickele, they are the productive norm and the income norm (distributive norm).[2]

The productive norm is a maximization of the national net value of want-satisfying goods and services. In other words, it is an allocation of all the agents of production in the economy—all forms of land, labor, and capital—in such a way that total net value production could not be increased further by shifting a unit of an agent from one line of endeavor to another. This is the "efficiency" criterion of Chapter 14.

The income norm is the achievement of a minimum subsistence level of all human beings, whether productive or not. Labor is assured the opportunity to produce and is awarded income commensurate with its productivity.

Recognition of these two basic precepts can lead to theoretically correct and fundamentally sound goals for public policy.

Viewing the matter more empirically, public policies toward private landowners are formulated to move unsatisfactory real conditions in the direction of an ideal. In practice, this approach tends to be forward looking: Policies are quite often developed to rectify anticipated deviations from the ideal.

Most public forestry policies aimed at private landowners are remedial in respect to the productive norm. That is to say, it is commonly assumed that insufficient resources are being directed to forestry, particularly to the tree-growing sector. It is assumed that if some resources were redirected to this sector, the total satisfaction of the consuming public, measured in market and nonmarket values of goods and services, would be raised—that is, economic welfare would be increased. It does not follow that all classes of resources would be redirected in the same proportion. It is quite possible that misallocation would be found to exist only in the case of labor and capital, while land was already available in ample supply in the private-forest sector.

POLICY NORMS: THE SOCIAL IDEAL

The theory of the idealized public-policy goal illustrates how easy it is for the process of public-policy formation relating to private forest owners to go astray. There is the problem of ascertaining whether there is now, or whether there is in the offing, a national misallocation of resources in respect to the private-forest sector. That is to say, would total national economic welfare be increased by shifting resources to or away from this sector? Substantial upward trends in the validly measured real prices of many types of forest goods and services constitute quantitative evidence that an improvement could be wrought by shifting resources from other uses into the private forestry sector. Some forest conservationists believe that public funds should be expended in order to plant trees on every acre of "idle land" lying within natural-forest zones, because all will eventually be required to satisfy our future "needs" for wood, a premise which rests on the assumption of an insatiable demand for timber products.

A great deal of improvement can be realized in the formulation of public policies applicable to private forests if the distinction between the productive norm and the income norm is kept in mind. In other words, (1) policies designed to move the private-forest sector toward the productive norm are not likely also to move the sector toward the income norm, and (2) vice versa. Actually, errors of the first type are much more common than those of the second type. And errors of the first type are made by persons responsible for applying policy as well as those who formulate policy: Many well-intentioned sylvan enthusiasts have no reservations about urging low-income owners to invest resources with a high earning potential in relatively low-yielding forest enterprises.

Perhaps some of the confusion in forestry circles between the productive norm and the income norm as a policy guide is a result of the close association between forestry and agriculture in the federal and most state governments. Both the stated and the implicit goals of most agricultural programs are based on the income norm. In forestry, on the other hand, most programs have come into being to meet production goals. Yet, upon close examination, the programs bear a striking resemblance, being administered in the same way and often by the same persons, or at least by persons within the same agency.

POLICY NORMS: REGULATORY AND OTHER MEANS

Public regulation has often been suggested as a means of assuring at least minimal productive performance by the private-forestry sector. Advocates of public regulation typically favor using the police power of the states to set minimum physical standards for private-forest management. These standards would fix limits to disinvestment in private forests, irrespective of profit.

Public-regulation proposals raise interesting questions of political philosophy. Many forest owners see regulation as an unwarranted and selective infringement of their rights, forcing confiscatory investment costs upon them. Others argue that the right to own and control forest property carries with it the responsibility of handling the property (including investment financial resources, if necessary) so that it contributes some prorated share of the national production goal, without regard to the owner's limitations in capital and labor.

Economically speaking, it may be efficient to consider policies that facilitate a shift of forest-land resources from low-income to high-income owners, from owners who have severe capital limitations to those whose capital supplies are ample enough to enable them to invest in relatively low-return ventures. Such policies may be more efficient than forest regulation, not only in promoting forest owners' welfare, but also in enhancing society's welfare.

Dilemmas of political philosophy also arise in considering the extra-market goods and services which society as a whole appears to demand from private forest owners. To the extent that such forest outputs have an indirectly measurable value, the productive norm indicates that more resources should be devoted to them on private forest lands. But the management objectives for such properties, based on owners' income goals and public acceptance of the income norm, militate against most extra-market endeavors. If society requires such endeavors to move the private forestry sector in the direction dictated by the productive norm, should society compensate private owners for the nonprofitable uses of their capital which they are thus forced to sustain?

Problems arising from differences in resource use under the income and productive norms are difficult enough in terms of economic theory and political philosophy. They are even more difficult in terms of policy application. Economic justice would seem to require that society's goal, founded on extra-market as well as market considerations, be estimated for each forest holding as a basis for appraising the dislocation, or damages, which each holding would sustain in fulfilling social aims. Making 4 million such appraisals would be a very difficult task indeed.

POLICIES FOR PUBLIC FORESTS

A large share of the U.S. timber supply, particularly the softwood sawtimber supply, originates on government-held land.

Since policy relating to public forest owners is a very broad topic, this discussion will simply concentrate on federal lands, particularly the national forests, since they are so significant in the total supply and since their policies provide an example for other public timber owners.

There seems to be little doubt that the goals for national and other public forests should relate almost totally to the productive norm rather than to the income norm. Early laws establishing the national-forest system and subsequent forest-related laws make such goals reasonably clear. Moreover, the public commercial forests constitute a convenient and logical institutional mechanism for moving a large part of the forestry sector toward timber-production goals based on the productive norm. Government can act quickly and effectively through the tax system or its massive borrowing power to generate large sums of capital, which can then be redirected quickly to timber-investment opportunities on government lands—in particular, national forests, since they are closely controlled by a centralized administration.

There are problems, however. One is the difficulty that a public agency has in accommodating special-interest groups, in both the formulation and administration of its policy goals. The difficulty arises because government enterprise is not compelled to be as responsive as private enterprise to the signals of the price system. Hence an opportunity is provided for special-interest factions to influence public policy for the public lands—either in the direction of extra-market values or in the opposite direction. Although the resulting distortions can manifest themselves in many ways, they probably appear most commonly in the management policies which come about as the result of administrative edict, rather than those established by legislation, and they probably relate most often to such things as the product mix to be produced from a given forest.

Fortunately, in recent years, investments basic to the management of federal forest lands have been increasingly subjected to scrutiny by the analytical economic techniques developed in the federal government during the last decade: the Program Planning and Budgeting System.

THE ALLOWABLE CUT FROM PUBLIC FORESTS

Perhaps no single policy issue for federal timber management has been more controversial than the allowable cut. The cut is ordinarily set by use of a formula, in which two variables play significant roles. These variables, rotation length and productive forest area, are weighed largely by administrative judgment, which is perhaps the immediate reason why they have become the center of controversy. Rotation length is especially controversial. The debate has been fueled when private industrial firms have announced the adoption of comparatively short rotations and intensive, high-yield timber programs. Many analysts have been unable to understand government rationale in clinging to long rotations in this era of high interest rates, since such rotations are difficult to defend economically except at extremely low rates. Dr. Brewer touches upon the rotation-length issue in Chapter 14.

One of the most sacred tenets of professional forestry for many generations has been "sustained yield." Largely biological in origin, this tenet has been the watchword of federal forestry. Sustained yield has been given a fairly strict interpretation: essentially equal annual or short-period yields. This interpretation has resulted in a policy for the handling of our forests quite inconsistent with other government policies on general economic welfare: A sustained-yield management program contributes to exaggerating both the peaks and the troughs of long-term price trends. The exaggeration is reflected first in stumpage prices and then in all prices throughout the industries dependent on timber as a basic raw material.

There is nothing inherent in the concept of sustained yield that prevents federal forests from being handled on a variable-yield basis, so long as the sustained-yield concept is adhered to on the average over the rotation. Thus the public timber cut could, in respect to the productive norm, act as a stabilizing force in our economy, particularly in those sectors which are heavily dependent upon such timber.

Moreover, publicly held forests could provide a stabilizing force in respect to the income norm as well: They could be managed under a regime of flexible inputs so as to provide a source of employment during recessions.

17   A LAYMAN SPEAKS

STEPHEN K. BAILEY*

As THE SINGLE NONEXPERT in a pride of timber and forestry specialists, I can only assume that my function is to place the problems of U.S. timber supply and America's forest policies in some kind of lay public-interest perspective. My mind being unsullied by substantive knowledge in this field, I am, I assume, judged to be in a good position to weigh evidence judiciously and to take a totally objective view of the U.S. timber-supply problem and some related questions of national forest policy. I shall try to be objective. Alas, it will not be easy. In Lovell, Maine, in the foothills of the White Mountains, eighteen miles due east of Mt. Washington, on the shores of Kezar Lake, there are sixty magical acres of woodland. Here I have spent each summer since 1950. Here my wife and I have raised our children. Here we look forward to spending the brighter months of our remaining years. There are no "board feet," there is no silviculture, in our forest. Old trees die natural deaths, and occasionally, as the north wind whips through the dark of a petulant night, and the dock frets at its moorings, we awaken to the awful single sob of the earth as a great tree falls.

My own small piece of wilderness surely gets in the way of my viewing the issues identified in this volume with complete objectivity. This bias needs a frank and early admission.

As a student of public policy, I found myself both fascinated and startled by the number of issues and actors described in the preceding chapters as being in serious contention. A cryptic list may help as a refresher.

This is far from an exhaustive list, but it is suggestive of the kinds of assumptive values that find themselves in combative array on the pages I have read.

*Chairman, Policy Institute, Syracuse University Research Corporation.

Major Issue	The Policy Question
Multiple use	In whose favor?
Public lands	For which public?
Housing	For whom, at what price?
Foreign trade	For whose comparative advantage?
Interest rates	For whose interest?
Substitutes	For whose biologically degradable profit?
Free market	Protected by whom, for whose benefit?
Prices	Of what, for whose delectation?
Sustained yield	At whose definition of allowable cut?
Protected environment	At whose sacrifice?
Small private forest landowners	Irrational in whose terms?
The people	Consumers or "great beasts"?
The Sierra Club	Saviors or swearword?
Further federal "investment"	On the basis of what "trade-offs"?
Taxation	Whose ox to be gored in whose cleared pasture?

A VIEW OF SILVICULTURE

In some cases the overt or hidden value conflicts run very deep. For example, according to some of the authors, clearcutting is not only more economical for the harvester, thereby promoting lower costs to processors and lower prices to consumers, but it is actually better for the quality and quantity of the new yield on the cutover site. From this point of view, there is obviously nothing but perverse romanticism in the archaic notion of selective timbering.

Alas, I can remember the summer when I first experienced clearcutting. We arrived earlier than usual that year. As we rounded the rocky curve below Joe McKeen's hill, suddenly all was desolation. On acre after acre, almost as far as the eye could see, were mutilated stumps, charred clearings, and tattered toppings. What welled up inside was an intense hatred for the despoilers—a sense of outrage as though we were colonial settlers entering a broken village littered with the corpses of scalped relatives and neighbors. In five years perhaps no one would notice. But five years—even a single summer—is a long time in the life of a 10-year-old girl.

For those of you who make great investments in tilling the forest and in processing timber products, and for the tens of thousands who earn livelihoods in the economy of wood, most of the competing in-terests (like mine) in the use of forest resources must seem madden-ingly perverse and even frivolous. I doubt that many of you are rapacious; but, judging from some of the chapters, some of you are extraordinarily insensitive. And this insensitivity has been passed on to some policy formulators in the federal government. In such pieces of proposed legislation as the National Forest Timber Conser-vation and Management Act of 1969, and in such official executive branch statements as the June 1970 report of the Softwood Lumber and Plywood Task Force and the timber section of the 1970 report of the Public Land Law Review Commission, I find a world-view, a public-interest framework, that does enormous credit to the experts and the lobbyists in the major timber and forest-products associations, but which is strangely archaic in its definitions of existing and pro-spective social values in this nation.

I say this with due appreciation for the emotionalism and the lack of sympathy for hard-choice trade-offs that untutored romantics like myself can infuse into discussions about policy alternatives in this troubled area. But until many of the most hard-headed of you can figure out the marginal productivity of a patch of sunlight on a bed of pine needles, and the ad valorem worth of the evensong of a woodthrush, you will have trouble figuring out an appropriate po-litical calculus for maximizing your own long-term profits. Until "multiple use" becomes something beyond a rhetorical cover for fairly single-minded objectives, you will fumble around in a political game that increasingly you are bound to lose.

THE FEDERAL POLICY ROLE

A stark political reality of our age is that the United States gov-ernment is not expressly organized for the purpose of defending the long-range profitability of the timber and forest-products industry. Nor, whatever some of you may think, is the federal government a handmaiden of the Sierra Club. The federal government, like most of the levels of government below it, is an instrument for resolving conflicts that cannot be resolved equitably by the market. It is a collectivity of legislative, executive, bureaucratic, and judicial devices for working out bargains among a myriad of contending interests. It is an homogenizer and moralizer of squabbles. It does not settle issues for all time. It settles issues tentatively, as imperfect knowl-edge, gifted rhetoric, squeaky wheels, and recent elections define and redefine what is good and what is evil.

Actually, as a political scientist, my key concern is not with the question of what is or is not the substantive public interest at the moment in the field of timber supply and forestry policy. My key concern is that the public procedures for arriving at tentative resolutions of conflict about such matters are in fact fair, informed, and well financed. I am particularly concerned with the last, for the substantive committees of Congress have a tendency to establish policies for whose administrative articulation and enforcement congressional appropriations committees are unwilling to supply adequate funds. I am happy to see this theme picked up and emphasized in some of the chapters in this book.

BOTTOM-HEAVY POWER

The main impediment to the determination of wise federal policies in the field of our concern has not been the existence in society of "vested interests," "greed," and "irrationality." These are simply words to describe the motives or imperfections of persons who disagree with us. America's search for the public interest in the field of forest policy has been hampered by structural anachronisms in both the legislative and the executive branches of government. To put the matter baldly, and in terms that the late Paul Appleby, former Undersecretary of Agriculture, would have endorsed, timber and forest questions tend to be settled at too low a level in both Congress and the bureaucracy. Too many important issues are determined by congressional subcommittees and by bureaus and sub-bureaus in the departments and agencies. The result of this bottom-heavy locus of power is that most of the maddeningly complex interdependencies so superbly articulated in preceding chapters are not "staffed out" before, while, and after policy is made. Timber and forest policies, and other social and economic policies of the federal government that impinge upon woodlands, tend to be promulgated intermittently, developed by myopic committee or agency specialists, and left to the mercies of a Darwinian administrative jungle for implementation. Oftentimes, the key victory for a lobbyist is not in influencing the language of a bill, but in helping to determine which subcommittee or which agency will get jurisdiction. "Multiple use" receives different interpretations in Agriculture, Interior, and the Corps of Engineers—and in their corresponding subcommittees in Congress.

In short, in both Congress and the executive branch, there are inadequate instruments, in Appleby's felicitous phrase, "to make a mesh of things."

Until recently, this structural lack was not a matter of serious consequence. We were a vast universe, and the galactic swarms of separate interests rarely collided in such a way as to cause much lasting damage. Today, and in historic terms quite suddenly, we are up to our eyeballs in affluent-effluent equations. We are also in a nightmare of punitive and partly ineffable policy trade-offs: High interest rates are needed to slow inflation; low interest rates are needed to house the poor. Import quotas are needed to protect American producers; free trade is needed to protect American consumers. Clear-cutting is needed to increase the efficiency of silviculture; selective timbering is essential for the preservation of watersheds and beauty.

These kinds of issues are not new to politics. Politics has always been concerned with who gets what, when, and how. What is new is the seriousness of the bewildering consequences that now seem to flow from parochial decisions in a totally interdependent world.

THE NEED FOR WEIGHT AT THE TOP

The real reason for the increasing gravitation of public authority from local and state to federal, and from technical and special to general, is not power-hunger, but sheer social necessity. Whatever judgments we may have about Mr. Nixon's performance and value priorities, it would be fatuous to suggest that he established a Council on Environmental Quality in the executive office of the President because he was an empire builder. The sad fact is that since the demise of the National Resources Planning Board in 1943, the presidential office has had no staff service committeed to examining the general consequences of specific governmental and private decisions in the whole field of natural-resource management. If such an instrumentality had existed, many of the issues that presently trouble us might well have been sorted out rationally on the basis of pictures taken with a wide-angle rather than a telephoto lens.

Hopefully, the Council on Environmental Quality, and the Domestic Council of which it is a part, will provide an intellectual center for spotting relationships and consequences unfathomable to more visceral, vested, and traditional political instrumentalities. The real question is whether any staff in the presidential office can bear the information and decisional overload that appears certain to develop in the field of environmental quality control. If an overload does develop, the executive branch may be forced into line reorganizations that would put together large parts of what presently constitutes the Departments of Agriculture and Interior—and even (God-Save-the-Mark) the Army Engineers, those redoubtable coopers of the congressional pork barrel.

Unfortunately, there is little sign that the legislative branch would be sympathetic to such executive branch rearrangements. And there is presently nothing to indicate that Congress is moving toward the construction of a committee system, or a party-policy system, that might superimpose general considerations upon myopic subcommittee policy determinations. Deference patterns being what they are and division-of-labor jurisdictional definitions being what they are, Congress is presently prone to make policy on the basis of log-rolls largely unencumbered with broad questions of public consequence. The accident of statesmanship, not the structure of responsible power, tends to determine the capacity of Congress to look beyond its nose.

In my estimation, no greater need exists in the structure of the American government than to induce Congress to reform its organization and procedures in such a way as to take large and cross-cutting views of the policy initiatives that stem from short-sighted private and bureaucratic interests. Gallant attempts by the President's office to see things as a whole, and in the round, do not accomplish much if subunits of Congress (often with the help of disgruntled bureaus and outside-interest groups) can then rip the broad picture to shreds and dispose of little pieces according to the whims of subcommittee chairmen responsible only to God and backwater constituencies. I may agree with the prejudices of a particular subcommittee chairman; I would still argue that it is wrong (in a governmental sense, immoral) for complex and portentous public policies to be decided by politically shrewd but programmatically unsophisticated feudal barons.

Failing a massive reform of the present congressional system, some improvement could be made by cultivating a more adequate mix of witnesses in committee hearings; by establishing one or more joint committees similar to the Joint Economic Committee, but concerned with resource and environmental issues; and by improving the quality and competence of relevant congressional staff. But before too many years, the national condition will probably mandate some more basic changes in the structure and procedures of Congress. It is difficult to see how a legislature constituted as Congress presently is can long endure in the face of the kinds of problems this book alone has surfaced.

ROLE OF THE MARKET

Thus far, I have come close to defining the public interest in terms of the way in which decisions are made in the federal government. To leave matters there, however, would be unfortunate. In the first place, a great many decisions affecting such an area as timber supply and forest products should be made by the market. I say this, not because I believe the market to be equitable, but because I believe that at some point far short of socialist faith, government regulation tends to make life bilious and unjoyful.

Where public decisions *are* necessary in order to modify market-set priorities, experimentation with local, state, and especially regional authorities should, in my estimation, be promoted. I am not particularly naive about the greater vulnerability of many local and state legislatures to concerted pressures, but it does seem that local, state, and regional variations, legal and administrative, are possible escapes from the inequities that tend to be secreted in all general legislation that is national in scope. Perhaps a better way to put the issue is to say that some tension between national norms and regional and local perspectives must be maintained if law is to be truly equitable and humane in its impact. One way to assure such tension is to provide consciously, in both legal and administrative terms, for its perpetuation. National and lesser levels of government must learn to live together even at the price of confusion.

PUBLIC INTERESTS IN FORESTRY

Is the public interest, then, simply a question of how, where, and by whom decisions are made? Are there not certain definable national goals that should take precedence over others?

At any earlier time, it is conceivable that many of us would have settled for a definition of the role of government in protecting the public interest as "equitable and efficient brokerage." In an apocalyptic world, procedural niceties are still important, but they are patently insufficient. The fact is that we are rapidly evolving an ethic of survival and of environmental felicity that will have major long-range consequences for the economy of timber and forest products. Whether these consequences constitute good news or bad news will depend upon the major schools of forestry in this nation.

Surely the first priority of all governments in this day and age must be the protection of the biosphere. If it were found, for example, that a combination of gaseous effluents from motor vehicles and from industry were dangerously lowering the oxygen content of the air, and that five billion more trees were needed within five years to maintain the world's photosynthetic output, the governments of mankind would not think twice about destroying the entire timber and forest-products economy in their respective nations. This may be a far-fetched example, but the fact is that we really do not know what the industrial and agricultural revolutions of this century have done to our ecologic balances. As we gear ourselves to finding out, every part of our economy that has major environmental effects is subject to the contingencies of the crises that new ecologic knowledge may produce.

Even if global issues are not immediately at stake, there are national priorities that must receive preemptive protection—for example, water. Forest practice that ignores or underestimates the importance of the nation's water supply and the need for ground cover to prevent floods from the runoffs of our major watersheds has no claim to public support or tolerance.

In short, air and water are matters of survival. Forest policy in the public interest must conform to the urge of the species to continue.

PUBLIC INTERESTS IN WOOD PRODUCTS

A related question emerges: Continue the species in what condition? If the younger generation can be taken seriously, we are about to enter, if not the Age of Aquarius, the age of diminishing marginal utility of gadgets, especially packaged gadgets. In the foregoing chapters much is made of the fact that wood products are biologically degradable. From certain points of view, this is a valuable long-range asset. Alas, most wood products are not left to self-destruct patiently in the moldering earth. The earth is not a big enough cemetery. Most wood and paper products that have served their initial purposes are subject to fire which, at least in the present state of the art, distributes ashes and soot via the wind to a lot of windowsills and mucous membranes. The very flammability of wood products presents both massive and subtle disutilities that have to be reckoned with in determining customer preference as well as larger public-interest standards. My untutored hunch is that part of the future viability of the wood-products economy will depend upon research and development directed toward new forms of forest-products waste disposal that do not pollute the atmosphere.

Parenthetically, I should like to add that until the paper manufacturers of this nation find a way of manufacturing their product without pouring nauseous, noxious, and acrid effluents into thousands of cubic miles of surrounding atmosphere, they will be hounded and despised by an increasingly vociferous and aroused horde of citizens. Anyone who has sniffed the State of Maine near Rumford or Westbrook knows the kind of skunk works to which I refer. Politically speaking, more and more people are becoming concerned about such matters. This means that priorities besides production and employment are emerging in our society and will inevitably affect the price and practices of forest-related industry and commerce.

RECREATION, WILDERNESS, TIMBER

Perhaps the most pressing new priority related to the quality-of-life issue for a massively growing and highly mobile population, is recreational lebensraum. This competes with timber interests on the one hand and with wilderness interests on the other. These inexorable forces will, in my estimation, become increasingly powerful politically. Greater public and private investments in the acquisition, servicing, and maintenance of recreational space and facilities come as close to a sure bet as any social forecast I can imagine. My guess is that both your interests in timber supply and my interests in the preservation of pieces of wilderness will be substantially compromised. Some three-way joining of hands in order to bargain out a series of competing values will be the order of the future day.

Perhaps a keen sense of emerging social necessities, an intensive research and development activity, and better management practices (supplemented by wiser laws and more flexible and realistic administrative guidelines) can give the timber and forest-products industry a new and enduring lease on life. I hope so, and not only for the sake of those who desperately need decent housing at a reasonable price or for those who earn their livelihood from forest products.

I hope so for personal reasons. For if I love my unkempt forest, I also love the smell and feel of freshly milled lumber. I love the pine ceiling in my summer bedroom, with its grotesque, knot-drawn caricatures of animals and fish and birds. And climbing up my chimney, above the mantel, are three ducks gracefully carved from hardwood and delicately painted, the birds obviously startled into flight by the noise of my screen door slamming.

Furthermore, I love to eat from wooden tables and sit in wooden furniture and feel the sanded and varnished sides of wooden beds.

And, anyhow, whoever heard of a plastic log or a metal heater spitting fireflies onto the hearth of a home?

18   IN REVIEW

GEORGE R. ARMSTRONG*

THIS CHAPTER seeks to identify and integrate the main ideas of the timber-supply conference and to draw together in this frame of reference the views expressed in earlier chapters and in the conference. Only the broad, general issues are stressed. The attitudes expressed towards them are summarized. Because such integrating and summarizing demands a significant amount of interpretation, conferees were invited to comment on an early draft of the chapter. Occasional comments in parentheses reflect the wishes of some respondents to amplify or to question statements made.

TOMORROW'S PROBLEMS

Foregoing chapters necessarily give some attention to price gyrations in the timber market and to economic adjustments for modifying them. But the real concern is for tomorrow's problems. The evidence presented suggests strongly that these problems will require early action if large economic dislocations are to be avoided. Moreover, the public is becoming convinced that there is greater need for the nation's resource managers to anticipate and prevent environmental troubles than to attempt belatedly to remedy them.

The fundamental problem is impending economic scarcity of timber, particularly of softwood sawtimber. The conditions that led to impending scarcity have been described as follows: The demand for wood products has tended to increase steadily over the years as population has grown, real incomes have risen, and consumer preferences have matured. Prospects are that the increase will continue. Meanwhile, sufficient supply responses have not been made.

Despite preventive efforts, real prices of stumpage (in dollars of constant value) have been rising at an average rate of about 2 percent per year for all timber and about 4 percent for softwood. Occasionally,

---

* Professor of Forestry Economics, State University of New York, Syracuse. Secretary to the 1970 Timber-Supply Conference, Harriman, N.Y.

when chance combinations of events have temporarily inhibited the flow of raw materials or have stimulated demand, prices have shot upward to worrisome heights.

Timber-inventory data suggest that for some kinds and sizes of timber, for many locations, and for several major markets, the rate of drawdown of timber stocks is such that unless strong and positive action is taken to increase supplies in the near future, prices will not only rise precipitously before the turn of the century, but will stay high, in spite of competition from other products, because the rate of timber replacement will be too low to permit meeting demands at lower prices, such a price surge is expected to have serious social repercussions. Wood, like steel, is firmly woven into the fabric of our economy. It is the sole support for a host of communities, a major source of support for several states, and a primary input for a large number of industries. Employment attributable to timber has been estimated at more than 5 percent of total civilian employment, and forest-related activities account for almost 6 percent of the gross national product. It follows that large and lasting disruptions in either quantity or direction of flow of timber and timber products stand to generate social costs of great dimension locally and of broad significance nationally and internationally.

CONTEXT FOR ACTION

We find ourselves today in rapid transition from one world to another. Yesterday's world was one in which the basic resources were available in virtually unlimited supply. Consuming them and transforming them into new complexes by application of knowledge and energy was obviously good and rational. The wastes and residues of production and consumption were considered to have a negligible effect on the environment. The conceivable future offered no threat to survival or to the ever-rising quality of life. Success was measured in terms of growth and gross national product.

As Kenneth Boulding has pointed out, tomorrow's world promises to be one in which available quantities of all the basic resources will be finite and relatively small, as in a space capsule.[1] In that environment, the production of goods will have an undesirable side, because production uses energy and creates residues and pollutants. Consumption will have unwanted aspects, too, because it creates more wastes and pollutants. Even growth will be questioned, because it creates further scarcity. The measure of success will be maintenance of the quality, quantity, and complexity of what will have become essentially a closed system.

The transition between the two worlds has not been clearcut or rapid. It has been in process for generations. Discoveries and innovations retard and even reverse the process; for each resource the realization of scarcity creeps in on us at different rates and at different times.

What to do in forestry? Two major positions have been taken. One advocates protecting the resource and the environment by limiting large areas of forest to uses other than timber production. This kind of action is said to have the virtue of enhancing the environment on the reserved areas by maintaining timber stock and concurrently reducing industrial pollution. (Several conferees point out that the effect may be to increase environmental damage elsewhere through heightened pressure on nonreserved forests and through industrial activity centered on the use of substitutes.)

The other major position holds that it is not correct to equate changes in the physical environment with changes in the quality of life. Quality of life is claimed to rest, not on one great inheritance, but on three. The first is the resource base. The second as its complement, the complex industrial pipeline through which society gains access to resources such as the multiple products of the forest. And the third great inheritance is our culture, including how we weigh and value things and how we govern our affairs. If we move to protect one inheritance without due regard for the effects that such action will have on the others—so the argument runs—the stability, security, and standard of living that we seek to maintain can be placed in great jeopardy.

The person who is not immediately threatened by the prospect of a declining rate of national or regional growth might be expected to lean toward the first viewpoint and to seek security in maintaining his physical inheritance. The industry spokesman, by contrast, seeks to protect and develop his technologic inheritance by holding to the national growth goals on which it has been built. Representatives of government are also cautious about moving away from a growth economy toward a maintenance economy, because they attach high costs to institutional changes which threaten employment and income.

Efforts to increase timber supplies can help ameliorate the problems as seen by both groups. By providing more forest land as well

TABLE 18.1 ACTIONS TO PREVENT ECONOMIC SCARCITY OF TIMBER

Strategy	Tactic	
	Short Run	Medium Run
Reduce demand	Reduce government purchases	Develop substitutes Monetary and fiscal controls
Increase rate of flow	Expedite delivery Speed boxcar turnaround Draw down inventories	Improve transport systems Stimulated foreign trade Improve marketing systems
Increase supply	Reduce log exports Accelerate timber sales	Increase imports

as timber, such efforts simultaneously broaden the base for nontimber forest uses and diminish threats of economic shock in many industries and regions. Each group finds security in the forests: their multiple values, their reproducibility, their biologically degradable wastes, their highly efficient utilization of solar energy, their role as natural factories, their contribution to the quality of the atmosphere, and the relatively low energy requirements for their processing and transformation.

ALTERNATIVE COURSES OF ACTION

Several types of action can be employed to prevent economic scarcity of timber, in both the short and the long run.

Price increases in the very short deriving from temporary breakdowns or slowdowns of the production-conversion-distribution mechanism due to strikes, bad weather, or the like may be at least partially offset by reducing government purchases, drawing down inventories, accelerating boxcar turnaround, reducing log exports, and enlarging timber sales.

In the somewhat longer run, demand can be affected by adopting substitutes and by controls such as interest-rate adjustments, which profoundly affect the housing market. And more can be done to increase supplies and rate of flow by increasing imports, intensifying forest management and wood utilization, and improving transportation and marketing systems.

In the still longer run, although the rate of increase in demand may be reduced by developing substitutes or changing preferences and cultural patterns, the working assumption of most concerned persons is that demand will continue to increase as new and replacement markets grow for a rising population. Thus the major need is to increase timber supplies. The broad array of alternative approaches is shown in Figure 18.1. To increase timber supplies in these ways, immediate concerted action is required of a wide variety of participants.

But action sufficient to eliminate threats of shortage in the longer run is *not* being taken. There are strong differences of opinion about how our nation's lands are to be used. Consequently, an alternative such as increasing the amount of land in commercial timber production presents special problems which extend far beyond forestry and require simultaneous consideration of agricultural, urban, and other needs. (Some conferees believe that the realistic long-term outlook is for continuing reduction in forest acreage.) Many of the actions projected in Figure 18.1 seem to require only financial justification. Yet those who are in a position to act apparently lack assurance that the payoffs will be sufficient to justify the investments.

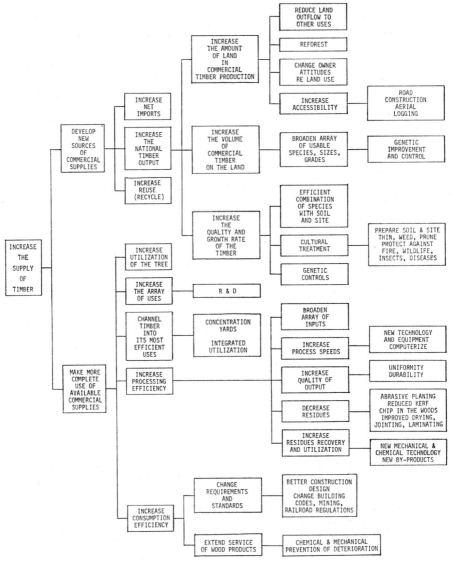

ALTERNATIVES FOR INCREASING TIMBER SUPPLIES.

FACTORS INHIBITING ACTION

Four major deterrents to remedial action have been named or implied by conferees. One is lack of knowledge. Thus it is claimed that the consumer or the average man in the street, particularly the city dweller, does not understand how the forest and its timber are hooked into his daily life. He fails to appreciate the social effects of his wood-using habits or forestry-oriented political activities. It is also argued that many small-scale landowners do not manage their holdings for increased timber production because they neither know how to go about it nor see the need. Similarly, lack of knowledge helps to keep the small sawmiller from achieving greater plant efficiency. In short, too many people in the forestry process fail to know what is best to do or how to do it.

A second deterrent is high rates of interest, which, like lack of knowledge, are related to scale of activities. Small-scale landowners, wood-using firms, merchants, and consumers are guided in their decisions by the high cost of borrowing and by important alternative uses for their resources. They consequently tend to discount the future strongly. So long-term planning and investment of the kind called for to assure a supply of timber at competitive prices are not widespread, at least partly because so many forestry firms are small.

A third reason for delay in taking remedial action is our inability to forecast. Traditional price instability in wood markets encourages short-term planning. The lack of assurance of continuity in timber supplies, in public management programs, and in financing in the face of strong competing demands for funds discourages even large firms from embracing ventures with distant payoffs, because high risk makes these payoffs, when discounted, look so small.

Fourth, there is the ineffectiveness of the present system either to separate social and private responsibilities in forestry or to place them on the shoulders of those who should bear them. Thus, efforts to put our ecologic house in order are attended by an eternal round of finger pointing and accusation which, because of the interconnectedness of events and because adequate means for measuring and assigning responsibility have not yet been developed, fails to find a culprit and to effect proper and timely repairs.

The timber-supply problem, if correctly stated here, does not allow the luxury of hesitation or delay or even slow progress. Yet present policies and programs are not doing the job. The responsibility for action to overcome serious systemic weaknessees resides with industry and other private groups as well as with government. But everyone seems to be looking to government to get the action started.

Critics have pointed out that to get on with the job, government will have to take such steps as these: Broaden and clarify its goals for forest-resource use. Centralize and unify decision making on forestry matters within its ponderous hierarchy. Place in better balance its several roles: timber owner and producer, consumer, coordinator, and arbitrator. And, as the nation's largest forest owner and timber grower, it behooves government to interpret such concepts as multiple use and sustained yield in ways which fit the new conditions and needs in our changing environment.

Further, government is being asked to reconsider some of the old timber policies. For example, financial-support programs for the small woodland parcels have not been demonstrably effective. Neither has regulation of their owners. New and happy amalgams need to be tried which can help to integrate small forests into workable units, permit continuity of policy despite continually changing ownership, and stimulate management activity. Tax incentives and private or government-controlled development corporations are cases in point.

GUIDES FOR POLICY

What policies are needed to give the timber-production side of forestry appropriate direction and thrust? Foregoing chapters and the conference discussions help to disclose, not what these policies should be, but what characteristics will fit them best to tomorrow's needs. First among these characteristics for forestry policies is that they adequately reflect the interrelatedness of things in tomorrow's world. Forestry goals cannot be determined independently of other goals. This implies that the outlines for the nation's forestry program have to be worked out at high levels, perhaps by means of a conference or panel representing broad viewpoints. And the responsibility for developing strategies within these outlines needs to be shifted upward, as from the local to the state or regional level, or from committees to joint committees, composed of representatives of major interest groups, to insure integrated planning. At the same time, there are arguments for strong expression of state and regional interests in planning the use of national resources, because of large variations in the nature, extent, and utility of local forests.

A second major characteristic of adequate policy is flexibility in both rate and direction of response to changing conditions. Some current policies set severe and arbitrary limits on adjusting the rate of forest use to short-term fluctuations of the market. Others inhibit or even prohibit shifts from one kind of use to another as social conditions change. Still others encourage actions which are either irreversible or extremely costly to reverse, for example, the breakdown of forest land into small parcels or the conversion of forest land to urban use.

A third characteristic of strong policy is adequate support. This implies, first, that the interest groups with a large stake in it have a voice in its formulation, agree on it, and will stand behind it. It implies, second, that the policy can be implemented, that is, that the program and the personnel are available to follow through on it, that the program is well financed, and that such financing is assured for the long periods of time often needed to complete a project or to maintain continuity. (Many conferees underscore the need for assured financing.)

A fourth characteristic of strong policy is that it be based on goals which have been carefully thought through and which fit the new environment which lies before us. For example, the big-wood-using firms are being taken to task, not because they are bad timber managers, but because they are not good environmental managers. Social critics seem to be saying that industry is not being a good intermediary, not providing a desirable combination of goods and services, not adjusting its goals to meet changing conditions. Under such circumstances, attempts to justify past actions or current programs carry little weight. The problem for wood-using firms is not to survive as timber processors under threats of timber scarcity but to grow, and grow profitably, by making a smooth transition from a resources-labor-capital complex, which manages timber and produces one mix of goods and services, to a new complex which manages land and produces another mix.

Government must also redefine some of its forestry goals and make clear the strategies with which it will support them. Timber owners, harvesters, and processors must know what will be expected of them and what the returns for their efforts will be. The answers to such questions lie deep in the marrow of our social structure and rest on reinterpretation of the concept of ownership in a society in which the rights of the individual and those of the group are becoming less and less separable.

Fifth, and finally, there is the expressed need for policy to be built increasingly on knowledge. Standards of value which comprehend recreation, watershed, and wildlife uses of the land as well as timber, and quantified production guides for each kind of use and combination of uses, will be welcome substitutes for the passion and partial analysis which now cloud the issues and delay or prevent helpful compromise.

Implicit here is the companion need for policies which will strengthen public understanding of the issues and public participation in their resolution. Too, policies are called for which will support research into the basic relationships among the natural and man-made systems of spaceship earth.

19   EPILOGUE 1971-1972: TURBULENT TRANSITION

JOHN FEDKIW*

THE TIMBER SUPPLY and price problems that emerged and quickly faded in 1966 and then surged in 1968–1969 reappeared strongly in 1971 and persisted tenaciously through 1972 as housing demands rose to new highs.

In 1971 and 1972, federal actions to contain general price inflation slowed lumber and plywood price rises and later complicated industrial efforts to expand lumber and plywood production. Lumber imports rose more than 50 percent, but did not turn the tide of rising prices. Environmental concerns reinforced by new disputes and court actions increased the complexity of the timber-supply problem and dampened the potential supply response of public forest lands to the rising timber demands. Efforts to enlarge the National Wilderness Preservation System were steadily intensified. Legislation to ameliorate timber-supply problems made little progress, as did legislation to restrict clearcutting on federal lands. Studies of the National Commission on Materials Policy and the President's Advisory Panel on Timber and the Environment and also the Forest Service's 1970 Timber Review progressed, but results were not expected until after 1972. Thus the timber-supply and environmental issues seemed to grow more turbulent, and solutions to become less evident.

The issues tended to focus on national forests. They polarized on increasing timber supplies vs. more wilderness. Both were social and humanizing needs—one for adequate housing, the other for preserving areas where men could wander among the mysteries of creation and wonder about the transcendental meaning of life. De facto wilderness was a rapidly declining resource on national forests. Increased harvests and road building threatened to accelerate the decline. So, given our reordered American priorities, the wilderness thesis was not inappropriate. But neither was its alternative: to expand timber supplies and to reduce the cost of housing and ease its availability,

* Deputy Director, Office of Planning and Evaluation, Office of the Secretary, U.S. Department of Agriculture, Washington, D.C.

particularly to low-income families. The latter thesis was less effectively vocalized but nonetheless real to national policymakers. It had its own overtones of environmental and spiritual values, though they seemed less obvious.

Projected declines in housing activity in the near future point toward a period of lower timber demands and perhaps lessened tensions as findings of the commission, the panel, and the Forest Service are explored and evaluated in the search for solutions. Longer-term projections, however, indicate that housing starts will remain at or close to 2 million units a year, a third greater than in the 1950s and 1960s; so the basic timber demand and supply issue is not apt to go away. Forest Service preliminary findings for the long-term timber outlook, presented in December 1972, showed a potential balance between softwood sawtimber demands and supplies about the year 2000 at a real price (in dollars of constant buying power) slightly above the high of 1972. But such a balance would require wide displacement of wood by materials from nonrenewable resources. The preliminary evidence is that the environmental impacts of using competing nonrenewable raw materials may exceed those of timber growing and processing. Thus environmentalists and timber producers may yet become allies in enjoying the forests' renewable resources.

The Forest Service has identified a wide range of opportunities for improving supplies. It has also completed the initial inventory of 55 million acres of roadless areas potentially suitable for inclusion in the Wilderness System. The need remains, however, for additional information, analysis, and enlightenment. And the natural-resource interest groups require a process for pursuing the policy issues and identifying appropriate tradeoffs to achieve national goals for ample materials and a good environment.

RESIDENTIAL CONSTRUCTION

Supported by public policy objectives, private demands, and adequate supplies of credit, housing starts (excluding mobile-home shipments) rose from 1.4 million in 1970 to 2.1 million in 1971, breaking all previous records. The 1972 performance exceeded the 1971 record by 15 percent, promising to reach 2.4 million starts when all the returns were in. For the first time since 1968, when a national housing goal was established by the Congress (26 million additional units by 1978), progress in housing, including mobile homes, exceeded the schedule for meeting the national goal.

Projections for 1973 and beyond indicate some fallback in residential construction as the national economy expands in other sectors. However, the outlook for housing demands indicates that the level of starts will remain at or close to 2 million units per year for the balance of the 1970s—and, indeed, to the end of the century. The possibility that major fluctuations in housing activity may recur in response to economic and policy changes continues to be a source of market uncertainty in the wood-using industry. But changes in mortgage institutions since 1969 have improved the ability of the mortgage industry to compete for lendable funds in times of credit stringency. Consequently the wide fluctuations in housing construction of the past may be dampened in the future and the demand for wood products may become more stable.

SOFTWOOD LUMBER AND PLYWOOD PRICES AND CONSUMPTION

Lumber and plywood prices rose sharply in response to the expanding demands from home builders. The real wholesale price of softwood lumber increased 30 percent during 1971 and an additional 12 percent during 1972. The real price of softwood plywood increased similarly: 19 percent during 1971 and 12 percent during 1972.

Softwood lumber consumption in 1971 increased 16 percent over 1970, to 37 billion board feet, the highest in history. In 1972, preliminary estimates indicate softwood lumber consumption of 40 billion feet, a new record.

Softwood plywood consumption in 1971 reached 16 percent above that of the previous year, topping 16 billion square feet. Preliminary estimates of consumption in 1972 are over 18 billion square feet. Both years represent new records for softwood plywood use.

SOFTWOOD LUMBER AND PLYWOOD SUPPLY RESPONSES

Both domestic production and shipments of softwood lumber responded to the rising price between 1970 and 1971. The former increased 10 percent; the latter, 13 percent. Softwood lumber mill stocks fell 11 percent during 1971, and the ratio of unfilled orders to mill stocks rose from .32 to .43, or 31 percent. Total domestic production in 1971 was over 30 billion board feet, about the same as peak levels attained in 1950 and 1959, when the real price was comparatively low.

From 1971 to 1972, softwood lumber production and shipments responded to further price increases at about the same rate as the year before. Both production and shipments expanded about 8 percent. Mill stocks declined an additional 12 percent during the first half of 1972, and the ratio of unfilled orders to stocks rose to .56, a 30-percent increase. Softwood lumber production in 1972 is estimated to exceed 32 billion board feet.

Softwood lumber imports were more responsive to price increases than domestic production and shipments. Between 1970 and 1971, net imports (imports minus exports) increased 37 percent. From 1971 to 1972, they increased 21 percent. Practically all lumber imports came from Canada: over 7 billion board feet in 1971, and about 9 billion feet in 1972.

Softwood plywood production responded more rapidly to price increases than softwood lumber. Production rose 16 percent from 1970 to 1971, while the year's average real price increased 9 percent. Between 1971 and 1972, production increased 11 percent, while the real price rose 17 percent, indicating a declining response to further price increases. Production in 1971 and 1972 was essentially the same as consumption, since softwood plywood exports and imports were negligible.

Mill inventories of softwood plywood remained quite stable at about 490 million square feet in 1970 and 1971. But they declined sharply to unprecedented lows in 1972, reaching 290 million square feet in October. Wholesale inventories followed a similar pattern, declining from 45 days of production in 1970 to a record low of 24 days in November 1972.

Softwood log exports in 1971 were 2.7 billion board feet, .4 billion feet less than in 1970. The decline in 1971 led to some improvement in domestic log supplies and probably helped the lumber-production response temporarily. The decline was due partly to a labor-management dispute that closed West Coast ports for a few months and partly to a fall-off of demand in Japan, the destination of 80 percent of all log exports in 1971. Softwood log exports in 1972 were 3.8 billion board feet, well above the 1970 peak. The increase is attributed to "catching up" on the 1971 lag, heightened economic activity in Japan, and some additional log exports to Canadian mills whose log supplies were reduced by a woods-workers' strike in British Columbia.

Congressional subcommittee hearings were held in the spring of 1972 on log-export issues. No legislative action resulted. The so-called Morse Amendment continued to limit export of logs from western federal lands to 350 million board feet annually.

CONSUMPTION AND SUPPLY OF SOFTWOOD SAWTIMBER PRODUCTS

The domestic softwood sawtimber harvest in 1971 rose 3.4 billion board feet above 1970, and in 1972 it rose an additional 3.8 billion feet (table 19.1). The increases came primarily from private timberlands, largely those in the South, where softwood lumber production gained 1.5 billion board feet in 1971 and an estimated additional .7 billion feet in 1972.

Southern pine average sawtimber stumpage prices, as reflected

TABLE 19.1 CONSUMPTION AND SUPPLY OF SOFTWOOD SAWTIMBER PRODUCTS, 1970–1972

Item	1970	1971	1973*
	Billion board feet, lumber tally		
Consumption:			
Housing	14.5	20.3	23.0
Other†	32.7	32.4	33.8
Totals	47.2	52.7	56.8
Supply:			
National forests	11.5	12.3	13.9
Other lands‡	34.2	36.8	39.0
Subtotals	45.7	49.1	52.9
Net log exports	−3.1	−2.7	−3.8
Net lumber imports	4.6	6.3	7.7
Totals	47.2	52.7	56.8

Source: Forest Service.

* Preliminary.

† Includes the lumber and plywood used in nonresidential construction, manufacturing, and shipping and the softwood sawtimber used in pulping and for miscellaneous timber products.

‡ Other public, wood-using industry, and nonindustrial private lands: 13, 47, and 40 percent, respectively, in 1970.

by sales from southern national forests, advanced 18 percent between 1970 and 1971. Softwood sawtimber production in the South, however, rose only about 10 percent.

Forest Service statistics for softwood sawtimber in the South indicated an excess of growth over removals of 5 billion board feet in 1970. Thus, by 1972, increases in the harvest were substantially reducing the growth margin for improving southern softwood sawtimber inventories and long-term supplies.

During the years 1965 through 1970, softwood sawtimber harvests from national forests approximately equaled sales, about 13.2 billion board feet per year, with some variation from year to year in response to market demands. (The board foot, here, is lumber tally by current recovery standards; the figure excludes a long-term sale of 9 billion feet in Alaska, 1968.) In 1971, the softwood sawtimber harvest declined to 12.3 billion feet, while sales fell to 10.6 billion feet. For 1972, sales of 12.4 billion feet were planned, while the harvest was expected to total 13.9 billion feet. The excess of harvest over sales shrinks the backlog of sold but unharvested softwood sawtimber by several billion feet, reducing somewhat the flexibility of the industry in responding to high demands for construction lumber and plywood.

The poor response of national forest timber sales to high timber demand and prices in 1971 and 1972 has been attributed largely to the Forest Service's increased environmental awareness, greater emphasis on a multiple-use approach to timber-sale planning, lawsuits and administrative appeals, and reductions in staffing. The sustained-yield level of the allowable cut remains at about 15.4 billion feet, lumber tally, for softwood sawtimber, substantially above sales. Prices for sawtimber sold from national forests increased from an average of $23.00 per thousand board feet, local scale, in 1970 to $26.90 in 1971 and $36.20 in the first half of 1972.

PRESIDENT'S ECONOMIC REPORTS FOR 1971 AND 1972

The President's Economic Report for 1971, sent to Congress in February, perceptively observed that the annual consumption of softwood lumber and plywood by the housing industry may have to increase by as much as 75 percent over current levels if the nation's housing demand in this decade is to be met (cf. table 19.1; the actual 1970–1972 gain was 59 percent). It also stated, "There are few areas where Government has as much direct control over the supply of natural resources as it has in timber."

The report emphasized that "an increase in the timber harvest through intensified management promises broad public benefits. Not only will consumers of wood products, particularly purchasers of housing, benefit through lower prices, but this can be achieved while keeping our timber resources intact. Unlike other natural resources, forests are renewable. . . . Indeed, it appears that, with proper planning and management, the permanent yield of forest lands can be increased." The report further advised, however, that "growing concern for our environment necessitates that increases in timber supply be achieved in a manner which is consistent with the preservation of natural surroundings," but recognized that "intensified forest management can also result in a natural increase in wildlife and improved opportunities for recreation."

The Economic Report for 1972 anticipated further increases in housing construction, but did not comment on the outlook for lumber and plywood demands or supplies. Timber harvesting and clear-cutting issues, likewise, were not mentioned in discussions of environmental resources and related problems of environmental quality.

The Interagency Task Force originally appointed in March 1969 was reactivated in March 1971 as rising lumber and plywood prices renewed concerns about the adequacy of timber supplies to meet housing requirements for lumber and plywood. The purpose of the reactivation was "to appraise what steps have been taken by the agencies with respect to the earlier Task Force recommendations . . . [and] to determine what additional measures might be taken to relieve the situation." Inquires were made into federal timber-sale contract-extension policy, freight-car shortages, lumber and plywood futures-market effects upon cash prices, and potential increases in timber supply through intensification of forestry practices.

Later in 1971, the Forest Service modified its policy on extending timber-sale contracts and limited extensions to a one-year period, effective on all timber sales contracted after June 30, 1971. The objectives were to ensure that contracts would be carried out in a timelier manner and to discourage unrealistic speculative bidding on stumpage by reducing the opportunity to delay harvesting of high-priced timber. For the industry, this action culminated discussions with the Forest Service that had been underway for two years.

NATIONAL COMMISSION ON MATERIALS POLICY

In June 1971, the President named the members of the National Commission on Materials Policy, established by Congress in October 1970. The commission assesses national and international materials requirements and investigates the relationship of materials policy to population size and environmental quality. Its charge is to recommend (1) means for extraction, development, and use of materials which are susceptible of recycling, reuse, or self-destruction and (2) how best to implement a national materials policy. In providing funds for the commission, the Senate Appropriations Committee also recommended that "special consideration and priority" be given "to the practice of clearcutting, a timber-harvesting policy which has been severely criticized in recent years."

In an Interim Report to Congress in April 1972, the commission noted growing demands for wood and wood-fiber products, a prospective shortfall in supply, and higher prices—if the present low level of forest management continued or was accentuated by losses of commercial forest land and constraints on timber management. It also noted that substantial environmental, economic, and social costs were likely to be associated with the increased use of substitute materials.

In May 1972, the commission requested the National Academy of Sciences to provide a "critical" discussion and recommendations on environmental elements that should be included in a national materials policy. The study is to be administered by the Environmental Studies Board and the Committee for International Environmental Programs of the academy. Five study teams have been formed for investigations into the following areas: economics, renewables, nonrenewables, fuels, and environmental policies.

The final report of the commission to the President and the Congress is due June 30, 1973.

PRESIDENT'S ADVISORY PANEL ON TIMBER AND THE ENVIRONMENT

On September 2, 1971, the White House announced the appointment of the President's Advisory Panel on Timber and the Environment as recommended by the Interagency Task Force in 1970. The panel's charge included making recommendations on such matters as "the desirable level of timber harvest on federal lands and methods of accomplishing the harvest while ensuring adequate protection for the environment; the costs and benefits of alternative forest-management programs; citizen involvement in forestry programs; timber-sale procedures; and possibilities of increasing productivity on nonfederal lands." The panel was also asked to review and report on issues associated with clearcutting.

The panel consulted with environmentalists, conservation groups, housing interests, wilderness representatives, timber industries, and state and federal forest and land-management agencies. It investigated environmental, conservation, wilderness, and timber-management and supply issues on federal, state, and private lands in the South, the West, and Alaska. Special studies were contracted out to experts on various aspects of the issues. The panel's report to the President is expected early in 1973.

THE CLEARCUTTING ISSUE

The clearcutting issue expanded to new proportions in 1971 and and 1972, beginning with the Senate Interior Public Lands Subcommittee hearings on federal forest-management practices in the spring of 1971. A total of 91 witnesses appeared, including members of Congress, environmentalists, state officials, professional foresters and other scientists, representatives of the timber and housing industries, the Forest Service, the Bureau of Land Management, and the Department of Housing and Urban Development. Much of the testimony focused on management practices on the Bitterroot, Monongahela, and Bridger National Forests, focal points of earlier controversy over management measures.

The practice of clearcutting was attacked vehemently by environmentalists, but strongly defended by representatives of the timber industry, the Forest Service, and representatives of the Society of American Foresters. The environmentalists attacked both the concept and its application. The others defended both, but acknowledged that serious mistakes in application had been made in some situations.

During the hearings, Senator Gale McGee announced his intention to introduce legislation calling for a two-year moratorium on clearcutting on federal forest lands and designation of a commission to study federal management policies, especially clearcutting, because he had come to share the concern of an ever-growing number of private citizens who felt that federal policies were wreaking havoc with the environment. His bill, S. 1592, was introduced on April 20, 1971.

The subcommittee reported in March 1972 that it had become aware that certain forest areas with special scenic values, fragile soils, or other limiting physiographic conditions should not have been subjected to timber harvesting. It recognized that there were problems in selecting harvest methods and that careful supervision and enforcement of road-building techniques and changes in timber-sale contracts were necessary to avoid environmental damage. It also recognized that measures to assure adequate timber supplies were essential to house people and serve other wood-product needs at reasonable cost. In its report, the subcommittee suggested guidelines for timber harvesting on federal lands: allowable harvest levels, harvesting limitations or constraints, location of clearcutting, and timber-sale contracts.

The Forest Service Chief, Edward P. Cliff, announced approval of the suggested guidelines, calling them "technically sound and generally compatible with a series of studies and reports which have been completed by the Forest Service and others, all involving public comment."

In January 1972, the Council on Environmental Quality released five regional studies of the environmental impacts of clearcutting and alternative harvest methods. The studies had been made during the preceding year at the council's request by the deans of five forestry schools. All the reports stressed the complexity of the problem and the need for policy changes and continued research. None recommended a complete ban on clearcutting. Also in January 1972, the Council on Environmental Quality prepared a draft executive order proposing new standards for cutting on federal lands and placing major importance on scenic and aesthetic considerations. But the Departments of Agriculture and Interior and the council, in a joint action, concluded that an executive order was not needed. Adequate control of clearcutting practices could be achieved by other measures, including new guidelines stressing environmental protection in timber harvesting.

The legislation proposing a moratorium on clearcutting and a clearcutting study commission was not enacted.

PRESIDENT'S ECONOMIC STABILIZATION PROGRAM

On August 15, 1971, the President, acting under authority of the Economic Stabilization Act of 1970, announced an immediate 90-day freeze of prices, rents, and wages and creation of a cabinet-level cost-of-living council to administer the freeze and advise on further stabilization policies and actions. The purpose of the freeze, phase I, was to halt general inflation while providing time to develop a long-range program to stabilize the economy. During the freeze, softwood lumber and plywood prices subsided slightly, even though housing starts remained above 2 million units at seasonally adjusted annual rates.

Phase II, designed to provide more flexible controls, began in November. A Price Commission and a Pay Board were established to control price and wage increases. The Internal Revenue Service received responsibility for monitoring the program. The goal of phase II was to reduce the rate of inflation by holding average price increases across the nation to no more than 2.5 percent per year. Price increases above freeze levels were permitted only to the extent of increased costs. Stumpage and log prices, like raw agricultural commodities, were not subject to controls. They could be reflected as increased costs in pricing lumber and plywood products. However, prices could not be increased if they raised the company's current profit margin above the average profit margin for the best of the past three years.

Phase II failed to limit lumber and plywood price increases to the stabilization goals. Softwood lumber and plywood wholesale prices, led by the powerful demand-pull from housing construction, rose an average of 12 and 16 percent, respectively, from August 1971 to August 1972, while wholesale prices of all commodities increased about 4 percent.

In May 1972, all small firms with 60 or fewer employees were exempted from price and pay controls. But failure of lumber and plywood prices to respond to stabilization objectives brought reimposition of price controls on small wood-products firms in July and, subsequently, intensive investigations of their pricing practices by the Internal Revenue Service and extension of quarterly reporting (of price changes and profit margins) to firms with annual sales of $5–$50 million. At public hearings in October on lumber and plywood price-control problems, the Price Commission heard testimony from manufacturers, consumers, distributors, and independent economists. Observers reported the general message of the testimony: that price controls had not been effective and might be contributing to price and production problems. In November 1972, the Price Commission issued briefings highly critical of the industry, reporting "evidence" of "illegal and unorthodox practices," and indicating that 30 percent of the firms with sales over $5 million had illegally raised prices.

At the end of 1972, the administration was seriously considering asking the Congress to extend the legislative authority to control prices and wages beyond April 30, 1973, when the current authority was to expire. The outlook for general expansion of the economy in

1973 indicated further excessive-demand inflationary pressures from sectors in addition to lumber and plywood.

WILDERNESS AND ROADLESS AREAS

The National Wilderness Preservation System was created by act of Congress in 1964. The act defined wilderness in this way: "A Wilderness in contrast with those areas where man and his works dominate the landscape, is hereby recognized as an area where the earth and its community of life are untrammelled by man, where man himself is a visitor who does not remain." A size criterion of at least 5,000 acres or of sufficient acreage to make practicable the use of the area without impairment was specified in the act. Authority to classify areas as wilderness was vested in Congress.

In 1971, the wilderness system included about 10 million acres of federal land. Most of it was on the national forests, but some had been set aside from national parks and national wildlife and game refuges. There were 89 separate wilderness areas. An additional 4.5 million acres of national forests were classified as "primitive areas." They carried the same restrictions as wilderness, since they were to be evaluated for suitability as wilderness. The Forest Service had also identified at that time an additional 36 million acres of roadless and undeveloped land in the contiguous 48 states. Another 54 million acres of roadless areas were available for wilderness consideration in the national park system and national wildlife refuges.

In January 1971, the Sierra Club's Wilderness Classification Committee report suggested that within the 48 contiguous states, the "two extremes of land utilization—wilderness and total development—should be approximately equal." To assure that some balance would be preserved, the report suggested that a guideline of a least twice the area devoted to urban uses be considered an adequate wilderness reservation. The area included in urban uses specified by the report constituted 55 million acres in 1964. Thus the report was suggesting a wilderness target about equal to the combined area of the established wilderness, the designated primitive areas, and other roadless federal lands in the 48 contiguous states. But no official total-area target was announced by the wilderness groups.

In a special Wilderness Message to Congress in April 1971, the President asked that 14 areas be added to the National Wilderness Preservation System. The following August, the President's annual report on the status of the system noted that 28 wilderness proposals totaling 2.8 million acres were pending before Congress.

In July 1971, a *New York Times* editorial mentioned that a draft executive order, proposing to withdraw from management as much as 40 million acres of public land in roadless areas, was being "circulated in the upper reaches of the Administration." In a "white paper" on the subject, the National Forest Products Association recommended that the President defer any executive withdrawal action until the Forest Service had completed its surveys to determine which areas should be studied in detail for possible inclusion in the National Wilderness Preservation System. In the fall, at the 12th Biennial Wilderness Conference, the Sierra Club criticized the administration for not issuing the Executive Order, the forest products industry for blocking its issuance, federal agencies for delays in reviewing proposed areas for inclusion in the system, and Congress for not acting on the President's legislative proposals for additions to the system. The executive director of the Sierra Club said, "If the President fails to act . . . our only option is to try to amend the Wilderness Act itself. We need an omnibus amendment to the Act placing all of our proposed units in the national preservation system."

In his Environmental Message of February 1972, the President proposed 18 additional wilderness areas. He also observed the lack of wilderness areas in the East and directed the Secretaries of Agriculture and the Interior to accelerate the identification of areas in the eastern states having wilderness potential. Legislation was subsequently introduced in Congress to create a system of National Forest Wild Areas in the East.

In June 1972, the Sierra Club brought suit to enjoin the Secretary of Agriculture and the Chief of the Forest Service from allowing any activities in any "de facto wilderness area" which would affect its character as wilderness. The suit also sought to require the filing of an environmental-impact statement prior to any action in areas being inventoried for possible wilderness withdrawal. A court injunction prohibited new timber sales, road construction, or other action that would change the wilderness character of the roadless areas.

Five timber-industry associations and seven forest-products firms with timber-sale contracts listed in the Sierra Club affadavit intervened as codefendants. The seven firms also brought a counter suit for $10 million in actual damages and an additional $10 million in punitive damages. Later, the U.S. Ski Association; the State of Alaska; Alaska Loggers Association; Douglas, Josephine, and Curry Counties in Oregon; and the State of Washington also intervened as codefendants. Approximately a billion board feet of the fiscal year 1973 timber-sale program on national forests was included in the roadless area. A total of 36 million acres in the eleven contiguous western states was affected, involving an annual allowable cut potential of 1.75 million board feet. The Forest Service and the codefendants argued that environmental impact statements were not necessary for studies of the roadless areas, since no actions were being proposed.

During the summer and fall of 1972, discussions among the Sierra Club, the Forest Service, and the forest industry considered possibilities for out-of-court settlement. A pretrial agreement was reached in December. The Forest Service declared it would file environmental impact statements before letting any future timber-cutting contracts in any roadless areas. The Sierra Club accepted this new policy as settling its main issue. The court withdrew the preliminary injunction, dismissed the suit, and counter suits were dropped. However, there remained the task of preparing environmental impact statements before letting timber-sale contracts in roadless areas. Timber-sale offerings could be significantly slowed in these areas.

The initial phase of the Forest Service's roadless-area study was completed in June 1972. An inventory of 55 million acres of roadless and undeveloped national forest lands in the western states and Alaska was submitted to the Forest Service Chief. It included 1,450 individual tracts. Recommendations of candidate areas for more intensive study are expected early in 1973. Public comment will be solicited before final selections are made.

Adjournment of the 92nd Congress led automatically to expiration of all pending legislative proposals for new wilderness areas and the proposals for establishing wild areas in the East. Thus the close of 1972 was marked by much unfinished wilderness business.

RENEWABLE NATURAL RESOURCE FOUNDATION

On January 24, 1972, 12 professional societies with common interests in the management and use of renewable natural resources joined in the incorporation of the Renewable Natural Resources Foundation with headquarters in Washington, D.C. The participating societies are:

> American Association for Botanical Gardens and Arboreta, American Association for Conservation Information, American Fisheries Society, American Geophysical Union, American Society of Horticultural Sciences, American Water Resources Association, Association of Interpretive Naturalists, Ecological Society of America, The Institute of Ecology, Society of American Foresters, Society for Range Management, The Wildlife Society.

Members of the constituent societies represent a wide range of professional and scientific capabilities: biologists, hydrologists, foresters, conservationists, zoologists, ecologists, agronomists, geochemists, ichthyologists, botanists, geologists, naturalists, horticulturists, and others.

The formation of the foundation is symbolic of the need for natural resource interests to work together more closely in meeting the diverse demands of the public on resources and their environment. The operational mode of the foundation is still in its early formative stage. It will include establishment of a center to house the societies and to serve as an educational facility for the public. The approach is expected to be multidisciplinary. The program will encompass informational services, scientific lectures, demonstrations, and special studies and research on critical environmental projects.

COURT SUITS ON PUBLIC LANDS

Twenty-four legal actions against the federal government affecting the management of national forests were filed or decided in federal courts in 1971 and 1972. Some also involved lands administered by the Department of the Interior. The majority of these suits was brought against the federal government by conservation interests, the Sierra Club being the most frequent plaintiff. The issues involved environmental quality statements, mineral exploration and development, road construction, timber-harvest and sale operations, long-term commercial-recreation developments, protection and preservation of wilderness characteristics, administration of the Multiple Use and Sustained Yield Act, and use of public lands for industrial sites. The Forest Service reported that about 2 billion board feet of timber sales were tied up in litigation, an unprecedented management experience.

Only three cases involved complaints from industrial firms operating on national forests. Two were concerned with timber-sale practices unrelated to environmental considerations. One complained against a Forest Service environmental constraint to protect the endangered condor.

Although the courts often rendered judgments favorable to the federal government in 1971 and 1972, it became increasingly clear that environmentalists could achieve many of their goals through the courts. In addition to the influence of changing American values, the flurry of cases involving public forest lands arises from relaxation of criteria for "standing to sue" in the federal courts. Standing becomes an issue when a person or group claims injuries inflicted by statute or by an administrative agency pursuant to the statute. The Sierra Club case against the proposed Walt Disney Recreation Development of the Mineral King area of the Sequoia National Forest, for example, went all the way to the Supreme Court on the issue of standing to sue.

Standing to sue requires that the plaintiff in a case have a personal stake in the outcome. Traditionally, two criteria were involved. The plaintiff had to show a private legal interest which was affected by the alleged governmental misconduct, and the harm had to be economic in nature. However, Supreme Court decisions since 1968 have reduced the economic value criterion to a triviality. And court decisions since enactment of the National Environmental Policy Act of 1970 have granted standing to conservation groups and individual conservationists without requiring them to show a private legal interest. And so the problem of standing to sue has become practically nonexistent for conservation groups.

The Mineral King decision in April 1972 appears to have reversed the trend and retightened the criteria. The Supreme Court affirmed the Circuit Court denial of standing to the Sierra Club. The majority opinion held that conservationists have to do more than assert their own value preferences in court. The opinion implies that suits cannot be initiated solely in the name of an organization, but that organizations can continue to finance suits in the names of individuals who have a direct or local interest. As a result, the Sierra Club has amended its complaint to allege facts sufficient to show proper standing. The issues will now be tried on their merits. The case, which has blocked the Mineral King project since July 1969, will probably come up for trial in 1973. The prolonged litigation in this case illustrates the growing problem of delays and added expenses in public-land management resulting from court suits. It also points toward a need for greater citizen participation in public-land management decisions so as to reflect citizen concerns and avoid or reduce delays and costs.

FOREST MANAGEMENT LEGISLATION

Two comprehensive forest-management bill were introduced in the 92nd Congress. Both had extensive hearings, but neither was enacted. The American Forestry Act, sponsored by Senator Mark O. Hatfield of Oregon, was introduced in January 1971. In several ways it was a broadened version of the unsuccessful National Forest Timber Conservation and Management Act of 1969. It applied to all public and private commercial forest areas. It included programs to reforest and restore the quality of public and private forest lands, to enhance and expand recreational opportunities, to provide financial incentives to improve state and private forest management, to establish a Federal Forest Land Management Fund from timber-sale receipts for forest and environmental management and research, to facilitate public participation in federal resource management, and to enhance the quality of the environment and resources of the public lands. The bill would also have established an American Forest Policy Board to advise the Secretaries of Agriculture and the Interior on "national forestland policy." The board would have included representatives of major interest groups such as professional forestry, wood products, outdoor recreation, fish and wildlife, wilderness, labor, forestry education, minerals, air quality, and the general public. "Physical disturbance" of undeveloped areas not included in multiple-use plans would have been delayed until public hearings were held to determine whether the lands should be developed or preserved. This proposal had the support of the wood-using industry.

The Forest Lands Restoration and Protection Act was introduced in April 1971 by Congressman John D. Dingell of Michigan in the House, and Senator Lee Metcalf in the Senate. It had the support of the Sierra Club. Title I provided for states to adopt standards for timber harvesting and land management on nonfederal commercial forest areas, subject to approval by the Secretary of Agriculture. It also provided state licensing requirements for foresters. Federal technical assistance would be provided for small holdings within legally established "cooperative management units." Title I essentially proposed state regulation of forest practices on nonfederal lands.

Title II directed that timber harvesting on all federal forest lands be conducted in accordance with the Multiple Use and Sustained Yield Act, which now applies only to national forests. It proposed that timber-harvest plans on federal lands be published, with provision for review every three years. Harvest plans involving clearcutting would have to be evaluated for effects on the environment and other resources, for effects on long-term forest productivity, for reforestation practicability, and for feasible and prudent alternatives to clearcutting. Existing sale contracts would be reviewed and cancelled if the required work was not consistent with sound forestry practice. Tracts that failed to meet the area criteria, but otherwise met the wilderness definition, would be given primitive-area status. Export of logs from federal or private commercial forest areas would be prohibited until domestic supplies were adequate to satisfy projected timber needs. A Federal Forest Land Fund would be set up from timber-sale receipts and from appropriated funds for national-forest land acquisition, reforestation, and environmental improvement activities.

Spokesmen for both the Forest Service and the Interior Department at March 1972 hearings recommended that neither the Hatfield nor the Dingell-Metcalf Bill be enacted. The Forest Service view was that "adequate authority exists now to accomplish balanced funding of the national-forest programs." Administrative regulations and statutory authority were more than adequate to consider all environmental values. Both bills would duplicate existing authority. The Interior viewpoint was that the bills were not "sufficiently comprehensive . . . to accommodate the diversity of interests involved." The Environmental Protection Agency neither supported nor opposed the bills.

Separate legislation providing financial assistance to improve forest management on small nonindustrial private tracts and nonfederal public lands was introduced in April 1972 under the title,

"Forestry Incentives Act of 1972." The proposal was an outgrowth of an idea originally formulated by the Forest Service and refined by the Southern Forest Resource Council, the Trees for People Task Force sponsored by the American Forestry Association, and other industry and nongovernment groups. The bill was passed in the Senate, but sidetracked in the House. The opposition saw the bill as inflationary and lacking guarantees that woodlands improved with federal funds would not then be sold for other developmental purposes. The administration also viewed the special-purpose, cost-share approach as conflicting with its policy and proposals for revenue sharing to meet domestic assistance needs. In October 1972, at the National Tree Planting Conference, the principal congressional supporters for the bill made it known that the legislation would be reintroduced in the 93rd Congress—"This is a good program." More wood has to be grown and "it must be grown on privately-owned nonindustrial lands, and this is an equitable way to go about it."

Other, less comprehensive legislation was passed by Congress and signed by the President. This included increases in funding authorizations for the cooperative forest-management and the cooperative forest-fire-control programs with states. The use of cooperative funds for urban forestry activities was also authorized. Legislation was also passed authorizing $65 million to be appropriated annually to reforest 4.8 million acres of unstocked and understocked national-forest lands. Other successful legislation related to federal cooperation in enforcement of state and local laws on national forests, expansion and extension of the Youth Conservation Corps, and acceptance of services of volunteers in areas managed as national forests.

PUBLIC LAND-USE POLICY

In June 1970, the Public Land Law Review Commission published recommendations from its comprehensive studies of federal lands. The following April, Congressman Wayne Aspinall of Colorado, chairman of the commission, introduced the Public Land Policy Act of 1971 as one of two pieces of "foundation" legislation for implementing the 137 specific land-use recommendations in the commission's report. It declared a basic national policy to retain and manage or dispose of public lands for the maximum benefit of the general public. The proposed policy required federal agencies to consider the views of all elements interested in the public lands before any plans were promulgated. The plans had to provide for maintenance or enhancement of environmental quality. Sustained-yield and multiple-use policies were endorsed, but with provision for dominant-use management. The bill provided for a Federal Public Land Use Coordinating Committee in each of the 10 public-land regions and an

Interstate Land Use Coordinating Commission with representatives from the regions and from state and local governments.

The administration opposed the Aspinall Bill in favor of its own National Resource Lands Management Act, which applied only to lands managed by the Bureau of Land Management. A coalition of national conservation organizations also opposed the Aspinall Bill. They feared the bill could lead to widespread public-land disposals if planning showed that disposal would achieve greater public benefits than retention. The coalition also criticized provisions that would have abolished the authority of agency heads to withdraw lands from mining and other development, including logging. The bill was not reported for floor action in the House. Congressman Aspinall was defeated in his effort for re-election in the Colorado primary, leaving the work of the Public Land Law Review Commission and its chairman unfinished. The findings and recommendations of the commission, however, remain available. Some may still be implemented administratively, others through new legislation.

NATIONAL LAND-USE PLANNING

Three major bills were introduced early in 1971 to provide for a national land-use planning policy. An administration bill was directed toward encouraging states to take the lead in planning and regulating major developments affecting the use of critical land areas. Amendments also broadened states' responsibilities for setting the location of major transportation facilities. National guidelines focused on identifying and planning environmentally critical areas such as "coastal wetlands, marshes, and other lands inundated by tides" or "scenic or historic areas," but did not prescribe how states should plan for these areas or require a land-use plan for an entire state. Proposed funding provided $20 million annually for 5 years for planning grants to states.

The Land Use Policy and Planning Assistance Act, introduced by Senator Henry M. Jackson of Washington, went beyond the administration bill. It required that states develop both a land-use planning process and a land-use program. Greater emphasis was placed on a federal role in developing and implementing a national land-use policy, and provision was made for an Office of Land Use Policy Administration in the Department of the Interior. State attention was directed to planning for environmentally critical areas, for key facilities, for land use having regional benefits, and for large-scale developments. The funding authorization provided $40 million annually for 3 years and $30 million annually for 2 more years.

A third bill, introduced by Congressman Aspinall, was similar to the administration's proposal. It was combined with the proposed

Public Land Policy Act of 1971 and then redesignated the National Land Policy, Planning, and Management Act. In this form, it was the only one of the three bills to include federal lands in its coverage. It repealed all or part of 160 statutes, including various settlement laws and withdrawal authorities that would be replaced by a public land-use planning and classification program on federal lands.

None of the national land-use planning bills was passed by the Congress. The Land Use Policy and Planning Assistance Act introduced by Senator Jackson made the greatest progress. It was passed by the Senate.

DEPARTMENT OF NATURAL RESOURCES

On March 25, 1971, the President transmitted to the Congress his plan for reorganizing federal domestic programs under four new departments: Community Development, Natural Resources, Human Resources, and Economic Affairs. The proposed Department of Natural Resources was to be concerned with the natural environment and the preservation and balanced use of the natural resources. The natural resources were to be grouped on the basis of common purposes into five administrations: Land and Recreation Resources; Water Resources; Energy and Mineral Resources; Oceanic, Atmospheric, and Earth Sciences; and Indian and Territorial Affairs.

Forestry programs were to be housed in the Land and Recreation Resources Administration, whose functions were to include the following:

Formulation and implementation of national recreation policy
Nationwide recreation planning
Technical and financial assistance to states for planning, land acquisition, facility development, fish and wildlife management, and the preservation of historic sites
Formulation and implementation of national timber policy based on supply and demand projections
Technical and financial assistance to states for fire control, forest management, tree planting, and insect and disease control.
Research and information services
Management of federal lands

Agencies to be transferred to the Land and Recreation Resources Administration were the Forest Service, Bureau of Outdoor Recreation, Bureau of Land Management, National Park Service, and Bureau of Sports Fisheries and Wildlife. Inclusion of the Forest Service with Interior agencies was justified on the basis of common purposes: "The rapidly increasing use of forest lands for timber and forage, recreational areas, management of wildlife, preservation of scenic beauty, and protection of downstream lands from floods and erosion dictates their placement in the DNR, where all competing claims may be balanced."

The Department of Natural Resources Secretary was to be concerned with the strategy of the department, its goals, priorities, and performance, and he would be spokesman to the President, the Congress, and the public. A deputy secretary was to serve as general manager of the department, responsible for allocating resources, evaluating program performance, and harmonizing line and staff elements. Two undersecretaries were to provide leadership for (1) general policy, strategy, and implementation of plans and (2) organization and management efficiency and effectiveness. An administrator appointed by the President and confirmed by the Senate was to be the implementor and manager of the Land and Recreation Resources programs, accountable for their success or failure.

Hearings were conducted by the Government Operations Committees in the House and Senate on the objectives and common features of the departmental bills. The Senate Committee on Interior and Insular Affairs also held hearings on the Department of Natural Resources bill. No final action was taken in the House or Senate on any of the reorganization bills. At the end of 1972, the administration was considering reorganization strategy for 1973, including the possibility of implementing all or part of its reorganization plans through executive action.

NADER REPORTS ON FOREST SERVICE STUDY

On December 3, 1972, two days before the Forest Service released preliminary findings from its timber supply and demand projections for the period 1970–2000, consumer advocate Ralph Nader released the report of a 3-year study of the Forest Service, made by his Center for the Study of Responsive Law. The report was generally critical. It described the Forest Service staff as "competent and dedicated," but asserted that the agency "often under enormous pressure from private timber interests, had begun to emphasize timber production at the expense of recreation, wilderness, wildlife habitat, and range." The *Washington Post* reported that Nader accused the White House and Congress of deliberately exposing the vast national forests to excessive private timber cutting at the expense of wildlife, recreation, and reforestation.

In a separate statement, the Forest Service pointed out that the Nader group failed to note recent agency changes, notably "massive" restudies and more public involvement. Some of the Nader proposals would have a "severe" impact on local communities and industry.

Nevertheless, the Forest Service said the Nader study would help "in making substantive changes" to accommodate to both environmentalists and industry.

Nader's group proposed 54 changes, many of which, the *Washington Post* reported, had the support of industry as well as Forest Service officials. The main proposed changes included:

Congressional enactment of a long-range protection and development plan and provision of $61 million a year to meet the "reforestation backlog" on national forests

Slowing down road building on national forests pending long-range planning; setting higher standards for loggers; and declaring a two-year moratorium on clearcutting of areas larger than 40 acres pending evaluation of environmental effects

Gearing "allowable cut" to the level of federal funds for "quality land management"

Granting legal power to the Environmental Protection Agency to enforce new standards for logging and reforestation on private holdings of 5,000 acres or more, to reduce logging waste and erosion

Setting up a National Forest Commission to develop long-range multiple-use plans, and holding annual public hearings and formal meetings in Washington with all interest groups to offset "informal" timber-industry pressure

Reducing local pressure by means of congressional abolishment of the 25-percent payment from federal timber receipts to the counties where the timber is cut, and substitution of federal school aid to "impacted areas."

TIMBER OUTLOOK FOR THE YEAR 2000

On December 5, 1972, the Forest Service presented preliminary findings from projections of timber demands and supplies to the year 2000. Softwood sawtimber demands from U.S. forests, based on 1970 price levels, were projected to increase from 47 billion board feet in 1970 to 74 billion board feet by 2000—more than 50 percent. With higher prices, projected demands would reach about 48 billion feet.

Supplies from domestic sources, based on current forest-management levels and 1970 prices, were projected at about 54 billion feet in the year 2000. This indicated a potential demand and supply balance at a real-price level for softwood lumber only slightly higher than the highest level reached in 1972. The projected level would be substantially above the 1970 softwood lumber real price and the prices experienced in the 1950s and 1960s. Still, it would be significantly below the long-term trend, which has been rising about 1.7 percent per year since 1800.

Timber supplies projected under the assumption of continuing current levels of management would lead to substantial replacement of wood products by structural materials from nonrenewable mineral resources. The latter involve potentially greater environmental impacts, arising from higher energy requirements and pollution effects of production processes. Thus the long-term national issue respecting sources of structural materials may evolve into a choice between (1) renewable timber resources, lower environmental impacts, and lower timber prices and (2) nonrenewable resources, higher environmental impacts, and higher timber prices.

The Forest Service's preliminary findings identified the following opportunities for improving long-term timber supplies:

More complete utilization of logging residues, plant residues, and trees lost by mortality

Increased product yields from improvements in mill equipment, manufacturing processes, and utilization of end products

Development and application of new technology in timber growing, processing, and use of end products

Some increase in dependence upon imports

More intensive management of all forest lands

The preliminary summary also reported that growing demands on nontimber resources and for environmental protection would have increasing impacts on timber supplies. For purposes of its projections, the Forest Service assumed that the commercial forest area would decline an average of 5 million acres during each decade after 1970. The decline between 1962 and 1970 was reported to be 8.4 million acres: federal commercial forest decreased 3.7 million acres and private, 5.2 million acres; while state and county commercial forest increased .5 million acres.

The Chief of the Forest Service, John McGuire, announced that review drafts would be distributed outside the service for comment and suggestions. The final report will be published in 1973.

THE NEW CONGRESS AND THE ADMINISTRATION

The turn of the year 1973 provided a brief pause before the 93rd Congress convened and the re-elected administration set forth its policies, programs, and budgets. The new Congress was busy in its first months with organization, committee assignments, and new bills. All bills expired which were not enacted during the 92nd Congress. Some will probably be reintroduced. New legislative proposals concerned with natural resources may also be expected.

Results of studies by the President's Advisory Panel on Timber and the Environment and by the National Commission on Materials

Policy are expected in June 1973. The Forest Service's final projections of long-term timber demands and supplies may also be available by that time.

Administration concerns are focused on planning for peace, constraining inflationary pressures, determining the extent of price and wage controls, reducing unemployment, holding down federal expenditures, effecting international monetary reforms, reforming the international trading system, and improving the performance of the federal government.

The thrust of apparently broader national concerns, the promise of new information and recommendations on forest resources after midyear, expected constraints on federal spending, and the possibility of reduced timber demands and prices with lower housing starts all seem to suggest a back-burner role for forestry policy issues in the early part of 1973, and perhaps through most of the 1st Session of the 93rd Congress. Congress is expected to concentrate on federal spending issues for fiscal 1973, fiscal 1974 appropriations, tax reforms, and national medical and health assistance. The forest-resource issues, however, remain pervasive on the domestic scene.

NOTES

CHAPTER 1

1. B. E. Fernow, *Economics of Forestry* (New York: Thomas Y. Crowell & Co., 1902), p. 85.
2. Same, p. 21.
3. "Forest Devastation, a National Danger and a Plan to Meet It," *Journal of Forestry*, December 1919, p. 915.
4. M. H. Wolfe, "Plan of Relation of Forest Regulation to Forest Communities," *Journal of Forestry*, May 1920, p. 491.
5. U.S. Dept. Agric., Forest Service, *Timber Depletion, Lumber Prices, Lumber Exports, and Concentration of Timber Ownership* (Washington, D.C.: U.S. Department of Agriculture, 1920), p. 68.
6. F. W. Reed, "Is Private Forestry Practicable in the United States?" *Journal of Forestry*, November 1926, p. 832.
7. C. A. Gillett, "Forestry and the Railroads," *Journal of Forestry*, January 1949, p. 13.
8. Aldo Leopold, *A Sand County Almanac* (New York: Oxford University Press, 1949), pp. vii and ix.
9. A. H. Carhart, "Recreation in Forestry," *Journal of Forestry*, January 1943, pp. 10–11.
10. L. E. Peterson, "New Developments in Forestry," *Journal of Forestry*, February 1941, p. 179.
11. Anonymous communication to the authors, 1970.
12. "Foresters Must Think," *Journal of Forestry*, April 1935, p. 365.
13. U.S. Dept. Agric., Forest Service, *A National Plan for American Forestry* (Washington, D.C.: U.S. Department of Agriculture, 1933), p. 90.
14. H. S. Graves, "A Look Ahead in Forestry," *Journal of Forestry*, February 1931, p. 168.
15. *A National Plan*, pp. 89–90.
16. W. Wyatt in *The Future, Forest Policy, and the 1970 National Timber Review*, ed. B. R. Wall (Society of American Foresters, Portland [Oregon] Chapter, May 1971), p. 15.

CHAPTER 4

1. *Proceedings of the Fifth American Forestry Congress* (Washington, D.C.: American Forestry Association, 1963).
2. Jeremy Main, "Conservationists at the Barricades," *Fortune*, February 1970, pp. 144–147, 150–151.
3. Garrett DeBell, ed., *The Environmental Handbook* (New York: Ballantine Books, Inc., 1970), p. 301.
4. "Capitalism v. Conservation," *Time*, July 6, 1970, p. 54.

5. T. P. Southwick, "Land Law Review Stirs Controversy," *Science*, July 3, 1970, p. 33.
6. Letter addressed to members of Congress by the Sierra Club, San Francisco, 1970.
7. Jeremy Main, "Conservationists."
8. Ralph R. Widner, ed., *Forests and Forestry in the American States* (Washington, D.C.: National Association of State Foresters, 1968), p. 7.
9. Same, p. 12.
10. Same, p. 6.
11. Orris C. Herfindahl, "What is Conservation?" Resources for the Future, Inc., Reprint 30, Washington, D.C., August, 1961.
12. Same.

CHAPTER 6

1. William C. Siegel and Sam Guttenberg, "Timber Leases and Long-Term Cutting Contracts in the South," *Forest Industries* 95:4, 1968, pp. 62–64.
2. Herbert A. Knight and Joe P. McClure, *South Carolina's Timber, 1968* (Southeastern Forest Experiment Station, Forest Service Resource Bulletin SE-13, 1969).
3. U.S. Dept. of Commerce, Bureau of the Census, 1941. Number of Inhabitants, United States, Summary, PC(1)-A1 (Washington, D.C.), pp. xiii and 1–74.
4. U.S. Dept. Agric., Forest Service, *Framework for the Future* (Washington, D.C.: U.S. Department of Agriculture, 1970).
5. Robert N. Stone, *A Comparison of Woodland Owner Intent with Woodland Practice in Michigan's Upper Peninsula,* doctoral dissertation, University of Minnesota, 1970.
6. Dwight Hair and Alice H. Ulrich, *The Demand and Price Situation for Forest Products 1969–1970* (Washington, D.C.: U.S. Department of Agriculture, Miscellaneous Publication 1165, 1970).

CHAPTER 7

1. Daniel Bell, "The Year 2000—The Trajectory of an Idea," *Daedalus, Journal of the American Academy of Arts and Sciences,* Summer 1967, pp. 639–651.

CHAPTER 8

1. U.S. Dept. Agric., Forest Service, *Timber Trends in the United States* (Washington, D.C.: U.S. Department of Agriculture, Forest Resource Report 17, 1965).
2. R. J. Marty and W. Newman, "Opportunities for Timber Management on the National Forests," *Journal of Forestry,* July 1969, pp. 482–485.
3. U.S. Dept. Agric., Forest Service, *Douglas-Fir Supply Study, Alternative Programs for Increasing Timber Supplies from National Forest Lands* (Washington, D.C.: U.S. Department of Agriculture, Regions Five and Six and Pacific Northwest Forest and Range Experiment Station, 1969), p. 29.
4. United States Congress, "Senate Committee on Agriculture and Forestry: National Timber Supply Act, Hearing before the Subcommittee on Soil Conservation and Forestry on S. 1832." 91st Congress, 1st Session, October 21, 1969, pp. 14 and 19.
5. Southern Forest Resource Analysis Committee, *The South's Third Forest, How It Can Meet Future Demands,* 1969.
6. United States Cabinet Task Force on Softwood Lumber and Plywood, "Memorandum for Cabinet Committee on Economic Policy, Findings, and Recommendations of Task Force," The White House, June 18, 1970.
7. H. J. Vaux and J. A. Zivnuska, "Forest Production Goals, A Critical Analysis," *Land Economics,* November 1952, pp. 318–327.
8. K. E. Boulding, "Economics of the Coming Spaceship Earth," *Essays from the Sixth Resources for the Future Forum* (Baltimore: Johns Hopkins Press, 1966).
9. Association of State Universities and Land Grant Colleges and U.S. Department

of Agriculture, *A National Program of Research for Agriculture* (Washington, D.C., 1966).

10. J. A. Zivnuska, "The Forest Products Mix in a Changing Economy," *Proceedings, 1960 Annual Meeting, Society of American Foresters* (Washington, D.C., 1961), pp. 57–63.

11. Southern Forest Resource Analysis Committee.

12. H. H. Landsberg, L. L. Fischman, and J. L. Fisher, *Resources in America's Future, Patterns of Requirements and Availabilities, 1960–2000* (Baltimore: Resources for the Future, Inc., 1963).

13. *Timber Trends.*

14. William A. Duerr, "The Long Trend in Wood Use," *Proceedings of the Forest Engineering Conference* (American Society of Agricultural Engineers Publication PROC-368, 1969).

15. U.S. Dept. Agric., Forest Service, *Possibilities for Meeting Future Demands for Softwood Timber in the U.S.* (Washington, D.C.: U.S. Department of Agriculture, Prepared for Working Group of Cabinet Committee Task Force on Lumber, September 29, 1969).

CHAPTER 9

1. K. P. Davis, "What Multiple Forest Land Use and For Whom?" *Journal of Forestry*, October 1969, pp. 718–721.

2. C. E. Hart, *Royal Forest, a History of Dean's Woods as Producers of Timber* (New York: Oxford University Press, 1966).

3. R. Nash, *Wilderness and the American Mind* (New Haven: Yale University Press, 1967).

4. J. C. Hendee, "Appreciative Versus Consumptive Uses of Wildlife Refuges," *Transactions of the 34th North American Wildlife and Natural Resources Conference,* 1969, pp. 252–264.

5. J. Harry, R. Gale, and J. Hendee, "Conservation, an Upper Middle Class Social Movement," *Journal of Leisure Research*, Summer 1969, pp. 246–254.

6. R. K. Hermann, "Some Observations on Forestry in Present-Day Germany," *Journal of Forestry*, March 1968, pp. 174–177.

7. T. W. Daniel, "European v. American Forest Practices, 15–Year Comparisons," *Journal of Forestry*, August 1969, pp. 550–553.

8. J. Fedkiw, "Forestry's Changing Economic Environment," *Journal of Forestry*, March 1970, pp. 137–138.

9. W. M. Broadfoot, "Problems in Relating Soil to Site Index for Southern Hardwoods," *Forest Science*, December 1969, pp. 354–364.

10. T. S. Coile, "Soil Productivity for Southern Pines," *Forest Farmer*, April 1952, pp. 10–11, 13; May 1952, pp. 11–12.

11. I. J. Craib, "The Place of Thinning in Wattle Silviculture and Its Bearing on the Management of Exotic Conifers," *Zeitschrift für Weltforstwirtschaft,* 1933, pp. 77–108.

12. Fedkiw, "Forestry's Changing Economic Environment."

13. T. E. Maki, "More Wood per Acre through Silviculture and Related Practices," *Proceedings of the First Forestry and Wildlife Forum* (Virginia Polytechnic Institute, Blacksburg, Virginia, 1969).

14. C. H. Stoltenberg and R. E. Phares, "Economic Considerations in Forest Fertilization" in *Forest Fertilization, Theory and Practice* (Knoxville, Tenn.: Tennessee Valley Authority, 1968).

15. C. O. Tamm, "The Evolution of Forest Fertilization in European Silviculture" in *Forest Fertilization, Theory and Practice* (Knoxville, Tenn.: Tennessee Valley Authority, 1968).

16. I. J. Craib, "The Place of Thinning."

17. D. Bruce, *Potential Production in Thinned Douglas-Fir Plantations* (Pacific Northwest Forest and Range Experiment Station Research Paper PNW-87, 1969).

18. R. L. Williamson and G. R. Staebler, *A Cooperative Level-of-Growing-Stock Study in Douglas-Fir* (Pacific Northwest Forest and Range Experiment Station, 1965).

19. F. A. Bennett, "Growth and Yield Research with Application in the Field of Thinning and Mechanization" in *Thinning and Mechanization* (Stockholm: International Union of Forestry Research Organizations, 1969).
20. R. G. McAlpine, C. L. Brown, A. M. Herrick, and H. E. Ruark, " 'Silage' Sycamore," *Forest Farmer,* October 1966, pp. 6–7, 16.
21. E. J. Schreiner, *Minirotation Forestry* (Gorham, N.Y.: American Pulpwood Association, Northeastern Technical Division, May 26, 1970).
22. W. A. Duerr, "The Changing Shape of Forest Resource Management," *Journal of Forestry,* August 1967, pp. 526–529.

CHAPTER 13

1. *Yale Alumni Magazine,* May 1970, p. 45.
2. Charles A. Connaughton, "The Revolt against Clearcutting," *Journal of Forestry,* May 1970, pp. 264–265.
3. Ellis T. Williams, *State Forest Tax Law Digest, 1967* (Washington, D.C.: U.S. Department of Agriculture Miscellaneous Publication 1077, 1968).
4. Ellis T. Williams, "Progress in the Assessment of Forest Land and Timber, 1956–1966," *Assessors Journal,* January 1968, pp. 25–35.
5. Same.
6. William B. Greeley, *Some Public and Economic Aspects of the Lumber Industry* (Washington, D.C.: U.S. Department of Agriculture, Report 114, 1917).

CHAPTER 14

1. Marion Clawson, *The Federal Lands Since 1956: Recent Trends in Use and Management* (Washington, D.C.: Resources for the Future, Inc., 1967), pp. 60, 95.

CHAPTER 15

1. Jules B. Billard, "Canada's Window on the Pacific, the British Columbia Coast," *National Geographic,* March 1972, p. 357.

CHAPTER 16

1. S. V. Ciriacy-Wantrup, *Resource Conservation Economics and Policy* (Berkeley: Univ. of California Press, 1952), p. 168.
2. Rainer Schickele, *Agricultural Policy—Farm Programs and National Welfare* (New York: McGraw-Hill Book Co., 1954), pp. 40, 44.

CHAPTER 18

1. K. E. Boulding, "Economics of the Coming Spaceship Earth," *Essays from the Sixth Resources for the Future Forum* (Baltimore: Johns Hopkins Press, 1966).

INDEX